CITIZENSHIP

The idea of citizenship is widely used in daily life. 'Citizenship tests' are used to determine who can inhabit a country; 'citizen charters' have been used to prescribe levels of service provision; 'citizens' juries' are used in planning or policy enquiries; 'citizenship' lessons are taught in schools; some youth organizations aim to instil 'good' citizenship; 'active citizens' are encouraged to contribute voluntary effort to their local communities; and campaigners may use 'citizens' rights' to achieve their goals. What is meant by citizenship is never static and its meanings are the subject of debate by academics, politicians and activists. These ideas are manifest and contested at a range of different scales. This book argues that geography is crucial to understanding citizenship.

The text is organized around a number of spatial themes to examine how spatialities of citizenship are played out at a range of scales. Ideas about locality, boundaries, mobility, networks, rurality and globalization are used to reveal the importance of space and place in the constitution, contestation and performance of citizenship. In doing so, the book reveals how different ideas of citizenship can include or exclude people from society and space. Consideration is given to ways in which different groups have sought to empower themselves through various actions associated with and beyond conventional notions of citizenship.

Written in an accessible way with detailed case studies to illustrate conceptual ideas and approaches, this book offers social scientists new spatial perspectives on citizenship while also bringing together strands of social, cultural and political geography in ways that deepen understandings of people and place.

Richard Yarwood is an Associate Professor (Reader) in Geography at Plymouth University, UK, with research interests in rural and social geography. He has published on a range of projects that include volunteering, policing, animal geographies, rural issues and governance.

Key Ideas in Geography

The Key Ideas in Geography series will provide strong, original, and accessible texts on important spatial concepts for academics and students working in the fields of geography, sociology and anthropology, as well as the interdisciplinary fields of urban and rural studies, development and cultural studies. Each text will locate a key idea within its traditions of thought, provide grounds for understanding its various usages and meanings, and offer critical discussion of the contribution of relevant authors and thinkers.

Published:

Nature
NOEL CASTREE

City
PHIL HUBBARD

Home
ALISON BLUNT AND ROBYN DOWLING

Landscape
JOHN WYLIE

Mobility
PETER ADEY

Migration
MICHAEL SAMERS

Scale
ANDREW HEROD

Rural
MICHAEL WOODS

Citizenship
RICHARD YARWOOD

Forthcoming:

Space
PETER MERRIMAN

CITIZENSHIP

Richard Yarwood

LONDON AND NEW YORK

First published 2014
by Routledge
2 Park Square, Milton Park, Abingdon, Oxon OX14 4RN

and by Routledge
711 Third Avenue, New York, NY 10017

Routledge is an imprint of the Taylor & Francis Group, an informa business

British Library Cataloguing in Publication Data
A catalogue record for this book is available from the British Library

Library of Congress Cataloging-in-Publication Data
Yarwood, Richard.
Citizenship/Richard Yarwood.
pages cm
Includes bibliographical references and index.
1. Citizenship. I. Title.
JF801.Y37 2014
323.6–dc23 2013017106

ISBN: 978-0-415-67963-3 (hbk)
ISBN: 978-0-415-67964-0 (pbk)
ISBN: 978-0-203-50164-1 (ebk)

Typeset in Joanna MT
by Sunrise Setting Ltd, Paignton, UK

Printed and bound by CPI Group (UK) Ltd, Croydon, CR0 4YY

For Elizabeth and William

Contents

List of illustrations

FIGURES

TABLES

BOXES

List of abbreviations

AFL-CIO	American Federation of Labor and Congress of Industrial Organizations
AGM	annual general meeting
AI	Amnesty International
AIDS	acquired immune deficiency syndrome
ANZAC	Australia and New Zealand Army Corps
BRU	Bus Riders' Union
CAFOD	Catholic Agency for Overseas Development
CFC	chlorofluorocarbon
CSCP	Community Safety and Crime Prevention
CSR	corporate social responsibility
DEFRA	Department of Environment, Food and Rural Affairs
DETR	Department of the Environment, Transport and the Regions
DoE	Duke of Edinburgh
ECJ	European Court of Justice
ECtHR	European Court of Human Rights
EU	European Union
FOI	Freedom of Information
GM	genetically modified
GPS	global positioning system
HA	housing association
HDB	Housing and Development Board
ICC	International Criminal Court
ICCPR 1966	International Covenant on Civil and Political Rights 1966
ICESCR 1966	International Covenant on Economic, Social and Cultural Rights 1966
ICHR	International Covenant of Human Rights

ILO	International Labour Organization
IMR	Income Management Regime
LANDSAR	Land Search and Rescue
LOC	locus of control
LOCOG	London Organizing Committee of the Olympic and Paralympic Games
MP	Member of Parliament
MTA	Metropolitan Transport Authority
NAG	Neighbourhood Action Group
NATO	North Atlantic Treaty Organization
NCS	National Citizenship Service
NGOs	non-governmental organizations
NHS	National Health Service
NI	Northern Ireland
NIMBY	not in my back yard
NRI	Natural Resources Institute
NSM	New Social Movement
NTNER	Northern Territory National Emergency Response
NW	Neighbourhood Watch
OCP	Office of Crime Prevention
OU	Open University
PCTs	Primary Care Trusts
PFS	People's Friendship Society
PGA	People's Global Action
QRA	Qualifications and Curriculum Authority
SARS	severe acute respiratory syndrome
SUV	sports utility vehicle
SYHA	Scottish Youth Hostelling Association
TAC	Treatment Action Campaign
TTT	Transition Town Totnes
UDHR 1943	Universal Declaration of Human Rights 1943
UK	United Kingdom
UN	United Nations
USA	United States of America
WA	Western Australia
WI	Women's Institute
WTO	World Trade Organization
WWW	Women Working Worldwide

ACKNOWLEDGEMENTS

This is a book I have always wanted to write. I have long thought that citizenship is a useful but underplayed concept that deserves more attention in geography. This interest comes from teaching courses on citizenship and geography for the past 20 years, first at Worcester University and then at Plymouth University. Over time the content of these modules has changed, reflecting changes in society and also geographical thinking, but they have always used citizenship as a thread to draw together diverse issues of contemporary interest. Citizenship has provided a helpful way of weaving social, political and cultural geographies together to provide rounded and critical views on society and space.

Citizenship has also been a long-standing research interest that has been manifest in my work on volunteering and voluntary groups. Citizenship has more often than not been implied in this work rather than being an explicit focus of research. Writing this book has offered me the space to think more closely about citizenship's relationship with geography and to tackle the subject head-on.

This is the second book in this series that owes a debt to the late Dr Bill Edwards of Aberystwyth University. Bill served as my undergraduate tutor and, later on, as my PhD supervisor. His enthusiastic, knowledgeable and reassuring tuition fostered my interests in human geography and considerably broadened my understanding of social issues. I am extremely grateful that he encouraged me to follow a career in geography and for all his support during my time at, and beyond, Aberystwyth.

There are many people I would like to thank for helping me to write this book. I'm grateful to the series editors and the four anonymous referees who commented on my proposal. David Storey and an anonymous reviewer provided constructive comments on the first draft and I am particularly grateful to Sarah Holloway for her extremely positive comments on that draft.

Thank you to my father, Andrew Yarwood, as well as Nichola Harmer and Ken Ringwood for the arduous task of proof-reading the text. I am also grateful to Jo Curtis, Carol Fellingham-Webb and Karen Greening for their work in proof-reading and preparing my text. I'm indebted to colleagues who read the proposal and/or draft chapters who include: Ian Bailey, Mark Brayshay, Clive Charlton, Agatha Herman, Jon Shaw, James Sidaway and Naomi Tyrrell. I think nearly everyone who commented suggested an area or idea I could have added to the book. I realize that the book has not covered everything and probably reflects my own interests and background. Apologies for the inevitable gaps but they serve to show the significance of citizenship to geography and how it can be effectively deployed in its many areas of investigation.

Thanks to Tim Absalom for drawing the maps and to Mike Knapman for the photograph of the Torch Relay. Thanks to Emma Quigley for the photograph of the Ten Tors Challenge and to Christina Birdsall-Jones for the photograph of Roebourne. Thanks to the Department of Immigration and Citizenship of the Australian Government for permission to reproduce questions for the Australia citizenship test. I am grateful to Curtis Brown Ltd for permission to reproduce W. H. Auden's poem 'The Unknown Citizen'.

Thanks also to Faye Leerink and Andrew Mould at Routledge for supporting this book and keeping me on track with it.

I am grateful to Ruth, Elizabeth and William for allowing me the time to write this book. It is dedicated to my children who have taught me more about citizenship than any text could.

1

WHY GEOGRAPHY AND CITIZENSHIP?

In July 2012, the Olympic flame was carried by 8,000 torchbearers in a relay around Britain and Ireland to herald the start of the Olympic Games in London (Figure 1.1). It passed within 95 per cent of the population, taking in settlements, landscapes and places of interest (London2012 2012a). While some of the torchbearers were international athletes or 'celebrities', the vast majority were nominated to carry the torch for their active contributions to local communities. They included people who had coached sports teams, supported disabled people, raised funds for charity, organized community events, managed youth organizations, led Guides and Scouts, served in the emergency services, or lived positively with illness or disability. The torchbearers were enthusiastically encouraged by members of the public who supported the torch as it passed through their localities. Although the 2012 torch relay did not explicitly celebrate the idea of citizenship, it provides an apt starting point for this book as it illustrates many important themes associated with it.

Citizenship, like the Olympics, has its origins in Ancient Greece and has been re-discovered and re-invented for the late-modern era. Defined in its broadest sense, it refers to an individual's membership of a political unit, often the nation-state, and the rights and duties that come with that relationship (Smith 2000; Cheshire and Woods 2009). Originally, the status of citizen was only conferred on certain men but today it is swathed in the language of inclusion and universality. Until the 1950s, Olympic torchbearers were male and usually chosen for their athletic prowess but the carriers of the 2012 flame included men and women of different ages, races, ethnicities, religions, sexualities and abilities/disabilities. All, though, were selected for their 'inspirational contribution' (London2012 2012b) to their localities, usually through committed and voluntary participation in community-based activities.

Many politicians have also championed forms of citizenship that emphasize active, voluntary service within local communities. In 2010 the UK's Prime Minister, David Cameron, stated in a Conservative Party conference speech that:

> 'Citizenship is not a transaction – in which you put your taxes in and get your services out. It's a relationship – you're part of something bigger than yourself, and it matters what you think and you feel and you do.'

The selection of active and committed volunteers to carry the torch suggests an alignment with these views. Others, by contrast, have argued that rights, rather than duties, should form the cornerstone of contemporary citizenship (Marshall 1950 [1992]) and that governments, rather than individuals, have obligations to provide, promote and safeguard their citizens' civic, social and political rights.

These rights, however, have not been given away. Instead, they have been achieved and maintained through a spectrum of actions (Short 1993; Parker 1999b; Isin 2009) that range from the conventional use of established political channels to more radical forms of direct action that challenge and disrupt authority (Routledge *et al.* 2007). Few, if any, torchbearers were recognized solely for their membership of campaign groups; taking part in direct action protests; striking or being politically active. Indeed, runners were accompanied by police escorts (Figure 1.1) that provided robust security against the torch being appropriated for political protest. In 2008, various attempts were made by demonstrators to seize the Olympic torch as a protest against a lack of human rights within the host nation, China. In 2012, the torch was diverted away from a protest in Northern Ireland which, although not aimed at the torch, detracted from the image of civic harmony that the relay was seeking to portray. Although efforts are often made to portray citizenship as universal, harmonious and inclusive, it can exclude many people who do not

Figure 1.1 The Olympic Torch Relay of 2012 implicitly celebrated and performed ideals of active citizenship. Here the torch is carried by Howard Otton in recognition of his voluntary service with Dartmoor Search and Rescue Team, Plymouth (Photo: Mike Knapman)

benefit from full membership of a state (Smith 1989; Valentine 2001; Lister 2007).

Concepts of citizenship, as well as who is considered a citizen and what this entitles them to, are contested. Although the 2012 relay privileged ideas of 'active' citizenship, it culminated in an opening ceremony that celebrated a much wider range of ideals. Using music, humour and performance, the event sought to foreground ideas, people and events that its artistic director, Danny Boyle, associated with the UK. It referenced, amongst many other things: the suffragettes' campaigns for women's political rights; the right to universal health care via the National Health Service (NHS); the first lesbian kiss on television; and notable citizens, such as the inventor of the World Wide Web, Tim Berners-Lee. It did not ignore 'active' citizenship (it was after all performed by 2,500 volunteers from across the world) or the place of tradition (a cameo appearance by Her Majesty the Queen in one sequence highlighted the significance of the monarchy), but it did offer a diverse, multicultural, fluid and often radical view of UK citizenship.

This emphasized that citizenship is not a static concept (Mullard 2004) but changes over space and time. While citizenship has in the past referred to the relationship between a citizen and his or her state, this connection has been increasingly challenged as private and voluntary actors have started to replace the state in many areas of service and welfare provision (Fyfe and Milligan 2003b; Desforges 2006). Privatization, voluntary actions and new forms of governance (Goodwin 1998, 2009) have made it difficult to determine the boundaries of responsibility (Shaw and MacKinnon 2011).

The torch relay again illustrated this. Runners were nominated by members of the public, including friends, family, co-volunteers, co-workers and employers, and selected by the London Organizing Committee of the Olympic and Paralympic Games (LOCOG), a private company formed to organize the 2012 Olympics in partnership with private and public stakeholders. Three multinational companies, Coca-Cola, Lloyds TSB and Samsung, acted as 'presenting partners' (London2012 2012b) for the relay with exclusive advertising rights. The torchbearers' participation was shaped by this partnership rather than any single organization or government body. The daily running of the relay reflected this heady mix of sectors, including spectators (members of the public), the police (from the state) and sponsored vehicles (from the private sector). Indeed, the supporting caravan was so large that the bearers themselves were sometimes difficult to spot (Figure 1.1; note also Staeheli 2011).

A series of staged events set the Olympic flame against backdrops of local landscapes, streets and people to enable, in the words of the organizers, 'local communities to shine a light on the best their area has to offer' (London2012 2012a). These events were spectacular but it is important to remember that they were celebrating the more routine contributions of volunteers to their communities. The torch briefly illuminated the work of a volunteer to the wider public but more mundane, actions are more significant to their everyday role and identity. For example, a Guide leader will be involved in organizing camps, leading weekly meetings, carrying out administration and so on.

In the same way, ideas of citizenship are reproduced through regular performances such as voting, collecting social security or carrying out national service. These everyday actions are probably more important to the idea of citizenship than spectacular events that celebrate it. Lyn Staeheli (2011: 399) argues that: 'the practices of citizenship – the daily repetitions that are part and parcel of the relationships that construct and disrupt citizenship – are important to the lives of people and to the potential of citizens to act'. If citizenship is to be more than just an ideal, it must be reflected implicitly or explicitly by daily life.

The Olympic relay operated simultaneously at a range of scales: while it celebrated an international sporting festival, the daily events focused on local actors, actions and places. Being a relay, the torch was defined by its mobility rather than an association with any one place. It moved continually between spaces and crossed boundaries, including national borders. Citizenship, like the relay, is multiscalar (Painter 2002) and mobile (Cresswell 2006a, 2009) rather than confined inside particular boundaries or spatial containers (Elden 2010). It has traditionally been coupled with the nation-state but it is increasingly associated with spaces below, across and between state borders (Painter 2002; Desforges *et al.* 2005; Staeheli 2011; Closs Stephens and Squire 2012a). Citizens are encouraged to act at a local level, perhaps as volunteers, and at the same time to connect to other citizens in other spaces, for example through global campaign groups.

In the following sections, more detailed consideration is given to the reasons why space and place are important to citizenship. Attention is given to the ways in which geography has informed understandings of citizenship and, in turn, how ideas of citizenship have contributed to geographical study. In doing so, the chapter argues there is a reciprocal relationship between geography and citizenship studies and provides a context for this book.

WHAT IS CITIZENSHIP?

Taken at its broadest level, contemporary citizenship traditionally refers to the relationship between an individual or group of people and a political community such as a nation-state (Smith 2000). This relationship is often expressed through a language of rights and duties. Citizens might be expected to have certain rights, such as the right to vote or speak freely, but, in turn, are also expected to fulfil duties such as military service.

Theories of citizenship are often normative and provide a framework for critiquing the gap between what rights a citizen should expect and what transpires in practice. Consequently, citizenship studies have paid close attention to social policy and the ways in which different institutions, such as schools or hospitals, deliver, deny or challenge human rights (Hill 1994; Mohan 2000, 2003a; Cowen 2005a). Although inclusion is often implied, many people continue to be excluded from full citizenship in *de jure* (legal) or *de facto* (actual) terms (Smith 1989; Valentine 2001; Lister 2007). As Turner (1997: 7) states, 'any bench-mark of citizenship would have to include some notion of egalitarian openness to difference and otherness'.

Citizenship is an important idea because it can be used to challenge and change existing norms in society (Mullard 2004). For example, the language of rights may be to contest racism, exploitation in the workplace, or poor access to services. What is viewed as good or acceptable citizenship is subject to contest and often reflects broader changes that are affecting society (Staeheli 2011). This fluidity means that citizenship eludes definition in any universal or lasting sense. Susan Smith commented:

> 'the literature on citizenship often seems confusing because the concept means different things to different people, not least because of the radical (and also conservative) rethinking to which the idea of citizenship has recently been subject'.
>
> (Smith 1995: 190)

Since Smith's article was published, further meanings have been heaped on to the idea of citizenship. It has been widely appropriated in policy circles to instil particular visions of citizenship that are associated with national identity and duties to the state. Consequently the term has gained a greater purchase in daily life. 'Citizenship tests' are used to determine who can or cannot become citizens of a country (Löwenheim and Gazit 2009; Samers 2010); 'citizen charters' have been used to prescribe expected levels of service provision from the state (Hill 1994); 'citizens' juries' are used in planning or policy enquiries (Huitema *et al.* 2010); 'citizenship' lessons are taught in schools (Pykett 2009b); voluntary, state and private organizations attempt to instil 'good' citizenship (Mills 2013); and 'active citizens' are encouraged to contribute voluntary effort to their local communities (Fyfe and Milligan 2003b; North 2011). These initiatives have stressed that citizenship, or at least the rhetoric of citizenship, has become important in the formation and delivery of political policies.

Increasingly citizenship is also being recognized as more than a political contract (Stevenson 2001; Pykett 2010; Isin 2012b). A person's identity as a citizen is not simply a reflection of national belonging but, rather, is shaped by a whole series of local and global cultural influences (Jackson 2010) that are played out on a daily basis upon a range of scales. Citizenship has often been associated with collectivity (Pykett 2010) and Staeheli (2011) argues that academics have often overlooked individual *citizens* in favour of studying *citizenship*. Perspectives from cultural geography have attempted to redress this imbalance by placing greater attention on the different ways in which people negotiate citizenship in their daily lives and practices (Stevenson 2001). The scope of work addressing the cultural geographies of citizenship is broad but has in common a desire to highlight the significance of hitherto neglected spaces and scales to the formation of citizenship.

Citizenship is, then, complex and multifaceted. It is played out across a range of spaces and scales that may intermesh and connect. This spatial complexity has challenged academics to think more carefully about the significance of place, space, territoriality and mobility to citizenship (Smith 2000; Desforges *et al.* 2005; Isin and Turner 2007; Isin 2012a). Box 1.1 illustrates some of the ways that geographers have defined citizenship and highlights the importance of space to these definitions.

Box 1.1 SOME GEOGRAPHICAL DEFINITIONS OF CITIZENSHIP

'The terms of membership of a political unit (usually the nation-state) which secure certain rights and privileges to those who fulfil particular obligations' (Smith 2000: 83).

'The rights and duties relating to an individual's membership in a political community' (Mitchell 2009: 84).

'The status of being a citizen, membership in a community and how an individual responds to membership in a community' (Chouinard 2009: 107).

Citizenship 'commonly denotes membership of a national polity to which certain rights and responsibilities are attached' (Cheshire and Woods 2009: 113).

Continued

Anderson *et al.*(2006: 1) conceptualize citizenship in three ways:

1. Citizenship describes people's collective political identities. It brings 'us' together and stands 'us' apart, and indicates people's senses of attachment and belonging in relation to people and places.
2. Citizenship relates to how society organises the involvement of individuals in decision making at a collective level. It refers to the ways in which we are governed and govern others, including rights and responsibilities.
3. Citizenship points to the central role of the nation-state, but increasingly to non-state institutions (for example, voluntary organisations, NGOs [non-governmental organizations], corporations, the EU [European Union]). (Original located at: http://www.geography.org.uk/download/GA_AUCWGJan-07ViewpointGuide.pdf)

'Citizenship is increasingly organised and contested through a variety of non-state as well as state institutions. This extends citizenship in the cultural sphere, to describe people's senses of belonging in relation to places and people, near and far; senses of responsibility for the ways in which these relations are shaped; and a sense of how individual and collective action helps to shape the world in which we live' (Anderson *et al.* 2008).

'Viewed from a geographical lens, citizenship is the unstable outcome of on-going struggles over how constructed categories of people come to be politically defined in space' (Barker 2010: 352).

'Dominant conceptualisations of citizenship still rest largely on an abstract, universal and western-centric notion of the individual and are consequently unable to recognize either the political relevance of gender or of non-western perspectives and experiences' (McEwan 2005: 971).

> 'Citizenship is constituted through a range of concrete political struggles. Our approach contrasts with those accounts that view citizenship as something that takes place and is achieved within a common unit, since we address this concept neither in terms of membership of a political community nor in terms of a body of rights and obligations. Rather, citizenship for us is conceived of as modes of political being that are enacted through encounters that can inhabit as well as exceed these delimitations' (Closs Stephens and Squire 2012b: 555).

These might be summarized by Lepofsky and Fraser's assertion that:

> citizenship is always connected to space and place . . . While one acts as a citizen of a sovereign power, this power is always defined through place (both representational and material). Furthermore, through participation as a citizen, one connects to an imaginary community through space.
>
> (Lepofsky and Fraser 2003: 130)

Geography has become so significant to the study of citizenship that Askins and Fuller (2006: 4, emphasis added) argued that '*only* geography as a discipline is uniquely placed to work through what citizenship may mean at a wide diversity of levels'.

THE GEOGRAPHIES OF CITIZENSHIP

It is difficult, if not impossible, to understand citizenship without a consideration of space. To begin to appreciate this, consider some of the questions in Box 1.2. They are seemingly straightforward but raise interesting points about citizenship and its geographies.

The first three questions are reasonably objective and can be answered in legal and political terms. Most people will probably identify themselves as a citizen of a particular country or countries, perhaps according to what is written in their passport. For most people their status as a citizen is one of coincidence that depends on where they were born or to whom they were born. For others, citizenship must be gained or earned by migrating

Box 1.2 WHAT MAKES YOU A CITIZEN?

Consider the following questions:

1. Of what country are you a citizen?
2. What did you do to achieve this status?
3. What rights do you have as a citizen?
4. What duties do you have as a citizen?
5. Do you ever consider your status as a citizen? When?
6. Is citizenship important to you on a daily basis? How are ideas of citizenship played out?
7. Are you a good citizen? Why?

to a new country and fulfilling a set of (increasingly arduous) criteria. The rights of citizens can be formally defined by the legal-political structures of a country and so vary considerably within and between places (Amnesty International 2012; Puddington 2012), reflecting political differences between states as well as social differences within them.

The last three or four questions are more subjective and are included to illustrate that citizenship is also negotiated by individuals in relation to prevailing social and cultural norms. While some of the duties that are expected of citizens may be prescribed in law, such as national service or jury duty, others may reflect a personal or ethical choice to engage with society in a particular way. Voluntary work may, for example, fulfil a sense of duty that might be prompted by government policy or by personal or religious belief. Others may feel no obligation to act.

Indeed, for many people their status as a citizen is only considered on rare occasions. Perhaps a need to show a passport to cross a border or to produce a social security number to negotiate officialdom may remind people that they are citizens of a state. If their rights are threatened or taken away, people may feel a duty to act or protest. By contrast, those who do not possess citizenship of a country (and are denied entry to it) or have partial citizenship (for example, can work in a country but cannot claim health benefits) are perhaps more likely to reflect on how their status as a citizen (or lack of it) affects their daily life. Equally, people who are excluded, or feel excluded, from places on the grounds of race, sexuality, age or gender may find themselves questioning whether they are full members of society.

The question of good citizenship is, of course, hugely subjective but how it is answered reflects personal ethics in relation to other people, agencies and places. Is, for example, a good citizen someone who obeys the law or someone who breaks the law to protest about something they see as unjust? Where are these ideas played out?

These generalizations start to show how places are important to citizenship. The following sections consider some geographical ideas and how they can be used to understand the diverse, complex and contested nature of citizenship and its importance to people and places.

Bounded spaces

The idea that someone is a citizen of a particular country reflects a well-established view that citizenship is associated with membership of a specific, *bounded* territory. In ancient times the territories of the city-state, such as Sparta or Athens, provided the geographical basis of citizenship. Today, the *nation-state* is usually the formal basis for conferring citizenship (Turner 1997). Its citizens can expect certain rights and duties that are contingent on its territory and are delivered through its political and legal structures. Janoski and Gran (2002: 13) write: 'citizenship rights are legislated by governmental decision-making bodies, promulgated by executive officers or enacted and later enforced by legal decisions'.

Through studying the apparatus of the nation-state it is possible to explain how different ideas of citizenship have emerged between and across nation-states. These have shaped the ways in which individuals or groups of citizens engage with the state through, for example, voting (Johnston 2000b; Johnston and Pattie 2006) or accessing welfare services (Lewis 2004b). Considerable attention has been given by academics to the importance of individual liberty, privacy and 'the right to rights' in different states and how these have been achieved (Shuck 2002; Bellamy 2008; Cheshire and Woods 2009). The foundations for much of this work were laid by T. H. Marshall's (1950 [1992]) seminal essay on 'Citizenship and social class' that discussed the development of civic, political and social rights in Britain. Although highly influential, it also meant that citizenship has widely been associated with the European concepts of the nation-state (Yuval-Davis 1997; McEwan 2005; Nyers 2007; Pain 2009) and, by contrast, much less attention has been given to forms of citizenship found outside the West (McEwan 2005; Chang and Turner 2011; Isin 2012b).

The territory of the nation-state continues to be hugely significant to citizenship and especially which rights and duties are attached to it. Its value is assessed in Chapter 2 as part of a broader discussion on the significance of bounded places to citizenship. Nevertheless, as the following sections argue, spaces below, above and across nation-states also contribute to the formation and performance of citizenship.

Mobility

Chapter 3 explores how globalized flows of ideas, people, materials and media cross the boundaries of states and challenge the idea that citizenship is exclusively linked to a single, defined territory (Appadurai 1990). For some groups of people wider opportunities to travel, work and live *between* states have led to what has been termed 'transnational' citizenship that draws on the rights and identities of more than one country (Linklater 2002; Mountz 2004; Chouinard 2009).

In 1992, the Maastricht Treaty formally established transnational European citizenship: 'Every person holding the nationality of a Member State shall be a citizen of the Union. Citizenship of the Union shall be additional to and not replace national citizenship.' Following directives established the rights of EU citizens to move between as well as work and reside in member states.[1] Most citizens of the EU member states also hold citizenship of the EU and, with it, social, civil and political rights at a supra-state level, including freedom of movement and the right to work anywhere in the EU. But, in contrast to the increased mobility enjoyed by EU citizens, those from outside the EU have been subject to more stringent border controls and legislation designed to reduce or deter migration (Kofman 2002, 2005; Samers 2010). Mobility and the right to retain rights in different places are becoming key components of contemporary citizenship (Cresswell 2006a).

Definitions of citizenship may also extend beyond the nation-state. Some people answering the questions in Box 1.2 might regard themselves as 'global' or 'cosmopolitan' citizens with wider responsibilites to the planet or to other people in distant places. Desforges *et al.* (2005: 444) upliftingly suggest that: 'it is the connections to strangers without – living, working and dying – in other places that form some of the most important, and potentially liberating, new geographies of citizenship in the contemporary world'. This statement reflects the idea that people associate themselves with a much wider set of identities (such as gender, age, sexuality, ethnicity, race, interests, faith or politics) that draw on global as well as national influences and challenge the assumption that citizenship is based on an identity that is fixed in and by the nation-state (Jackson 2010).

Locality

Local places also continue to hold significance for citizenship. Chapter 4 examines how governments in many Western countries have used 'active citizenship' policies to encourage their citizens to undertake voluntary work in their local communities, often with socially and spatially uneven results (Kearns 1992; Yarwood and Edwards 1995; Fyfe and Milligan 2003a; Skinner and Power 2011). Rather than citizenship being universal across a state, a more parochial form may develop in which citizens of vocal, well-organized and compliant local communities are granted more rights and duties than residents who are unable or unwilling to volunteer (Desforges *et al.* 2005).

Spatial networks

By contrast, other citizens use local actions to challenge rather than comply with state interpretations of citizenship (Routledge 2003). These can be local, tactical protests, perhaps against services being lost, but, as recent events have shown, they can also be part of much wider, global movements. These have the potential to 'jump scales'. Local protests or actions may be able to secure rights at a national or global scale because they are part of transnational or translocal networks (Haarstad and Fløysand 2007; Routledge *et al.* 2007). The 'Occupy' movement against global capitalism gained strength and publicity by combining many, autonomous occupations of public space in cities across the world. Citizens from many different countries were enrolled into a global network with shared goals that transgressed national boundaries and articulated rights for the poor. Similarly, Fairtrade networks link the consumers of food to its producers, often in faraway places, in an effort to develop ethical trading networks that avoid exploiting people and the environment (Cloke *et al.* 2007).

Chapter 5 examines the transnational nature of citizenship and the significance of local sites and international networks in its formation.

Everyday spaces

Although some people assert their citizenship through political protest or action, citizenship is something that is given meaning though daily life for the majority of people. Painter and Philo (1995) called for a more 'human' appreciation of the importance of everyday spaces, places and actions to citizenship. Consequently, much attention has been given to exploring how neighbourhoods, communities, symbolic public places, and different institutions help to reinforce ideas of citizenship. This is so much so that Bullen and Whitehead consider that the:

> contribution of geography to the study of citizenship has been . . . a changing spatial focus concerning where citizens are to be found – from the town hall to the ghetto; the public square to the private home; the city to the edge community.
>
> (Bullen and Whitehead, 2005: 499)

Chapter 6 considers some of the ways in which citizenship is played out in everyday life and the importance of particular sites to the way citizenship is understood on a daily basis. Schools, for example, are sites that enforce ideas of citizenship through specific lessons as well as extracurricular activities, such as team sports, aimed at promoting the qualities of good citizenship (Pykett 2009b, 2011). They also reflect a diverse mixing of values, people and ideas (Staeheli 2011). The 'public site' of the schoolroom is shaped by clashes over religious belief, scientific thought, school curricula and the Constitution of the USA that are also played out in courts, the home, churches and across the media. The social and legal controversies surrounded the teaching of 'Intelligent Design' as an alternative to evolution in some American schools illustrate this point. Equally, schools are places that offer a chance for different religious and secular views to be introduced and mixed (Hemming 2011, 2012). The site of a state-run school extends beyond its physical location and connects with wider social, cultural and political practices that cross, mix and shape everyday public and private spaces (Holloway *et al.* 2010).

Indeed, many geographers have emphasized and distinguished the relative importance of public and private space to citizenship. Women may feel excluded from public spaces due to concerns of sexual assault (Valentine 1989; Pain 2000, 2001). Laws aimed against anti-social behaviour may ban all young people from public spaces, reflecting adult-orientated viewpoints (Staeheli 2010). Although legislation exists in many countries to ensure the rights of minority groups to live their lives fully, exclusion from some places can occur because of *de facto* (actual) cultural practices that discriminate by age, ethnicity, race, sexuality or physical ability (Painter and Philo 1995; Isin and Wood 1999).

Others have suggested that a blurring is occurring between private and public spaces, with implications for citizenship. Mitchell (1995, 1997, 2005) has charted how public space is being eroded by private agencies to support consumptive practices that leave little room for diversity. Conversely, David Bell and Jon Binnie (Bell 1995; Bell and Binnie 2000, 2006) have also argued that the state has sought greater control of private space through efforts to regulate sexual practices.

When analysed at scales below the nation-state, citizenships appear fragmented, uneven and out of reach of some. Chapter 7 examines how some groups of people are excluded from citizenship and considers how new ideas about citizenship and space can be used to empower them. Attention is paid to private and public space in the formation of citizenship. Chapter 8 extends this analysis to non-human actors and examines how nature, animals and other non-human agencies are enrolled into networks and debates about rural and environmental rights.

SPATIAL CONNECTIONS

This book draws together geographical literature on citizenship and has two broad aims. First, it demonstrates that geography is crucial to understanding citizenship. Geographers' understandings of spatiality are leading to a greater appreciation of the role of space and place in the formation, contestation and performance of citizenship (Desforges *et al.* 2005; Staeheli 2011). To demonstrate this, the book is organized around a number of spatial themes, namely bounded space, mobility, locality, networks, everyday places, public and private space, and rurality.

It demonstrates that the significance of this work extends well beyond geography and contributes towards many areas of social science and citizenship studies.

Second, the book argues that citizenship should be a key concept in geography. To date, citizenship has had a sporadic and rather underplayed role in geography but, as this chapter has argued, it has the potential to bridge various strands of social, cultural and political geography in ways that deepen understandings of people and place.

This, as far as I am aware, is the first effort to draw together geographical literature on citizenship into a book. The breadth of citizenship geographies is immense and it is not the intention of this book to produce an inventory of the geographies of citizenship as, inevitably, many studies would be overlooked. Nor does the book aim to compare models of citizenship between different countries or places. Instead, three main themes interweave throughout. First, there is an emphasis on space and place. The book is organized around a number of spatial themes to emphasize the importance of place in the constitution, contestation and performance of citizenship. Second, the book explores the meanings, ideals and theories of citizenship. Consideration is given to normative aspects of citizenship from different political perspectives (Marshall 1950 [1992]; Smith 1989) and to the ways in which different geographical theories can be deployed to analyse it. Finally, concepts of citizenship are used to examine inclusion and exclusion from society and space. Consideration is given to ways in which different groups have sought to empower themselves through various actions associated with and beyond conventional notions of citizenship. Drawing these themes together, this book aims to provide a reading of the spatialities of citizenship that will be of interest not only to geographers, but to those in other disciplines who seek to understand the significance of space and place to the understanding of citizenship.

FURTHER READING

Definitions and introductions to citizenship from geographical perspectives can be found in various editions of *The Dictionary of Human Geography* (Smith 2000; Mitchell 2009) and the *International Encyclopedia of Human Geography* (Cheshire and Woods 2009; Chouinard 2009). Three key papers have effectively argued the value of spatial perspectives to the study of citizenship. Joe Painter and Chris Philo's (1995) editorial in a special edition of *Political Geography* on 'Spaces of citizenship' is a significant review article that makes a strong case for positioning citizenship more centrally in geographical research. It is still widely cited and the subsequent articles in the special issue illustrate some of the ways that different spatial perspectives can be used to study citizenship. Another editorial, this time in *Citizenship Studies*, by Luke Desforges, Rhys Jones and Mike Woods (2005) makes an excellent contribution to this work by outlining how new forms of citizenship are emerging at different spatial scales. Lynn Staeheli's (2011) report in *Progress in Human Geography* also discusses how new understandings of space challenge traditional understandings of citizenship. More information can be found about the 2012 Olympic relay and the torchbearers who took part in it at the official website: http://www.olympic.org/news/london-2012-olympic-torch-relay (last accessed 6 August 2013).

NOTE

1 After expansion in 2004 member states, with the exception of the UK, Ireland and Sweden, put some restrictions on mobility from the new accession countries. With the accession of Romania and Bulgaria in 2006, most countries placed restrictions on movements from these countries until 2014.

2

CITIZENSHIP AND BOUNDARIES

INTRODUCTION

In his inaugural lecture at the Open University (OU), Engin Isin (2012a: 6) asserted that 'citizenship is a bounded concept'. This is in two ways. First, citizenship is widely defined as membership of a political community that has formally recognized boundaries (Smith 2000; Painter 2002; Isin and Turner 2007; Closs Stephens and Squire 2012b; Turner 2012). In other words, citizenship is territorial and *bound to* the dimensions of a particular geographical unit. Second, as Isin expounds, people are also *bound into* the authority and territory of a political body through the idea of citizenship. Citizenship might be thought of as a 'social glue' that binds people to each other and the state. The relationship between citizenship and territory is therefore significant and mutually constituted.

Over time the territories of citizenship have changed (Painter and Philo 1995) but today are most closely associated with the nation-state. Nation-states confer *de jure* entitlements on citizenship and provide the political and legal apparatus for implementing and supporting the rights and duties of their citizens (Isin and Turner 2007; Isin 2012a). But, as the political power of the nation-state has been eroded, questions have been raised about the extent to which they continue to provide the *de facto* basis of citizenship (Sassen 2002, 2009). Likewise, in a world characterized by globalized flows of people, ideas and information, the very concept of bounded citizenship is also being challenged (Closs Stephens and Squire 2012a). Instead, it has been suggested that new and multiple spaces of citizenship are emerging that are linked to different, overlapping and boundary-less spaces (Desforges *et al.* 2005; Staeheli 2011; Closs Stephens and Squire 2012b).

This chapter considers the changing spaces of citizenship and questions whether it is still possible to link the concept to bounded territories. To do so, it charts some of the historical roots of citizenship and traces how these have continued to have an important bearing on the spatial nature of citizenship. It starts by examining how territorial forms of citizenship emerged in the pre-modern era and how these influenced the development of the nation-state and its citizenry in the West. In doing so, it traces how different forms of citizenship have emerged across different Western nation-states and, in turn, how these find expression spatially in daily life. Following this, consideration is given as to how different spatial histories have led to different understandings of citizenship in non-Western countries. The chapter concludes by questioning whether citizenship continues to be bounded or whether it has now moved beyond bordered communities.

FROM CITY-STATE TO NATION-STATE

Concepts of citizenship developed during the Classical Period that, in turn, influenced ideas and practices of citizenship in the West (Burchell 2002). Two traditions emerged that were based on Greek and Imperial Roman ideas of citizenship (Bellamy 2008).

The forms, privileges and duties of Greek citizenship were confined to the territories of city-states (Figure 2.1) (Painter and Philo 1995). Citizenship was associated with a particular city-state and could not be transferred to another. Thus, a citizen of Athens was not a citizen of Sparta and had no rights or duties there.

The duties of citizenship were onerous and required an active contribution to public life including participation in the political assembly, legal service, taking public office, working for local government and military service. The spaces of citizenship were public, with private duties of the home or business relegated from the view and remit of citizenship (although citizens relied on the labour of others, such as women and slaves, in private to enable them to fulfil their public duties as citizens).

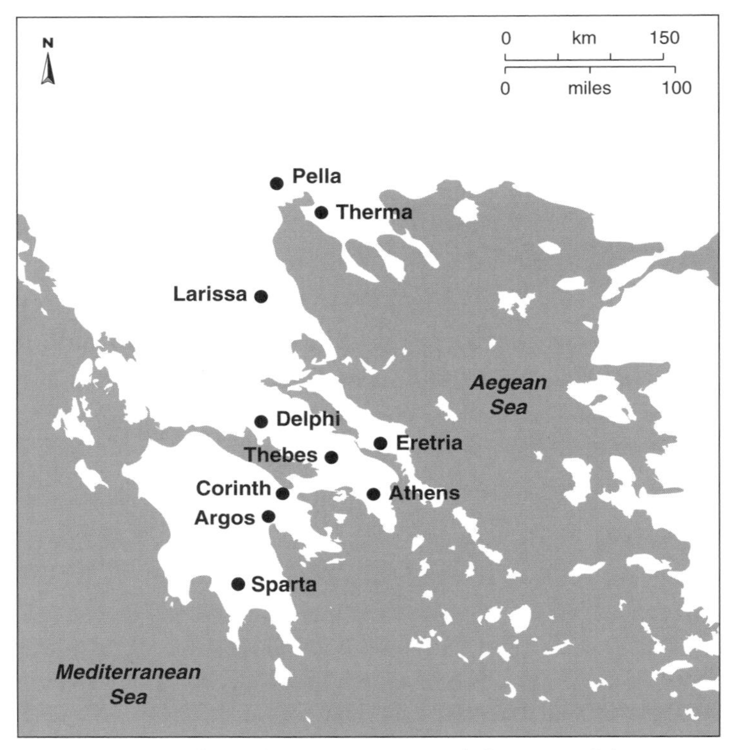

Figure 2.1 Map of Greek city-states around the time of the Persian Wars (c. 490 BC). Source: Oliphant 1999, drawn by Tim Absalom

City-states emphasized different aspects of citizenship: in Athens, democracy; Sparta, military service; (Republican) Rome, the law. Gender and class were the main determinants of citizenship. Citizenship was exclusive: to be a citizen of Athens it was necessary to be male, over 20, born to an Athenian citizen family, to be a warrior, a patriarch and an owner of slaves (Bellamy 2008). Immigrants could not attain citizenship but could be free and liable to tax and military duty.

The rise of the Roman Empire (27 BC onwards) brought significant changes to the Greek model of citizenship (Bellamy 2008). People from conquered territories were granted a form of 'second class' Roman citizenship that could be gained through service to the Empire, for example as an auxiliary in the army (Box 2.1). This afforded legal rights (*civitas sine suffragio*) but not political ones, which continued to be associated with

Box 2.1 MILITARY GEOGRAPHIES AND CITIZENSHIP

Military geographies often reflect much about society (Woodward 2005). The spatial organization of the Roman Army of the Republican period (509–27 BC) reflects many Roman ideas of citizenship and service (Sekunda *et al.* 2000) (Figure 2.2). Military service was the duty of all male *adsidui* (citizens who owned property worth 400 denarii or more) between the ages of 17 and 46 who were normally expected to serve continually for six years in an allocated legion. Soldiers were required to buy their own armour and so wealth determined the quality and type of equipment each soldier used and, hence, his place in the legion. Legions of 4,200 infantry were divided into ten cohorts that each comprised one maniple of *triarii* (60 men); one maniple of *principes* (120 men); one maniple of *hastai* (120); and one maniple of *velites* (120 men). In battle, these troops fought in four lines. The front line comprised the *velites*, lightly armed skirmishers drawn from the poorest citizens. Behind them were drawn the *hastai* in centuries of 60 men. The *hastai* would throw their two pila (javelins) before closing with the enemy with sword and shield. They were better armed than the *velites*, having a breastplate and greaves for defence, but comprised younger and, more likely, poorer men. The *principes* were arranged behind the *hastai* (in a chequerboard formation, filling the gaps between the centuries of the *hastai*). These were men in the prime of life and able to afford more body armour but, otherwise, armed and organized as the *hastai*. The final line comprised the *triarii*, the oldest and wealthiest citizens armed with chain mail and long spears. These troops were usually kept in reserve and used only as a last resort. The Roman cavalry, the *equites*, drew their ranks from the elite of society who could afford the most expensive weapons and armour (although horses were provided by the state).

These military geographies say much about citizenship. The poorest and more expendable citizens were in the front line (with

Continued

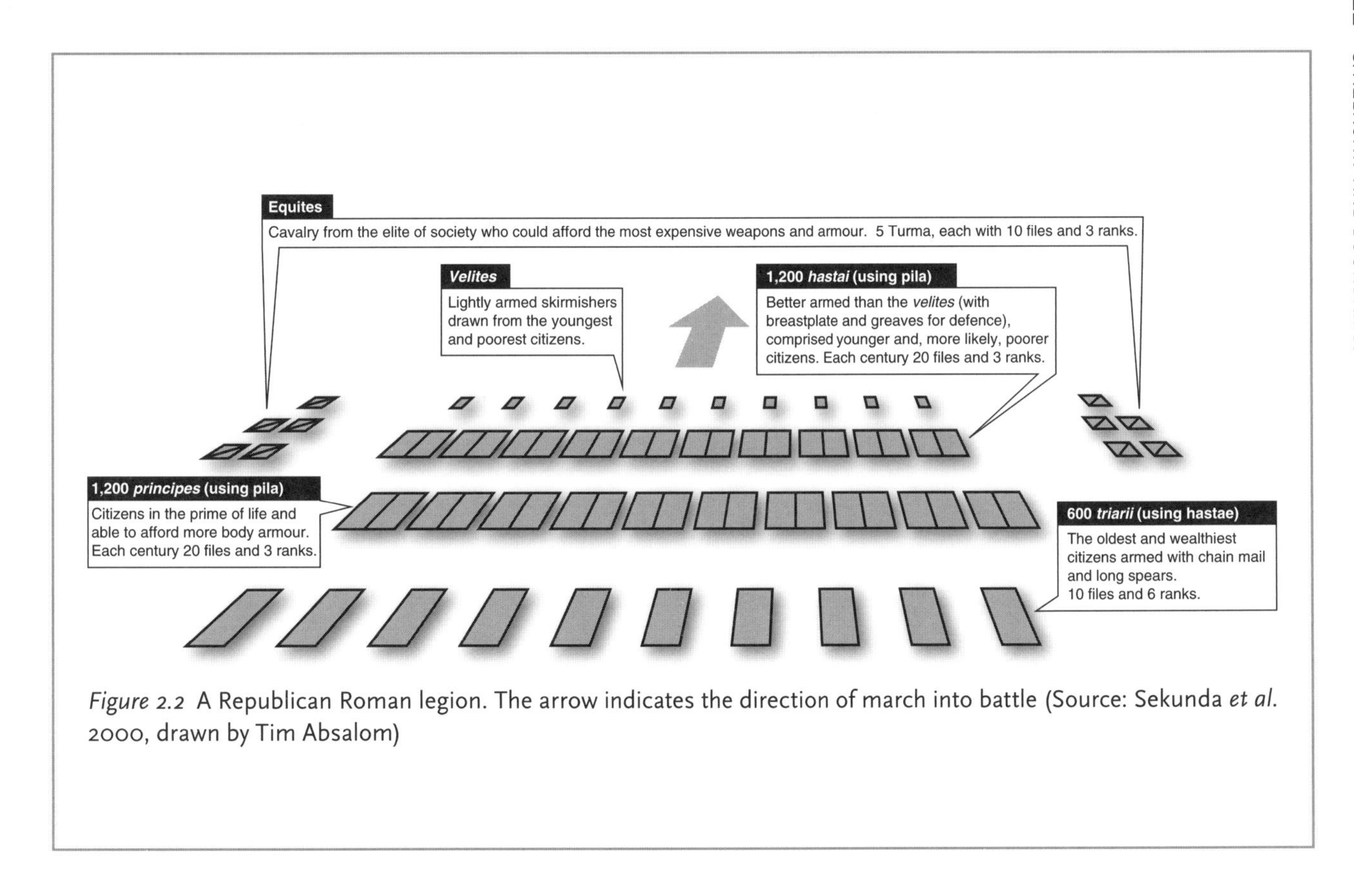

Figure 2.2 A Republican Roman legion. The arrow indicates the direction of march into battle (Source: Sekunda *et al.* 2000, drawn by Tim Absalom)

more chance of becoming casualties) while the wealthiest and most valued citizens were kept in the rear with a greater chance of survival. Those with property of less than 400 denarii, criminals, slaves and convicts were not recruited into the army. This, however, was not viewed advantageously as the deprivation of military service meant they were not recognized as Roman citizens with full political rights.

At the end of the Republican period, Roman armies expanded and needed more soldiers. Consequently the levy was extended to the proletariat (those with less than 400 denarii) and increased use was made of auxiliary troops from other states.

During the Imperial period between 104BC and AD284 the army became divided, more simply, into legionaries and auxiliary troops. Legionaries were citizens (who wore the classic *lorica segmentata* armour often associated with Roman soldiers) and auxiliaries were not. The latter tended to be placed at the front of battle or left to guard remote outposts, but after 25 years of service had the right to full, hereditary citizenship (Sekunda *et al.* 2000).

The spatial organization of armies throughout the Roman Empire reflected not only Roman society and citizenry, but also a formidable state bureaucracy capable of surveying, recording, organizing and administering its soldier-citizens.

local tribal systems and places (Oliver and Heater 1994; Smith 2002). In this way legal rights were extended across the Roman Empire and were not associated with an attachment to a local place or territory. This is exemplified by St Paul, who was born a Roman citizen in Tarsus in Asia Minor by virtue of his father's services as a tent maker to the Roman Army. According to Biblical accounts (Acts 22: 25) Paul drew upon his Roman citizenship to spare him from cross-examination under torture: 'is it lawful for you to scourge a man that is a Roman and uncondemned?' In contrast to Paul, who had been born a citizen, the captain of the guard who held him had gained his citizenship and so was inferior to him.

This widening of membership was necessary given the sheer scale of the Empire (Figure 2.3) and the necessity to bind diverse peoples into its

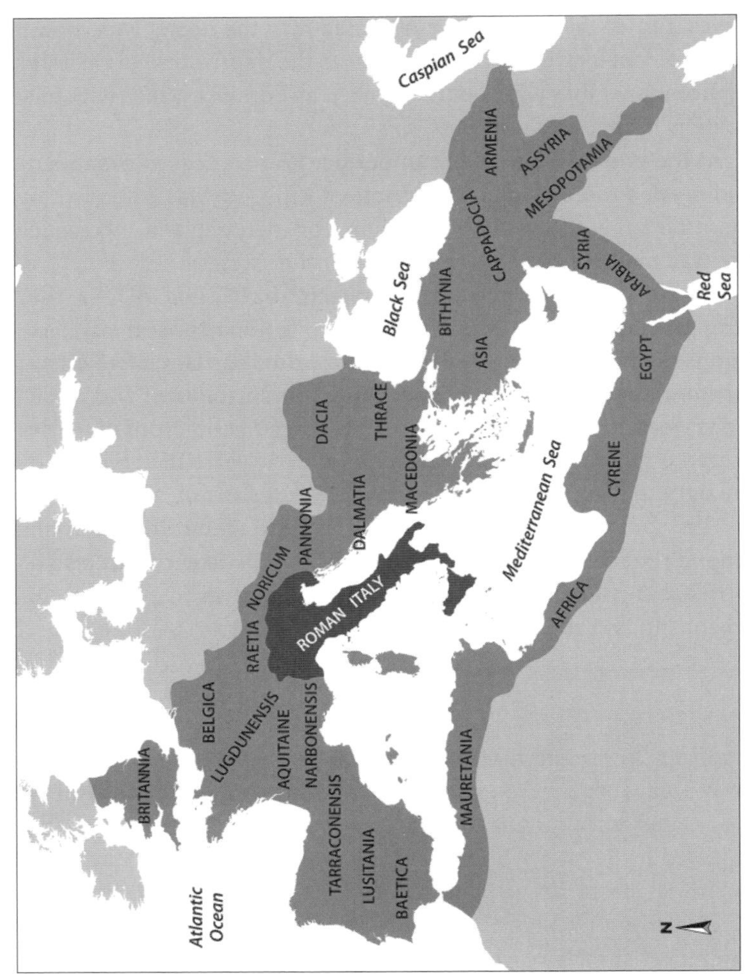

Figure 2.3 The Roman Empire at its height in 116 AD. Drawn by: Tim Absalom

authority. With its emphasis on legal rather than political rights, Imperial Rome encouraged a more passive version of citizenship than the public, duty-focused Greek model. Neither form gave consideration to social citizenship (Turner 2012).

Classical thinking cast a 'long shadow' (Bellamy 2008) over citizenship in the West, helping to define models of liberal and republican citizenship together with passive and active roles for citizens (Painter and Philo 1995; Faulks 2000; Burchell 2002). Above all, it associated the idea of citizenship with bounded, territorial space.

Of course, these ideas did not continue uninterrupted to the present day. Following the collapse of the Western Roman Empire, the concept of citizenship was largely lost in Europe. Instead of citizens, people were *subjects* of feudal and religious orderings. Ideas of charity, rather than rights, were used to provide (extremely limited) forms of alms or welfare provision to those who were deemed members of local communities (Marshall 1950 [1992]; Cresswell 2009). Rulers exacted duties and obligations over their (frequently disputed) kingdoms and territories without any reciprocal rights for the vast majority of people. In some towns 'burghers' had limited forms of local political power that were manifested in manorial courts, stannaries, craft guilds and the like (Smith 2002). Locality and community were the basis of these social relationships.

Interest in Western forms of citizenship was rekindled in the Renaissance, with many political writers turning to and developing Classical ideas (Burchell 2002). Some Italian cities, such as Florence and Venice, achieved independent forms of self-governance (Smith 2002) based in part on neo-Roman ideas of citizenship that ensured power was shared amongst different groups (Oliver and Heater 1994). This distribution of power inspired Niccolò Machiavelli's (1469–1527) writings that later influenced the formation of republics in the Netherlands, the English Commonwealth, France and the USA (Smith 2002; Bellamy 2008).

The English philosopher Thomas Hobbes (1588–1679) drew upon and criticized Classical views of republican citizenship, blaming them for the religious bloodshed of the seventeenth century (Burchell 2002). He considered that human lives had a tendency to be 'solitary, poor, nasty, brutish, and short' if they were left unregulated. His solution, therefore, was for people to turn away from this 'state of nature' and towards a society controlled instead by a 'social contract' in which individuals surrendered some of their freedoms to a recognized sovereign authority ('be it monarchical or popular') in exchange for its protection against these 'natural' ills (Burchell 2002; Rasmussen and Brown 2005; Bellamy 2008).

John Locke (1632–1704), by contrast, had a more optimistic view of human nature and, building on the idea of social contract, offered a more liberal view of the state that championed the rights of its people to 'life, health, liberty, or possessions'. Shared, rather than absolute, power together with individual consent and participation were key to his ideas (Bellamy 2008). Inspired by Locke's work, Jean-Jacques Rousseau (1712–78) (Smith 2002) wrote:

> 'those who are associated in the [body politic] take collectively the name of a people, and call themselves citizens, in so far as they share in the sovereign power'.
>
> (quoted in Oliver and Heater 1994: 15)

Here citizenship was portrayed as an idea that was bound together by the sharing of power. Rousseau's work, together with the writings of Aristotle, Machiavelli and Locke, was influential in the revolutionary establishment of new republics in the eighteenth century, including France and the USA. In both cases written constitutions were established to verify the relationship between citizens and the state, reflecting the importance of the state and the role of public citizens in shaping it as collective, equal agents. Citizens were regarded as private individuals able to pursue 'natural' rights associated with liberty, property and happiness (Bellamy 2008).

Bryan Turner argues that the rise of modern citizenship was connected with the rise of democracy and has four characteristics:

> it is universal in its formal treatment of rights; it attempts to suppress familial and kinship ties as criteria for employment and promotion in the public arena; it is closely associated with the rise of an effective taxation system; and finally it changes the basis of involvement in the military through universal conscription.
>
> (Turner 2012: 16)

These rights and duties are applied to members of a state in a given territory (Turner 2012: 19). Specifically, development of formal citizenship became closely associated with the evolution of the nation-state (Bellamy 2008). As the following section outlines, this relationship was charted in a seminal essay by T. H. Marshall (1950 [1992]) that has strongly influenced the way that citizenship has been conceptualized within bounded space.

T. H. MARSHALL, LIBERAL CITIZENSHIP AND THE NATION-STATE

Thomas Humphrey Marshall (1893–1982) was an English sociologist with interests in social policy and welfare institutions (Turner 2009). His essay 'Citizenship and social class' was delivered at Cambridge University in 1949 and published in 1950. It became, and remains, an influential essay that charts the development of citizenship through the growth of civil, political and social rights in Britain.

Civil rights corresponded with those 'necessary for individual freedom – liberty of the person, freedom of speech, thought and faith, the right to own property and to conclude valid contracts and the right to justice' (Marshall 1950 [1992]: 8). The courts and judicial system were the institutions most closely associated with these civic rights. *Political rights* referred to 'the right to participate in the exercise of political power, as a member of a body invested with political authority or as an elector of the members of such a body' (p.8). Parliament and local government corresponded with these rights. Finally, *social rights* were associated with 'a modicum of economic welfare and security to the right to share to the full the social heritage and to live the life of a civilised being according to the standards prevailing in the society' (p.8). Social services and, in particular, education were connected most closely to these rights. Marshall argued that civic rights were mainly achieved in the eighteenth century (for example, the establishment of justice and employment rights), political rights in the nineteenth (the gradual replacement of economic substance with personal status to determine the right to vote) and social rights in the twentieth (including education, health and welfare services), although there were overlaps between these periods.

Marshall noted that there were spatial implications for these changes and, as the functions and institutions associated with particular sets of rights separated, they became geographically fused. The development of a national set of rights brought with it a shift in the geographical focus of citizenship, from the local to the national, and with it a rise in institutions and bureaucracies aimed at delivering specific rights: 'institutions that were national and specialised could not belong so intimately to the life of the social groups they served as those that were local and general in character' (Marshall 1950 [1992]: 9). Thus social rights, which had been delivered (such as they existed) through local communities and their charities, were replaced by national structures of welfare delivery (Box 2.2). Likewise, the development of the judiciary saw common law, rather than local custom, as the way of delivering justice. Marshall argues that the institutions responsible for these rights became remote (e.g. the Houses of Parliament) so that citizens needed to employ experts or use intermediaries to recognize and realize the rights afforded to them (Cresswell 2009). While it was the general 'view of charitable bodies that those who received their help had no right to it' (Marshall 1950: 20), the

Box 2.2 THE UK'S NATIONAL HEALTH SERVICE (NHS)

The NHS was established in England and Wales in 1946 (1947 in Scotland and 1949 in Northern Ireland (NI)) with the principle that health care should be universal and free at the point of delivery. The NHS reflected ideas developed in William Beveridge's (1942) 'Social insurance and allied services' report that called for the state to be responsible for its citizens' health and welfare. It aimed to make health care a universal right for citizens rather than a commodity that could be purchased according to wealth, class or other social characteristics (Desmoyers-Davis 2001). Aneurin Bevan, the Health Minister at the time of the NHS's formation, argued it had three core principles:

- that it meet the needs of everyone;
- that it be free at the point of delivery;
- that it be based on clinical need, not ability to pay (NHS 2013).

These principles exemplify what Marshall (1950) would later refer to as social rights.

Prior to the formation of the NHS, 'access to hospital care depended on the vigour of voluntarism and the political priorities of local governments' (Mohan 2003a: 56). The provision of the universal NHS aimed to reduce these geographical inequalities and, instead, provide national equality for all UK citizens. The NHS has arguably become a central tenet of UK citizenship in both political and cultural terms. It was celebrated, to widespread acclaim, in the 2012 Olympic opening ceremony (see Chapter 1) and threats to close hospitals are usually met with fierce local resistance. In 2001, an independent Member of Parliament (MP) was elected in opposition to plans to close Kidderminster Hospital (Brown 2003). Far from just serving passive citizens, the NHS is frequently the recipient of fund-raising and voluntary work from active citizens (Mohan, J. 2003b).

However, there continue to be widespread spatial differences in people's health and the provision of health care that have been referred to by the media as 'a post-code lottery' (where someone lives affects their access to treatment). This has been exacerbated by the devolution of power to Scotland and Wales. Patients in England, for example, must pay for prescribed medicines while these are free in Scotland, Wales and Northern Ireland. Reforms to the NHS have reflected changing political views about citizenship and social rights (Mohan 1995, 2002). During the 1980s, the NHS (as with many public services) was subjected to 'internal markets' and various performance monitors (Hill 1994) and, in 2000, Primary Care Trusts (PCTs) were introduced in England to manage the provision of health care at a local and regional level. At the time of writing PCTs are set to be abolished in England and replaced by providers that will be chosen by competitive tender on 'price, quality and safety' (NHS 2013). Opponents fear this reflects a move to privatize the NHS and, with it, a change in its relationship with citizen-patients. A particular concern is that the use of market principles erodes the political right of patients to have a say in how the NHS is run. Decisions are made by managers accountable to shareholders rather than politicians accountable to citizens.

development of state apparatus reflected a growing belief in the civic, social and political rights of citizens.

It has been suggested that this approach has led to a passive form of citizenship, one where the citizen expects rights to be delivered to him or her by the state rather than contributing to their delivery (Desmoyers-Davis 2001). Passive citizenship places less emphasis on the duties of citizenship or the need for citizens to engage civically, socially or politically with state or neighbourhood. This might be evidenced in declining political participation, few formal duties (such as military or civic service) and, at the time Marshall was writing, the growth of the Welfare State and the National Health Service (NHS) (Box 2.2).

Marshall, though, recognized the significance of duties within this framework. He argued that citizens had a public duty to exercise the rights afforded to them by, for example, using opportunities provided by state schools to educate themselves and thereby contribute to the state:

> 'the duty to improve and civilise oneself is therefore a social duty, and not merely a personal one, because the social health of a society depends upon the civilisation of its members'.
>
> (Marshall 1950: 16)

In turn, the fulfilment of these duties may lead to other rights. Thus, the provision and acceptance of public education, he argued, led to more social rights in the twentieth century, not least because an educated populace was in a better position to understand, campaign for and use these rights and services.

Given his liberal political views, Marshall saw the development of rights as something that challenged and negated the inequalities of class and capital but did not overcome or replace them entirely. Citizenship to Marshall was concerned with equality of status rather than income. It often 'consisted not in the creation of new rights but the distribution of old rights to new sections of the population' (p.12). He argued:

> what matters is that there is a general enrichment of the concrete substance of civilised life, a general reduction of risk and insecurity, an equalisation between the more and the less fortunate at all levels – between healthy and sick, the employed and unemployed, the old and the active, the bachelor and the father of a large family.

> Equalisation is not so much between the classes as between individuals within a population which is now treated for this purpose as though it were one class.
>
> (Marshall 1950: 33)

Rights under citizenship afforded equality of treatment and basic standards of living for all. Although class equality was not Marshall's primary goal, he recognized that 'the preservation of economic inequalities has been made more difficult by the enrichment of citizenship. There is less room for them and there is more and more likelihood of them being challenged' (p.45). As such, Marshall's view of citizenship transcended market forces and consequently remains a powerful critique of recent, neo-liberal modes of service delivery (Moore 1991).

Marshall's essay remains an influential piece of work that has shaped modern discussions of citizenship (Lister 2003). It usefully charts when rights were established in Britain and provides something of a liberal manifesto on the rights that might be expected and enjoyed by modern citizens in a democratic country. It is also important in recording some of the spatial changes that occurred with the development of rights and, in particular, how these came to be associated with the nation-state. However, this rather British view has been challenged by the notion that citizenship is no longer, if it ever was, moored to the spaces of the nation-state.

Critiques of Marshall

There are well-rehearsed critiques of Marshall's work. Read today, it seems very optimistic: it was written at a time when the NHS (Box 2.2) and Welfare State were being established in Britain and, as Marshall mentions, inequalities in income were being reduced. Indeed, the period is sometimes regarded as a 'golden age' of inclusive citizenship (Bottomore 1991; Young 1999).

Some have also viewed his essay as descriptive, charting rather than explaining how rights were achieved (Turner 1986, 1990). Marshall himself recognizes that the development of rights overlapped but perhaps pays less attention to some of the struggles that occurred to achieve them (Giddens 1982). Universal suffrage, for example, was not just given away but was fought for by groups such as the suffragettes. Similarly, employment rights in the UK have been achieved through a long political struggle spearheaded by the trade union movement. Although many *de jure* rights have been achieved, in everyday *de facto* terms these are still open to abuse (Smith 1989).

The assumption that citizenship is gender-neutral has been widely challenged by feminist scholars (Sassen 2002; Lister 2003; McEwan 2005; Chouinard 2009). A key argument is that citizenship has been rooted in the public sphere so that private practices, which have dominated or repressed women, have largely gone unnoticed (Isin and Wood 1999). Marshall's work is also very Anglocentric (Mann 1996) and it is unclear whether his work is meant as a general model of citizenship or one that just pertains to Great Britain. The implied progression from civic to political to social rights did not occur in many countries in the order and to the extent described by Marshall (Turner 1986, 2009). It is certainly important to realize that the rights outlined by Marshall, and often taken as keystones to modern citizenship, have not been realized, achieved, gained or taken in many states (Janoski 1998) as organizations such as Amnesty International (AI) reveal (Box 2.3).

The kind of passive citizenship found in the UK is also not inevitable. To take one example, some states have developed more active forms of citizenship due to a wariness of state power and a desire, instead, for self-governance and self-determination, reflecting republican ideals of participation. Written in the nineteenth century, *Democracy in America* (2003 [1835–40]) by Alexis de Tocqueville (1805–59) posited that strong civic society, expressed through local authorities, voluntary groups and religious assemblies, provided an important counterbalance to state power by advocating political pluralism and power (Oommen 1997; Miller 2000).

Forms of 'thick' (Table 2.1) citizenship have become an influential narrative in the USA (Staeheli 2005, 2013), encouraging participation in town-hall meetings, religious congregations (Turner 2002) and in voluntary and civic groups. Local churches, for example, provide a platform for voluntary participation, leadership and democracy (Turner 1990, 2002; Isin and Turner 2007). Participating in such activities, which require some sacrifice of time and effort, helps to preserve republican forms of citizenship that stress a duty to participate in local society (Dagger 2002). Voluntary associations continue to be championed by authors such as Robert Putnam (2001) who argue that not only are they locally significant but they also contribute to a stronger state as they enable participation in society (Delanty 2002). Consequently, the

Box 2.3 THE LACK OF HUMAN RIGHTS

Amnesty International is an NGO that monitors and campaigns for human rights across the world. Its 2010 Annual Report, based on data from 159 countries, revealed a shocking lack of basic political, civic and social rights in many countries. These included:

- unfair trials in 55 countries;
- prisoners of conscience in 48 countries;
- freedom of expression restrictions in 96 countries; and
- the use of torture in 111 countries (http://thereport.amnesty.org/facts-and-figures – last accessed 6 August 2013).

In 2013, it reported that more than 100 million women were missing from the world's population as a result of infanticide; two-thirds of illiterate adults were women; more than 60 million girls were forced to marry before the age of 18; 358,000 women died from pregnancy and childbirth-related causes; and 3 million girls were at risk of genital mutilation (source: https://www.amnesty.org.uk/content.asp?CategoryID=10220 – last accessed 6 August 2013). These data highlight that women may not have the same rights as men in many places.

The organization has highlighted a link between the lack of rights and poverty, stressing that a right to life requires good health care and that freedom of expression requires a high standard of education. In 2013 it reported that 840 million people were chronically malnourished; 100 million had no access to education; and 11 million children die before the age of five every year (https://www.amnesty.org.uk/content.asp?CategoryID=11173 – last accessed 6 August 2013).

Amnesty International profiles human rights on a country-by-country basis. No countries are exempt and abuses of human rights can also be found in democratic countries where citizens have politic rights. For example, the use of the death penalty and the indefinite detention of people in Guantánamo Bay by the USA have been condemned; French anti-immigration laws were viewed as incompatible with the right to asylum; and, in Australia, high levels

Continued

of disadvantage and discrimination were recorded against indigenous people. Sadly, the list goes on (see reports on human rights by country: http://www.amnesty.org/en/human-rights – last accessed 6 August 2013) and serves as a warning that the rights argued for by Marshall are far from a reality in many places.

USA has followed an 'active' model of citizenship that stresses the importance of the individual and local community over that of the state (Figure 2.4).

In states where citizenship was achieved from below, the relationship between citizen and state is often celebrated publicly, sometimes on a daily basis. American schoolchildren often repeat the Pledge of Allegiance at the start of the day. French citizens celebrate Bastille Day on 14 July as a symbol of both national unity and the start of the modern French nation. It has been suggested that such conventions celebrate citizenship to remind citizens that it was achieved through struggle and of their duty to the state (Desmoyers-Davis 2001). Box 2.4 summarizes some ideas of citizenship and suggests how they are spatially manifested in and outside the nation-state.

Based on an analysis of Western nations, Turner (1990) proposed a fourfold model of citizenship that reflects whether citizenship has been driven from above or below the state and whether it favours either public

Table 2.1 Thick and thin citizenship (Source: Faulks, 2000)

Thin citizenship	Thick citizenship
Rights privileged	Rights and responsibilities as mutually supportive
Passive	Active
State as necessary evil	Political community (not necessarily the state) as foundation of good life
Purely public status	Pervades public and private
Independence	Interdependence
Freedom through choice	Freedom through civic virtue
Legal	Moral

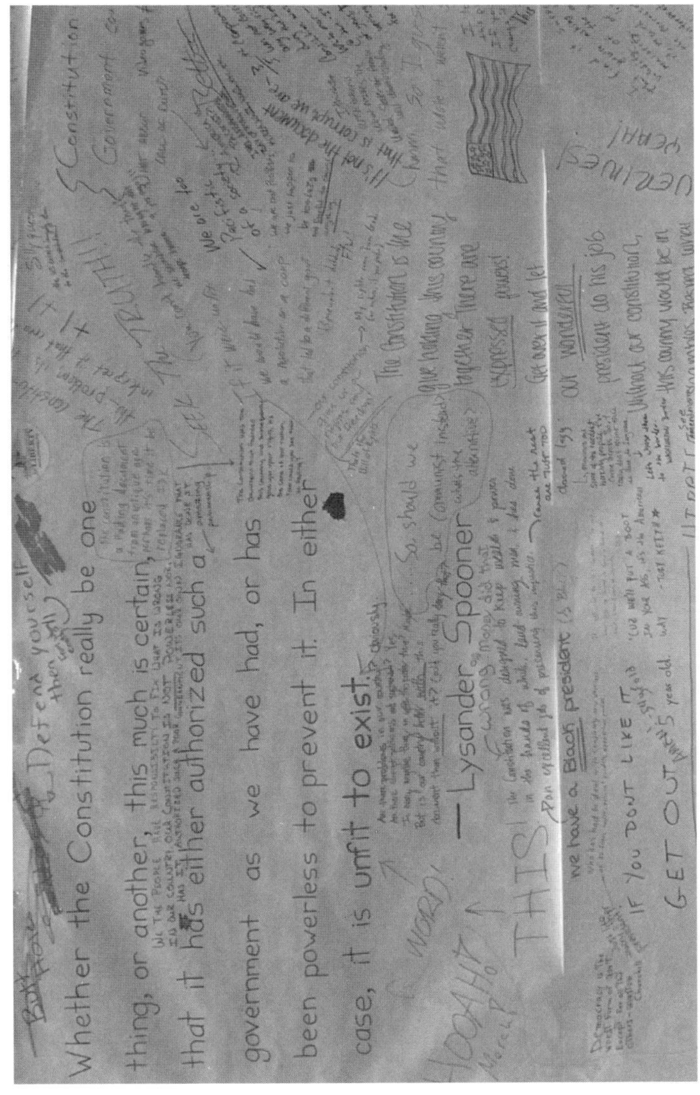

Figure 2.4 A public discussion in an American university about the American Constitution. Some of the comments reflect republican views of citizenship but, equally, show a diverse range of opinions about citizenship and the formal Constitution (Photo: Author)

Box 2.4 SOME NOMINATIVE THEORIES OF CITIZENSHIP AND SPACE (after Janoski and Gran 2002)

Liberal citizenship

Marshall's work is part of a *liberal* tradition of citizenship that emphasizes rights of individuals. This places less emphasis on the duties of citizenship and, consequently, citizenship is more passive. There is a greater expectation on the state and its institutions to ensure that the rights of individual citizens are met. Research has included work on welfare and service provision (Lewis 2004a) and the *de jure* and *de facto* rights of citizens.

Spatially, liberal citizenship is linked closely to the nation-state and its civic and political apparatus (Figure 2.5). Thus, council

Figure 2.5 The imposing Hotel de Ville (town hall) in Brest, France. Its dominant position in the city reflects the significance of the French state (Baker 2012) and its role in delivering rights and duties to its citizens (Photo: Author)

chambers, the welfare office, state-funded schools and hospitals are some of the sites where liberal ideas of citizenship are manifested, shaped and contested. A decision to close one of these sites may lead to protests that evoke the language of rights (Brown 2003).

Republican citizenship

Republican models of citizenship cover a wide range of ideas but tend to emphasize duties over rights. Active citizenship is championed as an obligation. Local participation and civic duty are seen to support a type of citizenship that stresses communal duties over individual rights. In his victory speech, President Obama made close reference to this idea:

> The role of citizen in our democracy does not end with your vote. America's never been about what can be done for us. It's about what can be done by us together through the hard and frustrating, but necessary work of self-government. That's the principle we were founded on.
>
> (President Obama, 7 November 2012)

This implies a consensus but forms of participatory republicanism recognize difference and aim to support an expansive democracy that represents the rights and participation of under-represented groups.

Academic work on active citizenship and volunteering, the development of social capital and civic participation has both advocated and critiqued republican views of citizenship (Putnam 2001; Fyfe and Milligan 2003b).

Republican citizenship is most apparent in places below the scale of the nation-state, especially those of local communities. These tend to be the spaces of formal voluntary schemes, civic centres or constituted community groups (Figure 2.6).

Continued

Figure 2.6 The premises of the Country Women's Association of Australia in the rural settlement of Jennacubbine, Western Australia, provides a place for women to engage in community affairs and decision making (Photo: Author)

Post-national citizenship

Post-national citizenship considers that the state may not be the only reference point for citizens.

It encompasses work on transnational and dual citizenship that examines how formal rights may be bestowed on citizens of one state by other states or superstates. More widely, the concepts of diasporic and cosmopolitan citizenship recognize the significance of international linkages based on cultural, if not political, formations of citizenship. Finally, work at scales below the state, in regional or devolved sites, explores how changes in state governance impact on citizenship.

It is therefore possible to examine post-national citizenship at a range of scales above and below the state. These may or may not be connected, although emphasis is often placed on tracing interconnections between these different sites. Figure 2.7 shows the

Figure 2.7 Protestors from the Occupy movement camped outside Drake Circus Shopping Centre, Plymouth, UK. This site was part of a wider transnational network campaigning against the accumulation of wealth in the hands of a few (Chapter 5). Similar, linked sites were found in urban centres across the globe (Photo: Author)

site of an Occupy protest (see Chapter 5) that is connected by media and common political causes to other sites, in other cities around the world.

Post-modern citizenship

Post-modern views of citizenship recognize diversity and difference, emphasizing cultural and social rather than national identities.

The scope of scholarly work in this area is diverse and includes studies of aboriginal peoples, gender, sexual citizenship, religion, age and disability (Figure 2.8).

Continued

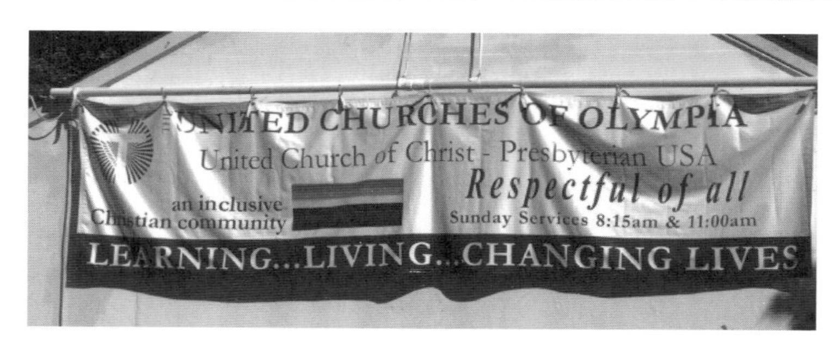

Figure 2.8 A church in Olympia, Washington State, USA displays the Rainbow Flag associated with gay pride. It attempts to offer an inclusive space on the basis of religious and sexual identities (Photo: Author)

Some work has examined efforts to reclaim space and assert *de facto* or *de jure* rights associated with belonging to a state. Other work has considered how local spaces can be used as sites of resistance (Pickerill and Krinsky 2012) or to confer identity and belonging as citizens (Holsten 2008) (Figure 2.8).

More broadly, some geographers have recognized the relational and multiscalar nature of space in determining identity. Thus, post-modern views recognize that identity as citizens comes not from the spaces of the state but also from spaces beyond and below its boundaries. Work focuses on how flows of ideas, information and people between spaces can shape cultural citizenship (Closs Stephens and Squire 2012b).

or private space (Table 2.2). Mann (1996) also outlines how countries which had liberal (USA, Switzerland), reformist (France, Spain, Italy), authoritarian monarchist (Austria, Russia, Japan), fascist (Nazi Germany) and authoritarian socialist (Soviet Russia) regimes followed different trajectories of citizenship that reflect their geopolitical and state histories. In all cases, however, these models are largely based on the experiences of Western or European countries, which has led Isin (2005: 35) to conclude that although various paradigms of citizenship have emerged, 'liberalism, republicanism and communitarianism are really different ways of telling the same occidental narrative' (Isin 2005: 35).

Table 2.2 Turner's (1990) typology of modern citizenship

Citizenship		
Below	**Above**	**Public space**
Revolutionary France	*Passive* England	**Positively emphasized**
Liberalism America	*Fascist* Germany	**Negatively emphasized**

BEYOND WESTERN BOUNDARIES

Ideas of citizenship have tended to reflect European values to the exclusion of non-Western ideas and states (Bulmer and Rees 1996; Isin 2002; McEwan 2005; Nyers 2007; Ho 2008; Isin 2012b; Kyung-Sup and Turner 2012). This is in part because the nation-state emerged from the European geopolitical arena. As European powers colonized other parts of the world, the European model of state-citizenship was imposed on other places as a dominant model of citizenship. This neglected or repressed existing forms of citizenship. Isin (2002, 2005) considers that a combination of what he terms 'orientalism' (a distorted view of the orient reflecting Western values (see Said 1978)) and 'synoecism' (incorporating tribes into a city-state) led to this exclusivity:

> Orientalism mobilized images of citizenship as a unique occidental invention that oriental cultures lacked and of the citizen as a virtuous and rational being without kinship ties. Synoecism generated images of citizenship as fraternity, equality, liberty, expressed as a unified and harmonious polity, and of the citizen as a secular and universal being without tribal loyalties.
>
> (Isin 2002: 118)

Max Weber's work has significantly influenced the association of citizenship with orientalism (Turner 1974; Isin 2005). Weber considered that Christianity played an important role in breaking down tribal associations, leading to the development of independent cities that became the basis of social organization and citizen contracts (Turner 1974). By contrast, oriental settlements were viewed as less autonomous because kinship, clan and tribe continued to be significant beyond their city walls. Kinship, rather than locality, therefore provided the basis for social organization that, in turn, led to different understandings of citizenship (Turner 2012). Weber's ideas strongly influenced the work of many twentieth-century scholars on citizenship to the extent that many efforts to critique or falsify them remained wedded to the occidental/oriental binary (for a full review see Isin 2005). Marshall discusses 'civilization' but affords little time to identifying what this is and, implicitly, takes a common culture for granted (Lister 2003). There is no reference to ethnicity or race in his thesis. More recent accounts have explored how the cultural and political nature of identity has impacted on citizenship (Isin and Wood 1999; Pykett 2010).

Consequently some scholars are critical of the whole concept of citizenship because of its Western bias. Cheryl McEwan (2005) traces how the use of Western concepts of citizenship has been problematic in South Africa. Here the state introduced formal methods of consultation aimed at empowering local citizens in local decision making. McEwan's analysis reveals that participation in these spaces is mediated by existing power structures and social relationships. In particular, established gender roles made it difficult for women to participate in consultation exercises, rendering the practice of citizenship 'a meaningless concept'. McEwan argues that these forms of citizenship should not be the *only* spaces for dialogue and, instead, she calls for greater attention to be paid to the voices expressed in more radical spaces that have been carved out by marginalized people, including women, the young and unemployed youths (see also Nyamnjoh 2007). For McEwan, conceptions of citizenship largely rest on the 'abstract, universal and western-centric notion of the individual and are consequently unable to recognize either the political relevance of gender or of non-western perspectives and experiences' (2005: 971).

Elaine Lynn-Ee Ho (Ho 2008: 1296) concurs with this view, championing the need for 'a fuller appreciation of citizenship experiences arising from alternative histories, contexts, intellectual traditions and political immediacies'. Greater attention should be paid to the cultural sensitivities of different people and places beyond Western Europe. She notes, for example, that the Korean, Japanese and Thai languages ascribe different meanings to terms such as state, territory or border that have such important associations for Western citizenship. It is important to move beyond Western definitions and linguistics to appreciate how citizenship plays out in different cultural settings.

To this end, more studies are being undertaken to understand citizenship from different, non-European perspectives (for examples of collections of studies see Chang 2012; Isin 2012b; Jakimów 2012; Shaw and Štiks 2012; Turner 2012). Isin (2005) proposed three directions for examining new political subjectivities of citizenship. First, efforts should be made to 'undo' citizenship through approaches that avoid orientalism or colonialism. Second, efforts should be made to 'uncover' forms of citizenship that have been hidden by hegemonic juridical-political discourses. This work should seek to recognize the legitimacy of alternative forms of citizenship that have been hidden by colonialism (Isin 2005). McEwan's work, for example, argues that greater attention should be given to the significance of African women's voices by examining their participation outside formal political channels (see also Chapter 7). Finally attention should be given to ways of 'reinventing' citizenship by studying acts of citizenship that allow new ways for people to act as political subjects (Isin and Nielson 2008). Examples might include new social movements that give spaces for previously excluded groups to express views and make local decisions (see also Chapter 7). These directions are being explored via Isin's Oecumene project (www.oecumene.eu/research – last accessed 6 August 2013) at the OU that aims to 'deorientalize' citizenship by, amongst other things, deconstructing colonial histories of citizenship (Harrington 2012; Nahaboo 2012); critiquing Eurocentric views of sexuality (Nahaboo 2012); examining Arabic performative traditions (Dajani 2012) and the political role of mathas (religious institutions) in India (Ikegame 2012); highlighting literary resistance to dam building in India (Marino 2012); evaluating the significance of Muslim family law in the UK (Pilgram 2012); and critiquing immigration regimes (Barbero 2012). This work has led Isin (2012a: 567) to conclude that it is now 'very difficult to imagine citizenship merely as nationality or membership in the nation-state'.

CITIZENSHIP BEYOND THE STATE

As heavily defended borders testify, territory can be used at a range of scales to define space and exclude groups from space (Amoore 2006; Staeheli 2008a; Elden 2010; Storey 2012). Borders, as Staeheli points out, are:

> important to the process of distinguishing citizens or potential citizens. These efforts are promoted as ways to protect citizens

> within a country from 'illegal' migrants or from those who would do harm, whether by taking jobs from citizens, by imposing burdens on taxpayers, by challenging social norms, or through physical violence. Yet these border controls are part of a larger dynamic of exclusion and 'othering' that is integral to nation-states and the ways that citizenship is often imagined and reinforced through discourses of fear.
>
> (Staeheli 2011: 394)

Desforges *et al.* similarly note that:

> border defences and crossing points, customs posts and immigration stations, meanwhile, form landscapes that demarcate the territorial limits of national citizenship. In this way, landscapes of national citizenship have tended to reproduce a model of citizenship as a singular identity awarded and controlled by the state.
>
> (Desforges *et al.* 2005: 442)

A territorial conceptualization of citizenship may be prone to reproducing these somewhat insular views. Instead of seeing citizenship as something that is contained or excluded by a state's borders, geographers have therefore started to consider how a citizen's identity is shaped beyond boundaries.

Doreen Massey (1991) has argued for a 'global sense of place' that recognizes that places are shaped by their global connections as much as by any local characteristics. People, goods, ideas and money move across and between different places in the world, producing global networks and flows that connect different places well beyond state boundaries (Appadurai 1990, 2008). National identity can also extend across state borders: diasporic communities may identify as citizens of places outside their state of residence (Nagel and Staeheli 2008) and more people than ever before hold dual citizenship (Sassen 2002). Similarly, work on mobility (Germann Molz 2005; Sheller and Urry 2006; Adey 2010; Cresswell 2010, 2011) has stressed the significance of movement between places and scales over static geographies embedded in territorial boundaries.

In keeping with this thinking, Closs Stephens and Squire (2012b) attempt to conceive citizenship 'without' community by describing it as a series of political *encounters* that can exceed territorial units. Employing the metaphor of a web, they argue for a relational understanding of citizenship that moves away from predefined identities, territories and political subjects. This is articulated clearly in Desforges *et al.*'s idea of a 'multi-levelled' sense of citizenship that:

> is defined and articulated by engagement with different scales of political authority and with a range of other social identities. Alongside this, it may be argued, are multi-scalar responsibilities of citizenship, expressed both through the different responsibilities felt by individuals towards the different contexts in which their citizenship is defined (nation, locality, faith and so on), and through the ways in which citizens are exhorted to act out the responsibilities of citizenship at different scales.
>
> (Desforges *et al.* 2005: 441)

By way of example, a householder who chooses to recycle goods is simultaneously engaging with his or her state though the local council (which may provide a recycling service), as well as with global initiatives to improve sustainability, and at the same time is acting in the private space of his or her home.

Given that many issues, such as climate change, recession, terrorism or military campaigns, are global in their extent, more cosmopolitan views of citizenship seek to persuade citizens that they have political and moral obligations beyond the boundaries of their state (Linklater 2002). This questions whether citizenship finds its strongest expression in the nation-state or whether people articulate a sense of citizenship at a global level.

CONCLUSIONS: NEW SPACES OF CITIZENSHIP?

This chapter has traced the spatial development of citizenship, from Greek city-states to the nation-state and beyond. Modern ideas of citizenship have been most closely associated with the nation-state and its boundaries, but as recent work has demonstrated, these associations can be problematic given changes in the power and institutional framework of the nation-state and new forms of cultural identity that are not always linked to territory (of the nation-state). In part, this signifies an erosion of political power as the nation-state has been 'hollowed out' through devolution, localism, privatization and transnationalism and, in turn, 'filled in' with a range of new governance structures and actors that span the public, private and voluntary sectors and operate in an increasingly complex web of overlapping spaces (Jessop 1997; Goodwin *et al.* 2005; Shaw and MacKinnon 2011). It also reflects a growing cultural diversity that challenges associations with a particular state and, instead, aligns citizens with different, non-territorial groups based on religious, social, sexual, racial or ethnic identities (Jackson 2010). Political communities are more complex than the boundaries of the nation-state and, consequently, new spaces of citizenship are emerging (Painter 2002).

Citizenship 'has multiple dimensions, only some of which might be inextricably linked to the national state' (Sassen 2002: 277). It might be concluded that the nation-state forms 'only one of the possible institutional forms of the community of citizens' (Balibar 2012: 438). Joe Painter (2002: 93) argues that citizenship should now be thought of as 'multi-level', reflecting 'individuals' simultaneous membership of political communities at a variety of spatial scales (local, regional, nation-state and European) and perhaps of non-territorial social groups, such as religions, sexual minorities and ethnic diasporas'. Thought of in this way, citizenship might be conceived as 'relational' rather than absolute, something that is constituted by its connections with different people and places rather than something defined by the borders of the nation-state (Desforges *et al.* 2005). Citizenship remains inherently geographical but, rather than being entirely defined by fixed boundaries, it is also fluid, mobile and multidimensional in nature.

This said, the nation-state continues to be the basis of *de jure* citizenship and so it would probably be premature to dismiss its significance in the formation and regulation of citizenship. Tim Cresswell (2009: 271) summarizes this dilemma, emphasizing the importance of space and scale in its resolution:

> 'The nation-state, however, configured is a key part of this assemblage but there is a lot of detail between the space of the nation and the body of the citizen that is brimming over with geography.'
>
> (Cresswell 2009: 271)

FURTHER READING

Engin Isin and Bryan Turner's (2002) edited collection *The Handbook of Citizenship Studies* provides an excellent introduction to the many forms of citizenship and how the term has been debated and understood by politicians and academics. Richard Bellamy's (2008) *A Very Short Introduction to Citizenship* is an accessible and widely available introduction to political citizenship. T. H. Marshall's (1950) 'Citizenship and social class' remains a seminal essay that should be read by students of citizenship. The OU's 'Oecumene: Citizenship after Orientalism' project, led by Engin Isin (2012b, www.oecumene.eu/research – last accessed 6 August 2013), reports on a range of exciting and innovative research projects that challenge orientalist and state-centred visions of citizenship. A recent issue of *Environment and Planning D: Society and Space* (2012, vol. 30.3) offers a set of papers on the theme of *Citizenship without Community* that challenges associations between citizenship and bounded communities.

3

CITIZENSHIP AND MOBILITY

INTRODUCTION

It is tempting to think of citizenship as something that is fixed and defined within national boundaries. However, as the world has become more mobile (Sheller and Urry 2006), questions have been raised as to whether citizenship continues to be defined by state borders or whether an interconnected world has loosened the moorings of state and citizen, leading to new formations of citizenship (Castles and Davidson 2000; Desforges *et al.* 2005; Ho 2008; Castles and Miller 2009; Staeheli 2011). After all, citizens are not static people:

> all the world seems to be on the move. Asylum seekers, international students, terrorists, members of diasporas, holidaymakers, business people, sports stars, refugees, backpackers, commuters, the early retired, young mobile professionals, prostitutes, armed forces these and many others fill the world's airports, buses, ships, and trains. The scale of this travelling is immense. Internationally there are over 700 million legal passenger arrivals each year (compared with 25 million in 1950) with a predicted 1 billion by 2010; there are 4 million air passengers each day; 31 million refugees are displaced from their homes; and there is one car for every 8.6 people. These diverse yet intersecting mobilities have many consequences for different

> peoples and places that are located in the fast and slow lanes across the globe.
>
> (Sheller and Urry 2006: 207)

Rather than disrupting citizenship, mobility defines it (Cresswell 2006a, 2006b). The ability to move between places and to claim universal rights within them are defining features of being a citizen (Marshall 1950 [1992]; Cresswell 2009). Restrictions on mobility are often associated with restrictions on the rights associated with citizenship. This chapter uses a range of scales to explore the relationship between mobility and citizenship. It begins by examining how new forms of international mobility are leading to new forms of citizenship that challenge its relationship with the nation-state.

CITIZENSHIP AND INTERNATIONAL MOBILITY

Citizenship, immigration and identity

For most, citizenship is granted through a simple coincidence of birth (Kofman 2002) and, occasionally, acts such as passing through immigration controls (where passports or visas are required to prove status and confer rights of entry/exit) serve to remind citizens of their status (Cresswell 2006a). These events aside, citizenship is often taken for granted and is rarely considered by citizens going about their daily business in their home country (Skelton 2006; Pykett *et al.* 2010). Yet, for others, citizenship is something that must be sought, gained, earned or approved (Alexander and Klumsemeyer 2000). Examples here include people who use citizenship for strategic reasons to support lifestyles or businesses, those who migrate for reasons of economic opportunity and those who are driven from their own countries as refugees (Samers 2010).[1] While status as a citizen can affect these various movements, it is important to realize that migration can also impact on how citizenship is defined and regulated (Ho 2008).

Increasingly, countries experiencing high rates (or perceived high rates) of immigration are seeking to regulate it more closely through tighter border security, limits to migration and the imposition of restrictions as to who can gain citizenship (Castles and Davidson 2000; Castles and Miller 2009). Legislation, quotas of migrants, more stringent border security, the streamlining of removal processes, confinement of asylum seekers, citizenship tests, a lack of welfare support and the withdrawal of rights to work are just some of the features of 'fortress policies' that have attempted to prevent, discourage and deport migrants (Kofman and Sales 1992; Robinson 1996; Leitner 1997; MacLaughlin 1998; Peers 1998; Tesfahuney 1998; Gallagher 2002; Koff 2008; Weber 2012). State policies and practices continue to play an important role in stratifying flows of EU migration, making movement easier for some groups than for others (Kofman 2002).

The UK, for example, introduced 16 pieces of legislation concerning citizenship and immigration between 2000 and 2010, compared with just two in the 1980s. In these ways, states are attempting to define, guard and reassert citizenship in relation to national identity (Kofman 2002). This is most strongly reflected in the adoption of citizenship tests in many countries, including Canada, Australia, the Netherlands, USA, Germany and France. Ostensibly, these tests aim to inform and examine prospective citizens on the daily life, history, politics and tradition of host states but they also link citizenship with national identity in a rather prescribed way (Box 3.1).

Box 3.1 AUSTRALIAN CITIZENSHIP TEST

A citizenship test was introduced in Australia in 2007 under John Howard's government to encourage 'people to find out more about Australia, as well as understanding the responsibilities and privileges that being an Australian citizen brings' (http://www.citizenship.gov.au/learn/cit_test/about_test/ – last accessed 6 August 2013). It is based on the publication 'Australian Citizenship: Our Common Bond' (Australian Government 2012), which contains three testable sections (see Table 3.1) on: 'Australia and its people', 'Australia's democratic beliefs, rights and liberties' and 'Government and the law in Australia'.

Fozdar and Spittles (2009) refer to the introduction of the test as a form of 'dog whistle' politics or one that contains meanings or ideas not discernible by the general populace. Despite a language of inclusion, the tests celebrated Australia's colonial past with its Judeo-Christian and Anglo-Saxon/Celtic heritage. The Australia citizen was viewed as 'a European citizen, accidentally located in the Pacific, with little connection to the Indigenous population nor the array of ethno-cultural heritages of the country's vast migrant population' (Fozdar and Spittles 2009: 512). Indigenous histories and cultures were mainly ignored, as were the contributions of non-Anglo-Irish migrants and cultures in

Table 3.1 Practice questions for the Australian citizenship test (Source: Australian Government (2012: 34–35))

Part 1: Australia and its people

1. What do we remember on Anzac Day?
   a. The landing of the Australian and New Zealand Army Corps at Gallipoli, Turkey
   b. The arrival of the first free settlers from Great Britain
   c. The landing of the First Fleet at Sydney Cove
2. What are the colours of the Australian Aboriginal Flag?
   a. Black, red and yellow
   b. Green, white and black
   c. Blue, white and green
3. Which official symbol of Australia identifies Commonwealth property?
   a. The national anthem
   b. Australia's national flower
   c. Commonwealth Coat of Arms

Part 2: Australia's democratic beliefs, rights and liberties

4. Which of these statements about Australia's system of government is correct?
   a. The Queen of Australia chooses people to form the Australian parliament
   b. The government is elected by the people
   c. The Prime Minister chooses our Members of Parliament
5. Which of these is an example of freedom of speech?
   a. People can peacefully protest against government decisions
   b. Men and women are treated equally in a court of law
   c. Australians are free to not follow a religion

Continued

Table 3.1 Continued

6. Which of these statements about government in Australia is correct?
   a. The government does not allow some religions
   b. Government in Australia is secular
   c. Religious laws are passed by parliament
7. Which of these is an example of equality in Australia?
   a. Everyone follows the same religion
   b. Men and women have the same rights
   c. Everyone belongs to the same political party

8. Which of these is a responsibility of Australian citizens aged 18 years or over?
   a. To attend local council meetings
   b. To vote in elections
   c. To have a current Australian passport
9. Which of these is a responsibility of Australian citizens aged 18 years or over?
   a. To do local community service
   b. To carry a passport at all times
   c. To serve on a jury if called to do so
10. Which of these statements about passports is correct?
   a. Australian citizens can apply for an Australian passport
   b. Permanent residents can hold an Australian passport
   c. Australian citizens need a passport and visa to return to Australia

PART 3: Government and the law in Australia

11. Which of these statements about voting in Australian elections is correct?
   a. People are free and safe to vote for any candidate
   b. Voting is by a show of hands
   c. People must write their name on their vote
12. What happened in Australia on 1 January 1901?
   a. The Australian Constitution was changed by a referendum
   b. The Australian Constitution came into effect
   c. The Australian and New Zealand Army Corps was formed

Table 3.1 Continued

13. What is the name of the legal document that sets out the rules for the government of Australia?
    a. The Australian Federation
    b. The Australian Commonwealth
    c. The Australian Constitution
14. What is a referendum?
    a. A vote to change the government
    b. A vote to change the Australian Constitution
    c. A vote to change the Prime Minister
15. Which arm of government has the power to interpret and apply laws?
    a. Legislative
    b. Executive
    c. Judicial
16. Which of these is a role of the Governor-General?
    a. The appointment of state premiers
    b. The signing of Bills passed by the Australian Parliament
    c. The appointment of the Head of State
17. Which of these statements about state governments is correct?
    a. All states have the same constitution
    b. Each state has its own constitution
    c. The states have no constitution
18. What is the name given to the party or coalition of parties with the second largest number of members in the House of Representatives?
    a. The Government
    b. The Opposition
    c. The Senate
19. What is the name of a proposal to make a law in parliament?
    a. Royal Assent
    b. Bill
    c. Debate
20. Who maintains peace and order in Australia?
    a. Public servants
    b. Police
    c. Lawyers

(Answers are given at the end of this chapter.)

Continued

Australia. Fozdar and Spittles conclude the test was introduced for 'the purpose of exclusion rather than inclusion' (p.512), arguing that it followed 'authoritarian communitarian' values that emphasized social order and limited individual rights (such as the ability to hold values other than those viewed as 'Australian'). The monocultural perspective of the test was reflected in the relatively high failure rates of refugees sitting the tests when compared with 'skilled workers'.

Following a review of the test in 2008 by Kevin Rudd's centre-left government, the test was linked more closely with the legislative requirements for becoming a citizen, rather than general knowledge about Australian history, culture and key figures (Fozdar and Spittles 2010). (In contrast, the UK citizenship test now places greater emphasis on culture and history rather than daily legalities.) Subsequently, the preparation for the test included additional sections on 'Australia today' and 'Our Australian story'. These included more information on indigenous histories and cultures, including the oppression of indigenous cultures by white settlers (so-called 'black armband' histories) (Australian Government 2012). However, applicants are not tested on these sections and English remains the required language of the test.

Citizenship tests are problematic because they attempt to link citizenship with one politically prescribed form of identity. They take little account of the dynamic, fluid and diverse ways in which individuals identify with citizenship and the nation-state (Isin and Wood 1999; Ehrkamp and Leitner 2006; Leitner and Ehrkamp 2006).

Although states grant *de jure* citizenship, identity as a citizen is increasingly seen as something that is gained beyond and below the state. Toby Miller (2002: 242) states:

> citizenship is no longer easily based on soil or blood. Rather, it is founded on some variant of those qualities in connection with culture . . . the state is no longer the sole frame of citizenship in the face of new nationalisms and cross-border affinities.
>
> (Miller 2002: 242)

Similarly, Peter Jackson (2010: 139) draws attention to 'cultural citizenship' which is 'much less territorially contained and tends to emphasise the emotional or affective dimensions of citizenship rather than its strictly legal or political aspects' (see Table 3.2). Rather than choosing a new state over the old, many migrants maintain transnational social and economic links between two nation-states (Ho 2008). It is unlikely that even those who pass a test actually identify with a single, prescribed view of citizenship.

Citizens' identities shape and are shaped by transglobal flows of people and information (Appadurai 1990) including religion (Hopkins 2010), politics (Routledge *et al.* 2007) or cultural practices (Ehrkamp 2006; Griffiths 2010) as well as the everyday lives and emotive experiences lived out in particular localities (Staeheli and Nagel 2006; Veronis 2006; Ho 2009; Pine 2010).

Efforts to 'fix' citizenship by the state are often short-term and subject to modification. This is because what is understood by citizenship is 'usually shaped more by historical experience, existing cultural norms and expedient political calculations than by deduction from abstract principles or compelling reasons of logical consistency' (Alexander and Klumsemeyer 2000: 2). In 2004, for example, a referendum in the Republic of Ireland led to an amendment of its constitution to remove citizenship from any future Irish-born children of immigrant parents (Tormey 2007). The favouring of *jus sanguinis* over *jus soli* reflected concerns about perceived increases in immigration, especially by asylum seekers, and 'baby tourism' (Harrington 2005) whereby women allegedly travelled to Ireland to give birth in order to claim citizenship for their children. Tormey (2007) suggests that the referendum succeeded as its

Table 3.2 Citizenship and identity (Source: Jackson 2010)

National identity	**Cultural identity**
Citizenship as a political and/or legal contract	Citizenship as a social or cultural construction
Based on established state boundaries and maintaining these	Fluid and transnational
Formal notions of political rights and identities	Wider geographical imaginations based on a global sense of place

advocates successfully positioned citizenship as 'a moral regime' with foreign nationals, their offspring and foetuses as 'suspect patriots'.

States experiencing net emigration also attempt to redefine citizenship for their advantage (Ho 2011). Mexico, for example, has sought to extend citizenship to emigrants in order to maintain formal links with their citizens who have moved abroad (Escobar 2006). Ho (2008) notes that in 2004 children born to second-generation emigrants from Singapore were granted citizenship of Singapore and that, in 2005, ethnic Indians who had become naturals of other countries were granted 'Overseas Citizenship of India' status. She argues that this courting of diaspora points to a form of 'extraterritorial citizenship' (Ho 2011) that provides 'an appropriate way of managing the multiple identities that arise from globalization' (Castles and Davidson 2000: 87). These forms of citizenship recognize that political and cultural identity extends beyond the neat borders of the state (Linklater 2002).

TRANSNATIONAL CITIZENSHIP

The concept of transnationalism recognizes that ideas and practices of citizenship cross national boundaries (Favell 2004). It emphasizes that immigrants engage in diverse practices that link their places of origin with their places of destination. For example, local groups may lend voluntary aid and charitable support to asylum seekers or illegal immigrants (Darling 2011). These interactions are so significant that it has been argued 'that sending and receiving societies should be understood as constituting a single field of analysis, given the multiple attachments and multi-stranded social relations experienced by migrants towards their societies of origin and settlement' (Ho 2008: 1287). Rather than considering places of origin and settlement in binary terms, research has focused on how these places are simultaneously linked by transnational flows of people and ideas.

In a study of British migrants to rural France, Benson (2011b, 2011a) demonstrates that migrants' mobile practices and their expectations of mobility contributed towards the perceived success of their new lives. These:

> included but were not limited to, physical, imaginative and communicative travel. As they travelled from their homes to those of their

> friends living locally and more distantly, as they walked around the local market, and as they sent an email or picked up the telephone to call their families, it became clear that mobilities were an important part of how they experienced their new lives abroad.
>
> (Benson 2011a: 228)

These connections also reinforced a feeling that they could return to Britain if an emergency occurred and a sense that they were not too far from family and friends.

While some migrants engaged in diasporic practices, such as playing in largely English cricket teams, others made efforts to engage in French daily lives and local organizations (Benson 2011c; Ferbrache 2011). Benson traces how these practices led to a range of complex identities and interactions. Some positioned themselves as part of the local community ('We are not expats; we are not migrants; we are Sauliacoise' (Benson 2011c: 80)) and, in doing so, differentiated themselves from immigrants who, they felt, had not integrated into French society. Benson's work highlights the need to understand transnational citizenship from a macro viewpoint (the EU regulations that allowed movement) but also that: 'it is no longer possible to ignore the local, even when exploring the lives of transnational migrants' (Benson 2011c: 80).

In an ethnographic study of migrants in Germany and the USA, Leitner and Ehrkamp (2006) note that ideas of national citizenship are important for migrants seeking equal protection under the law and access to social and political rights. At the same time, they also recognize that naturalized migrants experience discrimination, making it hard to belong within frameworks of national citizenship. They conclude that migrants negotiate multiple identities and allegiances, with varying outcomes. The desire to be part of more than one national community challenges the concept of bounded national citizenship as these extend across state boundaries. This supports the notion of 'post-national' (Soysal 1994; Sassen 2002) or 'multi-layered' citizenship (Painter 2002) of 'regional associations, international legal institutions, and transnational economic, cultural and political organisations, all "semi"-sovereign in some spheres of some people's lives, [which] are said to shape humanity's future more than existing national regimes' (Smith 2002: 112). More broadly, this underlines the need for empirical work on the daily lives of migrants to understand better the nature and impact of transnational citizenship and mobilities on citizen identities in host and sending countries (Favell 2003, 2004; Ho 2008; Pine 2011; Ehrkamp and Nagel 2012).

Studies of transnational citizenship have tended to focus on adults but it is important to consider the experiences of young people who often face migration in different ways to adults (Bushin and White 2010). Schools, playgrounds, clubs, sports clubs and informal spaces used by young people provide important sites for identities as citizens to be negotiated and performed, often in different ways to their parents (Ní Laoire *et al.* 2011; Tyrrell *et al.* 2012).

All too often transnationalism is applied to describe the often complex lifestyles and identities of 'super-rich', 'super-mobile' citizens of the West (Sparke 2006; Walsh 2006; Coles and Walsh 2010; Smiley 2010; Beaverstock 2011; Ho 2011; Pow 2011; Walsh 2012). Ho (2008) quite rightly calls for more attention to be paid to the transnational experiences of people leaving Asian and African countries. As well as adding empirical depth, such work also has the potential to challenge largely Western derived models of citizenship (Nyamnjoh 2007; Chang and Turner 2011). Through her own work on Singaporean expatriates in London (Ho 2009), she reveals that 'even though overseas Singaporeans are not under the direct purview of the Singaporean state, they are still emotionally and behaviourally self-conscious of their subjugation as subjects of the state' (p.799). She argues that emotions such as fear or aversion hamper the ability of these migrants to claim and articulate fully their claims on citizenship. In this way, Singaporean migrants are deemed to retain an 'emotional contract' with their home state that is just as important to their lives as more widely recognized (Western) political-legal and social-cultural aspects of citizenship.

Mobility is stratified (Kofman 2002; Cresswell 2006a, 2009; Sheller and Urry 2006; Adey 2010) and many citizens, especially in the majority world, have fewer opportunities and rights to move or migrate (especially in light of the 'fortress policies' described at the start of this chapter). In a study of young people growing up in eastern Germany, Hörschelmann and Schafer (2007) show that opportunities to travel, migrate or engage at a global level are unequal and reflect socio-economic and cultural disadvantage. Samers (2010) identifies a continuum of migrants encompassing full citizens of a single nation-state; dual, transnational and cosmopolitan citizens with varying rights and duties; denizenship; and, finally, illegal residents and aliens with no or few rights at all.

Within this spectrum, the term denizens refers to 'foreign citizens with a legal and permanent resident status' (Hammer 1990: 15) or 'non-nationals that enjoy social and civil rights but not "full political inclusion"' (Shearing and Wood 2003: 407) on the basis of '*jus domicili*' (law of residence). Alternatively, some denizens may have political rights. Denizenship can be a useful concept because it can help to break down the binary of citizen and alien and recognize that some people fall between these two categories (Cresswell 2009). For some people this is desirable because it is possible to claim some important rights without ceding citizenship of their home country. For example, Irish and Commonwealth citizens who are residents of the UK have the political right to vote in general elections in the UK but are able to retain the citizenship and identity of their home state.

In other cases, denizens and illegal migrants can suffer exploitation through dangerous, dirty and degrading work as well as social hostility. They may have little recourse to the law and no political voice (Chouinard 2009; Samers 2010). Bryan Turner notes a 'deep contradiction' between the need for mobile labour and the state's political need to assert sovereignty. The result is an 'enclave society' based on 'gated societies, ghettoes, quarantine zones, prisons, camps and similar arrangements' (Turner 2007: 287; see also Sidaway 2007). Given these circumstances, it would appear that transnational citizenship remains far from universal.

MOBILE LIFESTYLES

Tim Cresswell (2006a: 152) argues that 'to be a citizen you needed to have the ability to travel – to be mobile'. In feudal society, where 'the vast majority of people lived their lives pretty much where they were born' (Cresswell 2009: 259) strangers were easily identified. As society became more mobile it also became more anonymous. Passports, identity cards and national support networks developed in response to a need to define and classify who legitimately belonged in a place. These determined who were lawfully allowed into certain spaces and the rights and duties they held within them. People were identified not as strangers, but as citizens. Yet these rights have often rested on having a fixed place of abode. Addresses have been used to determine social rights (for example, access to services such as schools), political rights (the right to vote determined by an electoral roll that is usually based on the addresses of voters) and civic rights such as employment.

In contrast, mobile lifestyles are seen to challenge taken-for-granted assumptions of sedentary citizenship and many states have acted to restrict those who follow mobile or nomadic lifestyles (Cresswell 2001, 2006a). Some of the clearest examples of this can be seen in settler countries where efforts have been made to impose sedentary lifestyles on nomadic, indigenous groups through the imposition of reservations or settlements that have confined these people to particular territories (see also Chapter 7). Elsewhere, gypsies have often been subject to moral panics over dirt and disease (Sibley 1995), crime (Yarwood and Gardner 2000) and superstition (Halfacree 1996a) that have pushed them, literally and imaginatively, to the edge of settled society and have subjected them to legislation aimed at limiting both mobility and the right to reside in temporary sites (Sibley 1981, 1995; Cresswell 1996; Halfacree 1996b; MacLaughlin 1998; Holloway 2004, 2005). In 2010, up to 10,000 Roma people living in over 300 camps and squats in France were forcibly deported to Bulgaria and Romania. The identity and mobility of the Roma were constructed as a threat to the French state and society (Bergeon 2010; Barbulescu 2012; Nacu 2012). What was striking about the expulsions was that an ethnic group, rather than individuals, appears to have been targeted (de Nanclares 2011; Gunther 2012). In terms of citizenship, France contravened EU laws on the rights of its citizens to move freely between states and avoid prosecution on the grounds of ethnicity (O'Nions 2011: 361).

In other instances, mobility itself has been the target of legislation (Cresswell 2001). The emergence of lifestyle or 'new age' travellers during the late twentieth century added to the number of people pursuing mobile lifestyles in Europe and further threatened established forms of citizenship (Lowe and Shaw 1993; Earle 1994; Halfacree 1996b; Holloway 2004, 2005). Many travellers had a desire to live outside the conventions of settled society (Earle 1994), prompting new tranches of legislation aimed at limiting and criminalizing travelling and transient lifestyles (Sibley 1994, 2003; James 2011). In some instances, travellers were prevented from moving on some public highways if the police felt criminal acts were likely to occur. This reflected a stratified form of mobility that granted some citizens the right to travel, but not others.

These examples demonstrate the complex associations between mobility and citizenship. The right to be mobile is an essential part of citizenship (Cresswell 2006b), yet citizenship and the conferral of rights associated with it is often dependent on a largely settled lifestyle. Mobility is constructed and manipulated by the state in order to produce a social order and, when this is challenged, sanctions are taken to prevent mobility, raising questions about the extent to which citizens are indeed mobile. In other instances, mobility can be used to discipline or punish transgression, for example by transporting or exiling prisoners away from their homes (Moran *et al.* 2012). As the following section explores, immobility also challenges the ability of citizens to claim their social, political and civic rights.

IMMOBILITY AND CITIZENSHIP

Freedom of movement is ingrained into many ideals and ideologies of citizenship but these rights are uneven or impossible to access for many 'shadow citizens' (Chouinard 2001). These include physically and socially disadvantaged groups such as 'the disabled pedestrian . . . inner city residents trying to negotiate run down public transport, and people in the long lines at the Mexican border who cannot enjoy the mobility that comes with being an American citizen' (Cresswell 2006a: 167).

Disabled people are perhaps the most obvious group of citizens to suffer from reduced mobility (although Imrie and Edwards (2007) note that some commentators on mobility have ignored their situation):

> 'apart from being excluded and marginalised from the workplace disabled people are often segregated within schooling, unable to find suitable housing, and have restricted access to public transport'.
>
> (Kitchin 1998: 343)

Disability is a social rather than a physical construction (Parr and Butler 1999) in that the organization of society, rather than physical disability itself, is the underlying cause of exclusion. Thus, geographers have drawn attention to the way in which urban planners and architects have contributed to poor urban design that restricts the mobility of disabled groups and, consequently, reduces their opportunity to engage fully in society (Vujakovic and Matthews 1994; Matthews and Vujakovic 1995;

Imrie *et al.* 1996; Kitchin 1998, 2000). In a forceful piece, Rob Kitchin (1998) argues that space is socially organized to keep disabled people 'in their place' and 'written' to convey to disabled people that they are 'out of place'. Hastings and Thomas (2005) note that the design of the Welsh Assembly and Scottish Parliament buildings favoured the 'normalized' over the 'impaired' body, revealing a privileged form of embodied citizenship.

Vera Chouinard (2001) demonstrates that disability campaigns have focused on attempting to gain equality for disabled people in terms of law, access, mobility and, ultimately, citizenship with some success. In a case study of Canada, she notes many important changes to the formal rights of its disabled citizens but, despite these changes, she argues that disabled people remain 'shadow citizens' with rights in principle but not in practice. Mowl and Fuller (2001) also point out that 'stares' as well as 'stairs' can impinge on the mobility of disabled citizens, particularly in the case of mental illness (Parr *et al.* 2004). Despite *de jure* rights, citizenship and (social and physical) mobility continue to be contested daily on a *de facto* basis.

As Chouinard's (2004) work also shows, physical disability is not in itself the root cause of mobility exclusion. She notes that women and those on low incomes are particularly at risk of exclusion from 'embodied places of citizenship, in which differences of class, gender, race, sexuality and ability come into play in determining whether, where and how fully legal rights can be asserted in practice' (Chouinard 2001: 191). A clear example of this is provided by the (in)ability of many women to negotiate urban space through a fear of crime (Valentine 1989). Valentine argues that while domestic crime is often hidden, crime against women in outdoor spaces is highlighted. Consequently, women come to rely on men to escort them in urban places (especially after dark) and opportunities for leisure and work become restricted. Subsequent work has noted that this fear is amplified by social class, age, disability and motherhood (Pain 1997a, 1997b). Fear of crime is also place-dependent and, often, bound up with concerns about change (Pain 2000). Although some groups, including women, the old and people with disabilities, have their mobility and opportunity reduced by crime, certain groups of people are often 'othered' as potential threats or criminals, including the young, black people or the homeless. In turn, they may be subject to curfews or physical measures that limit their mobility or right to gather in public space (Collins and Kearns 2001; O'Dougherty 2006; Staeheli 2010; Yarwood and Tyrrell 2012).

In a detailed study of public transport in Los Angeles, Cresswell (2006a) highlights significant differences between users of the public bus system and those of a new light rail system, both operated by the state-funded Los Angeles Metropolitan Transit Authority (MTA). Eighty per cent of bus passengers were non-white and poor yet faced increases in the prices of tickets and the loss of bus passes that made travel between work, home and vital services difficult. By contrast, the light rail scheme (which received 70 per cent of MTA's financial resources compared with only 30 per cent invested in buses) carried passengers who were mainly white, professional and affluent. While 'some, principally white and sub-urban areas of Los Angeles were having their modes of mobility enhanced, the vast majority of poor, non-white, urban areas, were having theirs reduced' (p.172). Consequently, a collaboration of bus users called the Bus Riders' Union (BRU) sued MTA on the grounds that it was using funds in a racially discriminatory manner.

Cresswell demonstrates that citizenship is differentiated not only on the grounds of class, gender, ethnicity, ability and sexuality but also by mobility. Far from being universal or heterogeneous, citizenship and the rights to travel and access services and employment are 'transit dependent'. This dependency is described as a 'prosthetic citizenship' whereby citizens are reliant on material aspects (or prosthetics) of the urban environment, in this case public transport, to achieve full citizenship. As the example of Los Angeles shows, this extends to socially as well as physically disadvantaged citizens and points to a need to investigate fully how spaces of inequality impact on apparently heterogeneous understandings of citizenship. But, at the heart of these issues, argues Cresswell, should be an understanding and appreciation of mobility and unequal opportunities to be mobile. The ability, or otherwise, to move thus reveals uneven geographies of citizenship (Cresswell 2006a, 2009). As the next section examines, increased security is further impinging on the rights of citizens to be mobile.

CITIZENSHIP, SECURITY AND MOBILITY

Cresswell (2009) argues that a need to distinguish citizen from stranger emerged as a response to a progressively mobile world. The late-modern era has been characterized by an increasingly mobile society caused by 'the narrowing of travelling times through physical space and the implosions of glimpses of other societies and cultures provided by a growing and ever proliferating mass media. Business, tourism, television all bring us together' (Young 1999: 15). Jock Young has argued that these changes have propelled us from a post-war 'golden age' of citizenry, which enveloped 'the vast majority of adults' in a social contract with the state, to an era of individualism 'with its emphasis on existential choice and self-creation' (Young 1999: 14). Young suggests that this has undermined the relationship between citizen and state, contributing to a pervading 'ontological insecurity'. An 'exclusive society' has emerged that aims to 'hold at bay and exclude' those regarded as threatening its sense of security. Whether or not a 'golden age' of citizenship ever existed (Sibley 1995, 2003), concepts and practices of security are becoming increasingly significant to citizenship and mobility (Cresswell 2009; Philo 2012). Recently, a heightened sense of global fear, linked to international terrorism or pandemics, has given further impetus to security planning and regimes (Pain 2009).

Security, as Lucia Zedner (2009: 9) notes, is a 'promiscuous concept' that has been deployed inconsistently and widely across a range of spaces and contexts (see also Philo 2012). She argues that objective and subjective forms of security are impossible to achieve for 'absolute security implies a condition of being without threat, which, even if it could be achieved today, always remains liable to negation by new threats tomorrow' (Zedner 2009). Instead, many forms of security focus on 'preventing the worst' (Beck 1992; Johnston 2000a) through the creation of literal and metaphorical barriers to keep out things, ideas and people that are seen to threaten the security of a space (Young 1999; Herbert and Brown 2006; Loader 2006; Sidaway 2007; Yarwood 2010a). In these cases the right to enter space and, consequently, to be mobile is granted not by citizenship but through an agreement to behave and conform in specific ways.

This is most clearly seen in the regulation of highly secure private and semi-public spaces such as gated communities or shopping malls where access is conditional on behaving in ways that are compliant with and support the owners' purposes (Atkinson 2003; Shearing and Wood 2003). The Bluewater shopping centre in the UK aims to provide 'a safe, relaxed and friendly environment' for its 'guests' (i.e. customers) to be 'free to shop and relax' (http://www.bluewater.co.uk/content/cu_guestconduct – last accessed 6 August 2013). According to its code of guest conduct, activities deemed incompatible with or distracting from these activities such as 'leafleting, canvassing or the conducting of third party interviews or surveys . . . unauthorised busking' are banned. It states that 'all groups of more than five without the intention to shop will be asked to leave the centre' and that certain forms of clothing that restricts views of the face are banned. This code stresses the rights of the management company but says nothing about those of the citizen or even the consumer.

Increased security is also evident in public spaces. In residential areas, voluntary schemes such as Neighbourhood Watch (NW) (Yarwood and Edwards 1995; Yarwood 2012a) are innocuous enough (largely because most are dormant) but represent an attempt to treat public space as private, to be used as a preserve for those who are known and accepted in a neighbourhood. They have been supplemented in some places, for example South Africa, by armed security guards (Paasche 2011). Public spaces in city centres have also been subject to closer security regimes (Mitchell 1995, 1997) as part of a 'revanchist' turn in public policy that has sought to punish and exclude those who do not fit hegemonic notions of decent behaviour (MacLeod 2002; Staeheli and Mitchell 2007; Paasche 2012). Thus, direct and indirect legislation has sought to remove homeless citizens from the streets or to ban behaviour such as drinking in public, skateboarding or distributing leaflets, seen as 'anti-social' in public urban space. Mitchell (1995) argues that whereas public space was used to create inclusive forms of citizenship, for example through campaigns for civil rights, it is now the site of exclusionary practices. He considers that this has been driven by a desire to keep public space as a place for voluntary activity:

> citizenship is based on notions of volunteerism in contemporary democracies. Private citizens meet (if only ideally) in public to form a (or the) public . . . but they always have the option of retreating back into private, into their homes, into those places over which they presumably have sovereign control. The public sphere is thus a voluntary one, and the involuntary publicity of the homeless is thus profoundly unsettling.
>
> (Mitchell 1997: 321)

Memorably, Mitchell likens this form of citizenship to driving a sports utility vehicle (SUV):

> Cocooned in a sealed chamber, behind tinted glass, with the temperature fully controlled, and the GPS system tracking, and sometimes dictating, our every turn, our every stop and start, we are radically isolated from each other, able to communicate only through the false connectedness of the cell phone. We ride high and sovereign; we are masters of space; we are safe against all who might intrude, all who might stand in our way (and against the weather, too). That this is a false security has been amply shown in traffic accident statistics; that this is a false (or rather deeply regressive) isolationism has been proven in the way that the large consumption of raw materials and fuel the S.U.V. society requires makes us, in fact, even more radically connected to others in the world . . . In our S.U.V.s and with our S.U.V. citizenship, that kind of connectedness can always be banished beyond the shell of the Ford Explorer . . . We are now, truly, the liberal, autonomous subject. We own ourselves and no one can intrude upon us without our permission.
>
> (Mitchell 2005: 96–7)

In an effort to keep danger at bay, a complex geography of 'secure spaces' is emerging that encompasses different '"patchworks", "quilts", "bubbles", "corridors", "mosaics", "webs", "networks" and "nodes"' (Zedner 2009: 61) extending across different urban spaces in different ways. In a study of Maputo, Mozambique, Till Paasche and James Sidaway (2010) reveal how urban space is policed via a patchwork of public, private and 'ad hoc' actors that have reduced the city to a series of micro-security-enclaves that reflect and enforce existing inequalities in development and power.

Shearing and Wood (2003: 406) conclude that the emergence of these differing actor-spaces reveals a shift from state to nodal governance so that 'people now live within a world full of crisscrossing group memberships that simultaneously operate across and through multiple governmental domains'. They suggest that the term 'denizenship' is a more appropriate way of describing this relationship than 'citizenship':

> 'Denizenship' thus refers to an affiliation to any sphere of governance and its associated rights and responsibilities. Within this

> conceptualization, persons would have multiple denizenships depending on the number of domains of governance through which their lives are regulated. Each domain would carry with it expectations and obligations including expectations for new and different forms of political participation that would define the specific nature of the denizen's status.
>
> (Shearing and Wood 2003: 408)

So, those who live in a gated community are governed by its rules, those who shop in a mall by its regime and so on. Rather than being regarded as a second-class citizen (Hammer 1990; Samers 2010), denizens might be considered privileged members of a group and the spaces associated with it (Cresswell 2009). Shearing and Wood (2003) caution, however, that different sets of denizens have access to, or are excluded from, particular spaces. This is extending beyond private and semi-public spaces to encompass some public spaces. City Improvement Districts, for example, are public places that are policed by private policing companies to support commercial interests (Paasche 2011). Those unable to consume are barred not only from private space, but from public space too. Citizenship alone is not enough to guarantee a right to access and to move between these places.

At the start of this chapter it was noted that modern citizenship emerged from feudal society that had organized people in local spaces (Cresswell 2009). Shearing and Wood (2003: 410) suggest that the spaces emerging under new forms of nodal governance and security have 'a strong resonance with medieval common spaces legally controlled by feudal authorities to which certain people had rights of access'. Citizenship, it seems, has turned full circle.

Answers to Australian citizenship test

1a, 2a, 3c, 4b, 5a, 6b, 7b, 8b, 9c, 10a, 11a, 12b, 13c, 14b, 15c, 16b, 17b, 18b, 19b, 20b.

FURTHER READING

Tim Cresswell has written widely on mobility, rights and politics. *On the Move* (2006a) is an accessible collection of essays on these topics while his 2010 paper in *Environment and Planning D: Society and Space* provides a critical commentary on the politics of mobility. The BRU, discussed by Cresswell and outlined in this chapter, has a website that campaigns for the right to mass transportation: http://www.thestrategycenter.org/project/bus-riders-union/about (last accessed 6 August 2013). Michael Samers' (2010) book *Migration* has an excellent chapter on migration and citizenship that complements and expands some of the arguments in this chapter. An example of a citizenship test can be found at: http://www.citizenship.gov.au/learn/cit_test/practice/ (last accessed 6 August 2013). Authors such as Vera Chouinard (2001, 2004) and Gill Valentine and Tracy Skelton (2007) demonstrate how disability can exclude people from full citizenship. Don Mitchell's (2005) piece in *Political Geography* uses the metaphor of the SUV memorably to critique exclusion from public space.

NOTE

1 Michael Samers' book *Migration* (2010), also published in Routledge's 'Key Ideas in Geography' series, contains an excellent chapter on migration and citizenship. Readers are referred to this book for a detailed examination of these issues.

4

CITIZENSHIP AND LOCALITY

INTRODUCTION

Mobility and travel are important signifiers of citizenship but, for many people, citizenship is most closely identified with locality and community:

> while nation-states may be where the formal standing as citizen is vested, it is largely through *localities* that the horizontal bonds of citizenship operate to create identification with the 'we', as in 'we the people'. This has been a particularly influential narrative in the United States.
>
> (Staeheli 2005: 196–7; emphasis added)

Many commentators have suggested that citizenship is given meaning through daily acts and performances at the *local level* (Staeheli 2003a; Ghose 2005; Staeheli 2008a, 2008b). Rina Ghose (2005: 64) goes so far as to argue that:

> 'it is not enough to be a citizen through birth-right or naturalisation. Instead one has to understand how to perform actively as a citizen in order to claim a right to the city.'

Likewise, Lepofsky and Fraser (2003) consider that:

> 'there has been a shift in the meaning of citizenship from being primarily guaranteed as a status . . . to being primarily guaranteed as a performative act'.

In other words, people only attain full citizenship when they mobilize, use and perform their rights and duties. Local places below the scale of the nation-state provide an important setting for these activities (Desforges *et al.* 2005). Alexis de Tocqueville's *Democracy in America* (2003 [1835–40]) posited that citizen participation in local civic society was more efficient and democratically preferable to control by the central state and its large bureaucratic organizations (Isin and Turner 2007). William Beveridge (1948: 8–14) stated:

> 'Voluntary action . . . that is to say action not under the directions of any authority wielding the power of the State . . . [is one of] the distinguishing marks of a free society.'

Participation in local planning or policy decisions, such as taking part in local consultation exercises, is a way in which civic and political *rights* can be asserted to influence local decision making. Other forms of local participation also include voting in local elections, contacting a local councillor or participating in local electoral politics (Widdicombe 1986; Munton and Zurawan 2003).

These forms of formal participation offer members of the public the chance to engage more closely with the running of affairs in their locality and, in doing so, attain the rights and duties associated with being a citizen (Ghose 2005). However, discourses of locality and community can be problematic as they have the potential to exclude as well as include (Staeheli 2008a, 2008b; Closs Stephens and Squire 2012b). Although some people may benefit from the opportunity to participate in local community affairs, those unable, unwilling or prevented from doing so may also be excluded from full membership of citizenship.

These issues are significant because, over recent years, many Western governments have placed greater emphasis on citizen participation at the local level. Indeed, they have maintained that local involvement is not only a right, but a *duty* of citizenship (Kearns 1995; Lepofsky and Fraser 2003; Cheshire and Woods 2009). 'Active citizenship' aims to use volunteers to fill some of the gaps left by the state's withdrawal from service and welfare provision (Fyfe and Milligan 2003a; Staeheli 2013). As part of these policies, citizens are being made increasingly responsible for managing local spaces through involvement in planning (Ghose 2005; Scott *et al.* 2012), welfare provision (Fyfe and Milligan 2003b) and partnership working (Edwards *et al.* 2001).

In the context of these policies, this chapter critiques the ways that citizenship is manifested and performed at the local level. It questions how 'active citizenship' and the growth of the shadow state are reshaping relationships between state and citizen at the local level. It concludes by considering how appropriate concepts of community and neighbourhood are to citizenship. These themes are continued in Chapter 5, which explores more radical forms of local activism.

ACTIVE CITIZENSHIP

'Active citizenship' emphasizes *duties* over rights. In many countries this principle has become enshrined in policies that have encouraged citizens to contribute to the organization and management of their local communities through voluntary work (Figure 4.2). For example, in the 1980s Margaret Thatcher's Conservative Government in the UK made calls for citizens to 'recognize their moral responsibilities to care and meet their obligations to give their talents and skills in the management of public and welfare services' (Kearns 1992: 20). These ideas manifested themselves in numerous state-sponsored initiatives that encouraged people to take part in the management of local affairs through, for example, running Neighbourhood Watch (NW), schemes (Box 4.1) (Fyfe 1995; Yarwood and Edwards 1995), housing associations (HAs) (Kearns 1992), youth groups (Matthews and Limb 2003), voluntary transport schemes (Banister and Norton 1988) or rural development initiatives (Edwards 1998).

Despite the moral rhetoric of politicians, active citizenship polices complemented the restructuring of the local state. A shift from Keynesian to monetarist policies stressed the withdrawal of the local state from the delivery of local welfare and its replacement with private and voluntary actors (Goodwin and Painter 1996). For example, in the UK, local councils ceased building and managing social housing and, instead, passed these responsibilities to Housing Associations (HAs). HAs are charitable bodies that, traditionally, built affordable housing in response to local needs (Yarwood 2002). They are governed by committees of volunteers, the kind of unpaid service exemplified and championed by active citizen policies. However, a study of volunteers, revealed that they were mainly male, middle class, white and owner occupiers (Kearns 1992). Few actually lived in HA houses and many had offered their services because they had been asked to by existing committee members.

Box 4.1 ACTIVE CITIZENSHIP: THE EXAMPLE OF NEIGHBOURHOOD WATCH (NW)

In many countries, the restructuring of police forces according to neo-liberal principles has led to a greater emphasis on efficiency (Yarwood 2007a). The subsequent rationalization of policing meant that locally based community policing was replaced with reactive policing styles that have distanced the police from the public. Instead, 'active citizenship' policies have encouraged people to police themselves, with support from the state, through locally managed voluntary schemes (Fyfe 1995).

NW is a prime example of this (Fyfe 1995; Yarwood and Edwards 1995). The first formal schemes were established in Seattle in 1972 (Bennett *et al.* 2008) and by 1988, it was estimated that 20 per cent of the USA's urban population were members of a scheme (USAonWatch 2009). NW is now a presence in most first-world countries (Figure 4.1). Schemes operate in a locality that ranges from a few houses to a town. Members are required to be 'good neighbours' (see Painter 2012 for a critical dicussion of this term and its use) and stay alert for any suspicious activity or people. If they witness behaviour that is criminal or 'out of place', members tell a coordinator or the police. Specifically, NW aims to:

1. cut crime and the opportunities for crime and anti-social behaviour;
2. provide reassurance to local residents and reduce the fear of crime and anti-social behaviour;
3. encourage neighbourliness and closer communities;
4. improve the quality of life for local residents and tenants (Moley and Budd 2008).

Yet, within the context of neo-liberal restructuring, the aims of NW were 'not simply those of crime reduction and the alleviation of the fear of crime, but concern the creation of spaces of active or responsible citizenship where individuals recognize that they have obligations with regard to the well-being of their neighbourhood' (Fyfe 1995).

Yet, as numerous studies demonstrated (Hourihan 1987; Yarwood and Edwards 1995; Bennett *et al.* 2008; Yarwood 2012a), NWs are mainly located in low crime, owner-occupied areas where the need for NW in policing terms is lowest. Other policing initiatives, such as the deployment of 'special constables' (unpaid police officers), reflected a similar social geography that lead Fyfe (1995) to conclude that such efforts consolidated rather than extended the spaces of citizenship.

In a recent move, schemes in the USA have been rebranded as 'USA on Watch'. As well as preventing crime, the scheme aims to 'empower citizens to become active in homeland security' (USAonWatch 2009). Members are encouraged to look out for

Figure 4.1 A sign signifying the presence of a Neighbourhood Watch group in Western Australia and the involvement of the public, police and private sector (Photo: Author)

Continued

potential terrorists and terrorist activities. In doing so, active citizens in neighbourhood localities are linked into discourses of national security. Vigilance is no longer just a local duty but a national one too; a reminder, if it is needed, that active citizenship, although played out at the local level, reflects national priorities and views of citizenship.

Based on this evidence, active citizenship seems to do little to improve pluralistic participation or self-governance at the local level (Kearns 1995; Parker 1999b; see also Box 4.1).

Rather than pluralizing citizenship or extending local democracy, active citizenship does more to enable policies aimed at shifting service provision away from the state. If the public choose not to be active citizens they, rather than the government, can be blamed for failing to provide a service. At the same time, the local state's power as the sole provider

Figure 4.2 Volunteers engaged in litter-picking and street-cleaning activities in their town (Photo: Author)

of welfare was diminished in accordance with neo-liberal principles (Wolch 1990; Kearns 1992).

For these reasons, active citizenship is attractive to many Western governments and voluntarism has come to occupy a central position in policy making (Fyfe and Milligan 2003a). Britain's 'new' Labour government (1997–2010) embraced volunteering as part of the 'third way' policy that aimed to steer a course between the pro-state, anti-market views of the left and pro-market, anti-state views of the right. This relied on a 'conditional citizenship' that linked rights to duties, operating within the 'mixed economies' of welfare and service provision. The state, private and voluntary sectors were expected to work in partnership to deliver this model (Fyfe and Milligan 2003a). In doing so, the voluntary sector was expected to bridge the divide between state and market forces. In a speech to the Active Communities Convention in 2000, Tony Blair exhorted the private, public and voluntary sectors to involve themselves in voluntary working:

> I want to challenge employers to give their employees paid time off – the equivalent of one day's paid time in the next 18 months – to work in the community. Today five trailblazer companies are announcing their commitment to this – GE Electrics [*sic*], the Family Assurance Company, Dresdner Kleinwort Wasserstein's, Hasbro and Sainsbury's . . .
>
> The second challenge is to our public services. I know that our public services need funding and commitment from government. And they will get it. But I also know how much they can benefit from involving more volunteers . . .
>
> Third, I want to challenge Britain's older citizens to become involved. Many are already the mainstay of thousands of voluntary organisations but many, for a variety of reasons including the false belief they will not be wanted, do not get involved.
>
> (Blair 2000)

The government undertook to play a greater role in 'enabling and empowering voluntary action' (Brown 2000). This included establishing an office and minister for volunteering, monitoring participation in volunteering via an annual 'citizenship survey' (Munton and Zurawan 2003) and strengthening collaboration with the public and private sector through, for example, formal compacts to work in partnership (Fyfe and Milligan 2003a). The principles of formal partnership working have been adopted in many countries; Box 4.2 gives an example in Western Australia.

Although volunteering has been seen by the left as a way of improving local democracy (Wolch 1990; Martin 2004), these strategies aimed to make local communities and their citizens more responsible for delivering services in partnership with other actors, implying that they, rather than wider social or political forces, were the cause and solution of local problems (Rose 1996; Lockie *et al.* 2006). Although ministers suggested that these actions benefit citizenship through increased participation, other commentators have questioned whether they increase citizen autonomy (Rose 1996; Higgins and Lockie 2002; Herbert-Cheshire and Higgins 2004; Woods 2006a).

While direct government intervention may have been reduced, the state continued to influence local decision making 'at a distance' (Garland 1996). Far from leading to autonomous citizenship, voluntary working has been subject to increased surveillance, scrutiny and regulation by government agencies. Painter (2007: 222) states:

> from this viewpoint, citizenship is not so much a practice undertaken by citizens in relation to the state, but rather a technology of state governmentality. States produce citizens in all kinds of ways – through education, surveillance, the judicial system, urban and social policy and so on. Arguably, it is the state that gives life to citizenship, rather than the other way round.
>
> (Painter 2007: 222)

Box 4.2 PARTNERSHIP WORKING: CRIME PREVENTION IN WESTERN AUSTRALIA (WA)

In 2004 the Western Australian government implemented a 'Community Safety and Crime Prevention' (CSCP) programme as part of its crime prevention and reduction strategy. The CSCP programme was operationalized by the state government's Office of

Crime Prevention (OCP) that sought to develop partnerships with shire (local) authorities to identify and deal with crime and safety issues at a local level (Yarwood 2007b).

The policy gave local shires the option of signing a formal compact with the OCP. This committed shires to write a local policing plan based on a 'meaningful consultation' that recognized local crime and safety concerns, devised ways of dealing with them and identified appropriate agencies to implement these solutions. In return for signing, the OCP offered financial incentives, advice and opportunities to bid for further funding. Reaction to the CSCP initiative by the shires was mixed. Some shires were opposed to or sceptical about the partnerships as they felt they devolved costs and responsibility for policing from the state to local actors. Others felt it was not their responsibility. There followed a period of negotiation between shire councils and the OCP in which efforts were made to form and enrol local shires, volunteers and the police into common discourses about policing, safety and rurality (Yarwood 2007b). Nevertheless, by 2007, 120 shires out of 144 had signed a compact with the OCP to deliver a local policing strategy (Anderson and Tresidder 2008).

The case of the CSPC shows that the state government made local communities responsible for their own protection. Conditional funding streams and expert knowledge only became available when local shires formally complied with requirements that were laid down by state government, to write, monitor and respond to local crime plans. The alternative, which seemed unpalatable to the vast majority of councils, was to lose the financial and organizational support of the state government's OCP. Rather than withdrawing from decision making, WA's state government continued to influence the direction of local policing 'at a distance' (Garland 1996; Higgins and Lockie 2002). Whether shire councils liked it or not, the policy of partnership working moved the responsibility for policing policy squarely on to their shoulders (Yarwood 2011b).

In the UK, the most recent attempt by the government to encourage, and manipulate, voluntary working is David Cameron's idea of the 'Big Society'. It aims to reduce state bureaucracy but, like many forms of state-driven volunteering, appears to reinforce the idea of duty rather than politically empowering citizens (Box 4.3).

Box 4.3 THE BIG SOCIETY

The idea of the 'Big Society' has been pursued by the UK coalition government since their election in 2010. The policy draws upon various antecedents (Pattie and Johnston 2011) but, broadly, supports the 'active citizenship' tradition of expecting citizens to carry out a perceived set of duties. Prime Minister David Cameron positioned the 'Big Society' in opposition to 'Big Government' (Painter 2012):

> We want to give citizens, communities and local government the power and information they need to come together, solve the problems they face and build the Britain they want. We want society – the families, networks, neighbourhoods and communities that form the fabric of so much of our everyday lives – to be bigger and stronger than ever before. Only when people and communities are given more power and take more responsibility can we achieve fairness and opportunity for all.
>
> (Cabinet Office 2010, p.1)

The policy calls for power and responsibility to be shifted from state to society and has the potential, at one extreme, to recast radically the relationship between citizen and state (Pattie and Johnston 2011). Briefly, this envisages a stronger role for social enterprises, charities and voluntary organizations in the provision of services as well as a transfer of power to citizens so that 'when there are local issues to address, they take action themselves rather than waiting for the state to intervene' (Pattie and Johnston 2011).

The five stated elements to the 'Big Society' are to:

1. *Give communities more powers:*

We will radically reform the planning system to give neighbourhoods far more ability to determine the shape of the places in which their inhabitants live.

We will introduce new powers to help communities save local facilities and services threatened with closure, and give communities the right to bid to take over local state-run services [Figure 4.3].

We will train a new generation of community organisers and support the creation of neighbourhood groups across the UK, especially in the most deprived areas.

2. *Encourage people to take an active role in their communities*

We will take a range of measures to encourage volunteering and involvement in social action, including launching a national 'Big Society Day' and making regular community involvement a key element of civil service staff appraisals.

We will take a range of measures to encourage charitable giving and philanthropy.

We will introduce a National Citizen Service. The initial flagship project will provide a programme for 16 year olds to give them a chance to develop the skills needed to be active and responsible citizens, mix with people from different backgrounds, and start getting involved in their communities.

3. *Transfer power from central to local government*

We will promote the radical devolution of power and greater financial autonomy to local government, including a full review of local government finance.

Continued

We will give councils a general power of competence.

We will abolish Regional Spatial Strategies and return decision-making powers on housing and planning to local councils.

4. Support co-ops, mutuals, charities and social enterprises

We will support the creation and expansion of mutuals, co-operatives, charities and social enterprises, and support these groups to have much greater involvement in the running of public services.

We will give public sector workers a new right to form employee-owned co-operatives and bid to take over the services they deliver. This will empower millions of public sector workers to become their own boss and help them to deliver better services.

We will use funds from dormant bank accounts to establish a Big Society Bank, which will provide new finance for neighbourhood groups, charities, social enterprises and other non-governmental bodies.

5. Publish government data

We will create a new 'right to data' so that government-held datasets can be requested and used by the public, and then published on a regular basis.

We will oblige the police to publish detailed local crime data statistics every month, so the public can get proper information about crime in their neighbourhoods and hold the police to account for their performance.'

(Cabinet Office 2010)

Some actions, such as an 'Annual Big Society Day', attempt to nudge (Jones *et al.* 2011b; Pykett *et al.* 2011) people towards participation but others seem more of a push, such as proposals to make 'regular community involvement a key element of civil service staff appraisals'.

The Big Society also includes plans for a 'National Citizenship Service' (NSC) that has been described as 'something like national service' for young people (David Cameron quoted in *The Daily Telegraph* (Prince 2010)). The NSC aims to be universal but not compulsory, offering opportunities for young people from all social backgrounds to undertake a series of tasks, including residential activities, aimed at developing community cohesion and social responsibility (Mycock and Tonge 2011). The NSC is funded and supported by the state but will be delivered by voluntary groups, businesses and charities. Mycock and Tonge (2011: 65)

Your Local Library is Changing

Henley Library will close on
Saturday 3rd March 2012

It will re-open for business as a Community Managed
Library in April 2012

There will be a Mobile Library Service from Wednesday 7th
March 2012 until Wednesday 28th March 2012
The Mobile Library will be based at the Fire Station,
Main Street

2.00 pm – 4.30 pm

For more information visit
www.warwickshire.gov.uk/communitymanagedlibraries

Figure 4.3 The Big Society? This library in a Warwickshire (UK) town is now run by a local community group with support from the council (Photo: Author)

Continued

raised concerns that the NSC will do little to develop political citizenship and democratic rights (local authorities, for example, are not involved), but instead reflects a view that 'volunteering rather than political participation is seen as integral to citizenship and the establishment of a better society'. Such a position reinforces rather than challenges the view held by many young British people that citizenship is about doing duties rather than receiving rights (Lister *et al.* 2005). It cements visions of active citizenship that foreground voluntary duties over political rights.

The 'Big Society' received widespread criticism. In particular, it is viewed as a cover for deep cuts in public funding and employment (North 2011; Painter 2012). Rowan Williams, the then Archbishop of Canterbury, commented that:

> 'Big society rhetoric is all too often heard by many therefore as aspirational waffle designed to conceal a deeply damaging withdrawal of the state from its responsibilities to the most vulnerable'.
>
> (quoted in *The Observer* 24 June 2012)

The Third Sector, which has become increasingly reliant on government monies, has lost state funding because of spending cuts and, consequently, has become poorly placed to fulfil the aspirations ascribed to it by the 'Big Society'. There is also doubt that citizens have the time or aspiration to volunteer in the 'Big Society'. Based on evidence from the British Electoral Survey, Pattie and Johnston contend:

> the likely pool from which volunteers will probably be drawn is relatively small and skewed towards those already active in their communities; individuals from particular class backgrounds are most likely to participate while those from other backgrounds and those relatively discontented with life in general and politics in particular are more likely to opt out from community involvement.
>
> (Pattie and Johnston 2011: 420)

It remains to be seen whether the Big Society will lead to a radical reshaping of citizenship in the UK or whether it is simply 'aspirational waffle'.

CITIZENS OF THE SHADOW STATE

As the previous section demonstrated, over the past 20 years many Western governments have pursued a policy of 'active citizenship' that has placed emphasis on the duties of citizens, charities and voluntary organizations to provide services in their local communities. The state and voluntary sectors have always had a symbiotic relationship in the delivery and provision of social welfare and services (Bryson *et al.* 2002; Mohan and Mohan 2002) that has been characterized by a 'moving frontier' between the two (Finlayson 1994; Kearns and Joseph 1997; Mohan 2003b). The position of this frontier varies between states and over time, reflecting differences in political thinking and hegemonic values of citizenship (Bryson *et al.* 2002).

Thus, in the USA, as de Tocqueville (2003 [1835–40]) observed, citizenship has traditionally been seen as emphasizing civic participation at the local level. By contrast, in the years following World War Two, the UK placed a greater reliance on the state to provide a welfare service (Marshall 1950 [1992]), replacing the work undertaken by charitable trusts (Mohan 2003a) and limiting the role of the voluntary sector (Wolch 1990). Indeed, with the development of the post-war Welfare State in the UK, many commentators at the time felt that the voluntary sector would wither away (Bryson *et al.* 2002).

In her seminal work, *The Shadow State*, Jennifer Wolch (1990) drew on examples from the USA and the UK to demonstrate how their governments placed greater reliance on the voluntary sector to provide welfare needs. This was achieved through the development of formal business contracts between the state and voluntary organizations, including charities and NGOs, to deliver particular welfare services.

According to a recent report by Snowdon (2012), 27,000 charities in the UK are now dependent on the government for more than 75 per cent of their income. The voluntary sector as a whole receives more money from the state than it receives in voluntary donations (Snowdon 2012).

Between 1997 and 2005, the combined income of Britain's charities nearly doubled to £37.9 billion, largely as a result of government contracts. The sector employs more than 600,000 people and is regulated by a government department (Clark *et al.* 2009; Snowdon 2012).

Barnardo's, Shelter, the Catholic Agency for Overseas Development (CAFOD), Scope, Oxfam, Christian Aid, Action Aid and Age UK all receive significant state funding. Relate, a marriage counselling service founded in 1938, was awarded a £15,000 state grant in the 1950s to support its work. In 2011, 95 per cent of its £2,036,320 donations came from a grant from the Department of Education and the National Lottery (a further £2 million came from charitable activities, including payment for counselling services) (Snowdon 2012). The benefit for the state is that services can be delivered more cheaply and with a degree of consumer choice, a central tenet of neo-liberal government (Wolch 1990). In the case of Relate, government justified funding the charity on the grounds that it costs the state less than the expense of subsidizing divorce cases. Charities have also benefited from more resources that have enabled them to expand their activities as well as greater 'political clout' (Wolch 1990). However, the activities of the shadow state and volunteering are geographically and socially uneven (Wolch 1990; Munton and Zurawan 2003; Mohan *et al.* 2005, 2006).

Wolch (1989: 201) argues that a 'shadow state' has emerged in which voluntary organizations shadow the work of government by taking 'collective service responsibilities previously shouldered by the public sector, administered outside traditional democratic politics, but controlled in informal and formal ways by the state'. In other words, charities and voluntary organizations work for government and provide services previously administered by them. As a consequence voluntary groups and charities have been obliged to 'professionalize' their activities in order to win government funding/contracts and to ensure that services are delivered in a competent, efficient and appropriate manner (Wolch 2006; Milligan 2009; Milligan and Wiles 2010; Yarwood 2010b; Cloke 2011). This has included better transparency in record keeping, formalizing administrative practices and complying with national standards and practices (for example, health and safety requirements) that are also enforced through legislation (see Box 4.4).

Some voluntary groups are better placed, or more willing, to do this than others, leading certain commentators to speculate that a bifurcation

Box 4.4 THE SHADOW STATE IN NEW ZEALAND

New Zealand has been regarded as 'a social laboratory of the world' (Tennant *et al.* 2008: 26) given the pace and scale at which neo-liberal welfare, health and service reforms have been implemented in the country. State welfare provision was rolled back by successive Labour and National Governments (Murphy and Kearns 1994; Barnett and Barnett 2003; Crack *et al.* 2007; Sanders *et al.* 2008) and replaced with a greater reliance on the voluntary sector. Service provision was 're-moralized' so that community rather than state provision was seen as desirable (Gleeson and Kearns 2001; Barnett and Barnett 2003). This was strengthened by a more formal relationship between the state and voluntary sectors (Murphy and Kearns 1994). These moves took advantage of a strong tradition of volunteering in New Zealand: 34 per cent of the population over the age of ten participate, two-thirds of staff in non-profit organizations are volunteers (Sanders *et al.* 2008; Tennant *et al.* 2008) and unpaid staff make up a high proportion of the emergency services, including 80 per cent of fire fighters (Yarwood 2011a).

Until the late 1980s, voluntary groups that were concerned with sport, recreation and culture were viewed favourably by government (Sanders *et al.* 2008; Tennant *et al.* 2008; Yarwood 2011a). In the decade that followed more emphasis was given to organizations, especially faith-based groups, with social and welfare concerns (Conradson 2006; Crack *et al.* 2007). These started to play a greater role in the provision of health and welfare services, supported by government grants administered through formal contracts of service delivery that controlled, and limited, how they behaved (Owen and Kearns 2008).

The impact of these reforms has been geographically uneven, with rurality and cultural difference influencing the provision, use and effectiveness of voluntary services (Kearns and Joseph 1997; Barnett and Barnett 2003, 2008; Conradson 2003c). Areas with strong community leadership and professional support are

Continued

more likely to have better services (see also Brown 2003 in a UK context).

Owen and Kearns (2008) argue that increased state funding has made voluntary organizations more susceptible to political pressure, threatening their independence. Further, they suggest that 'the core business of third sector organisation should be as much concerned with participation and citizenship as it is about provision and services' (p.129). The need to professionalize has meant that as government funding has increased, so too have the overhead and staff costs of organizations. Figure 4.5 illustrates this in relation to LANDSAR (Land Search and Rescue Organization), a voluntary organization in New Zealand.

These changes are not uncontested and increasingly commentators are noting a need to look at the internal dynamics of third-sector organizations and how their volunteers perform ideas of charity (Conradson 2003b; Barnett and Barnett 2008). Although

Figure 4.4 Police and civilian volunteers provide search and rescue services in New Zealand. Here they train together in water rescue techniques (Photo: Author)

some organizations in New Zealand have become increasingly centralized, some of their members and branches have resisted these changes (Owen and Kearns 2008; Yarwood 2011a). In a study of major faith groups, Conradson (2006) notes that organizations funded by the state remain critical of its welfare policies, arguing that they are more than simply service providers. The case of New Zealand illustrates that welfare reforms and the development of the shadow state are significant, but the ways in which these are spatially manifested reflect the internal politics of different organizations, cultural traditions of volunteering, social differences and the performance of different ethical values (Figure 4.3). The death of citizen participation in the voluntary sector has perhaps been exaggerated. This emphasizes the need to understand change within local, place-specific contexts. What is the case in one locality may not be in another.

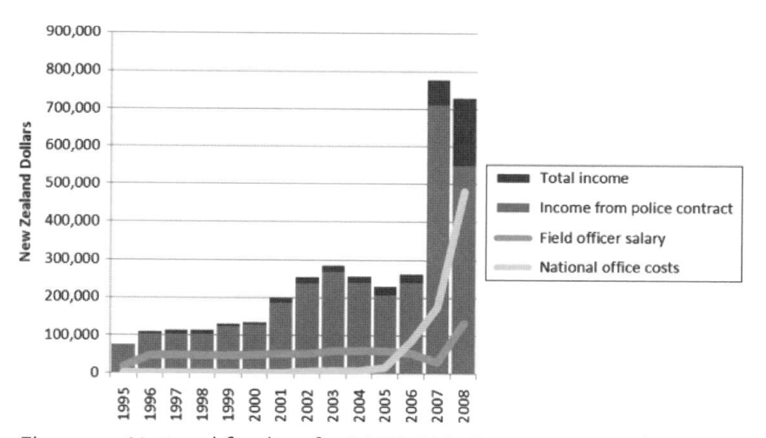

Figure 4.5 National funding for LANDSAR (Source: Yarwood 2011a)

of the voluntary sector has occurred (Milligan and Fyfe 2005) (see Table 4.1). At one extreme are large-scale corporatist non-profit organizations (such as those listed by Snowdon (2012) above) that are formal, hierarchical and 'top down' in their identification and resolution of problems. These are more likely to take advantage of state funding

Table 4.1 The bifurcation of the voluntary sector (Source: Milligan and Fyfe 2005)

	Grass-roots welfare organizations	**Corporatist welfare organizations**
Organizational structure	Informal, non-hierarchical, strongly democratic, maximizing participant input and control	Formal, hierarchical and bureaucratic with clear internal divisions of labour based on functional specialization
Basis of welfare service delivery	Mutuality, compassion and offering the resources for autonomous action	Standardized programmes offering a level of material security
Nature and sources of funding	Relatively unstable and mix of state and non-state sources	Relatively stable, state-dominated and may be contract-based
Distribution of power within organization	Symmetrical – minimization of distinctions between workers, volunteers and service users	Asymmetrical – formal separation between managers, 'welfare professionals', 'volunteers' and 'clients'
Form of engagement with community	Focus on community participation, development and empowerment	Focus on community classification, treatment and management
Form of citizenship fostered by organization	Active	Passive

streams, responding to state policy rather than needs identified by communities themselves (Milligan and Fyfe 2005). Organizations are likely to locate their branches and activities in places that most benefit from formal funding streams (Fyfe and Milligan 2003b; Milligan and Fyfe 2005) including, for example, territories that have been earmarked for urban development.

These groups fulfil the functions of the shadow state but offer less opportunity for active citizens to participate in their operations given their increasingly corporate and hierarchical nature (Gleeson and Kearns 2001; Barnett and Barnett 2008; Cloke 2011). Wolch (1990) argues that the voluntary sector can, and should, create spaces to counter, oppose or critique state policies. There is a danger that a greater reliance on state funding will mean that third-sector organizations may be unwilling to bite the hand of the state that is feeding them.

This is a view shared by commentators from the political right. Snowdon (2012: 4) objects to charities that lobby 'for bigger government, higher taxes, greater regulation and the creation of new agencies to oversee and enforce new laws'. In doing so, he contends, the government may fund pressure groups 'with the intention of creating a "sock puppet" version of civil society which creates the illusion of grassroots support for new legislation'. Snowdon (2012: 20) lists a range of third-sector groups, including 'Sustain, the Green Alliance, Alcohol Concern, the Women's Environmental Network, Action on Smoking and Health, the London Sustainability Exchange, Forum for the Future, Consensus Action on Salt and Health, the Fatherhood Institute, the Pesticide Action Network, the Climate Group and the Children's Rights Alliance for England' (Snowdon, 2012: 20), that he argues do little more than contribute to 'policy development, lobbying and enforcement . . . in so far as their objective is to "raise awareness" and "educate the public", they do so principally by producing policy documents for government and promoting new legislation via the mass media'. Snowdon clearly objects to the aims of some of these bodies (including those that campaign for increased foreign aid) and the use of taxpayers' money to fund their campaigns. More significantly, though, he argues that many corporate charities speak for the state rather than its citizens.

This relationship is not necessarily given. Conradson (2008) demonstrates that some large third-sector groups maintain a critical stance against changes in state policy (see Box 4.5). Further, different branches

Box 4.5 GRASS-ROOTS VOLUNTEERING: SOUP RUNS

Soup runs and kitchens are staffed by volunteers and provide emergency food, clothing, counselling and care to homeless people on the streets of urban centres, a practice that is not in keeping with state efforts to help people off the streets and to dismantle street lifestyles (Conradson 2003c; Johnsen *et al.* 2005). Soup runs and soup kitchens are places where citizenship is negotiated and performed, often in opposition to state policies or concerns.

Consequently, many soup runs have been pressured by local governments, the police and even homeless charities to work more closely with the state in achieving these policies:

> I think the biggest problem comes with what I call 'ad-hoc' agencies, not in receipt of funding, for example the soup run, who are out of the Loop . . . I think people choose not to accept funding for a variety of reasons, and it can be quite difficult getting these agencies, these organisations, on board in terms of ensuring a professional approach to the work that they're doing. Not just in health and safety and training issues, but more particularly, helping clients move away from a life on the streets – giving people opportunities to move forward in their lives, and I think very often that is missing in some of those voluntary organisations. Personally, I feel that it's quite irresponsible.
>
> (city outreach worker quoted in Johnsen *et al.* 2005b: 333)

In 2011, Westminster Council in London attempted to ban soup runs but relented in the face of public pressure; in 2012, the Mayor of Philadelphia, USA also tried to ban the serving of food to homeless people in public parks but faced legal challenges.

Many soup runs continue to operate, transforming 'seemingly insignificant outdoor public spaces such as car parks or sections of pavements into spaces of compassion' (Johnsen *et al.* 2005b). Cloke *et al.* (2007) argue that these activities continue because of a particular form of 'ethical' or 'moral' citizenship. Based on interviews with voluntary workers on soup runs, they argue that ethical citizenship is driven by 'volunteering because they *wanted* to rather than because they felt *obliged* to' (Cloke *et al.* 2007) through any government-directed schemes. In turn, the wish to help is driven by a desire to bring 'ordinary ethical beliefs' into the 'extraordinary' and marginal spaces of the city:

> ethical citizenship differs radically from politicised citizenship, being wrapped around self-recognition in and self-identification with the needs of the other. We therefore argue that volunteers will be people who use some kind of identification with the other to bridge over from their lifescape of ordinary ethics into some form of extraordinary ethical citizenship.
>
> (Cloke *et al.* 2007)

Often, but not always, the desire to act in this way is driven by religious or ideological convictions. In turn, these beliefs are performed, often emotively, within the institutional ethics and organizational contexts of soup runs. Supporters of soup runs would argue that their work creates spaces of care that are inclusionary in nature by providing homeless citizens with food, counselling and compassion. Many operate a 'no questions asked', non-judgemental approach to the provision of emergency care that encourages their use by those who feel unable to approach state welfare services for these reasons. Given this complexity, ethical citizenship is best understood as performative rather than something that can be 'read-off' from personal or institutional standpoints. The performance of volunteering on soup runs represents personal and institutional ethics rather than state ideologies of 'active citizenship'.

By contrast, other faith groups acting in the 'post-secular city' (Beaumont and Baker 2011) may elect to work more closely with state agencies in the performance of these ethics. For example, some Christian food banks will only provide food to people who have been referred to them by government agencies (Lambie-Mumford and Jarvis 2012), actions that have been criticized for

Continued

helping the state to relinquish its welfare responsibilities (Cloke 2011; Williams *et al.* 2012). Other groups work 'in parallel' with state agencies. Street pastors, for example, provide care in the night-time economy. They operate with the backing of the emergency services and local councils but work independently of them.

All of these faith groups bring personal but different ethics and faith into the performance of volunteering in different urban spaces, emphasizing the need to understand the socio-cultural contexts in which individuals and voluntary groups perform citizenship.

of large voluntary organizations may have different working cultures, environments and priorities that create local differences in the relationship between the organization and the state (Parsons 2006; Yarwood 2011a). Grass-roots organizations at the other end of the voluntary spectrum (Table 4.1) may provide better opportunities for citizen involvement. These groups are more informal in their management, organization and activities, responding to needs identified by volunteers or communities. However, they are in danger of becoming politically, socially and financially marginalized as the voluntary sector is restructured on more formal lines.

Milligan (2009) suggests that voluntary groups are now faced with a choice between 'renewing' (jettisoning independence in favour of working in partnership with the state) or 'de-centring' (actively relocating to the margins of state control and shunning the opportunities offered by partnership working). Yet empirical work suggests that the situation is more complex than this. Some voluntary groups are able to negotiate their position in relation to other agencies, policy initiatives and funding streams to maximize not only funding but the influence and effectiveness of the organization (Trudeau 2008b). Although voluntary groups may be a 'junior partner' in government funding schemes, many attempt to balance this with efforts to empower local communities (Trudeau 2008a). In the adage of development workers, these organizations are 'funding fed rather than funding led', using funding in a more tactical fashion to achieve their own goals. These complex and sometimes bureaucratic negotiations may open up new opportunities for active citizenship and participation (Woods 2006a). Although voluntarism has been strongly influenced by national-level restructuring, it is also apparent that local needs, interests and organizations remain influential and contribute significantly to a geographically uneven terrain of volunteering (Milligan 2008; Owen and Kearns 2008; Skinner and Power 2011).

Places are not only shaped by volunteering but can also shape the significance, magnitude, nature and performance of volunteering (Wolch 1990; Owen and Kearns 2008). Recent work has demonstrated how the spaces of charities, such as the soup kitchen or even a local branch office, give volunteers opportunities to perform personal, political, religious and altruistic beliefs and, in doing so, are able to shape the institutional frameworks of these organizations (Conradson 2006; Cloke *et al.* 2007). Socio-cultural approaches to the study of volunteering (Conradson 2003a, 2003b) emphasize that, despite the politicization of volunteering and the growth of the shadow state, the ethics and motivations of individual volunteers (Cloke *et al.* 2005), together with local leadership and circumstances (Milligan 2008), remain significant determinants of local action. It is important to appreciate not only how voluntary groups create or extinguish spaces for active citizenship through their relationship with the state, but also how citizens negotiate and perform within these spaces. An emphasis on the individual citizen (Staeheli 2011, 2013) and acknowledging his or her political and ethical engagement with community, however imagined, is crucial to understanding how local places are shaped by citizen action.

CITIZENSHIP AND COMMUNITY CRITIQUES

Active citizenship implies a vision of citizenship that is based on locality, inclusivity and civic virtue: 'through participation as a citizen, one connects to an imaginary community through space particularly when engaging in the language of rights to ground desires for social betterment' (Lepofsky and Fraser 2003: 130). Indeed, ideas of community and neighbourhood are central to the imagination and development of active citizen policies. This raises a broader question as to whether community is based on citizenship or vice versa (Staeheli 2008a). Delanty (2002: 159) notes that communitarians argue 'citizenship is rooted in a culturally defined community, while liberals argue that citizenship rests on individuals and that political community is derivative of its members'.

This debate is rendered more complex because the idea of community has been imbued with multiple meanings that hide as much as they reveal

(Newby 1986; Harper 1989; Liepins 2000a, 2000b; Delanty 2002, 2003; Panelli and Welch 2005; Painter 2007; Staeheli 2008a; Closs Stephens and Squire 2012a). The conflation of community and locality is problematic, not least because engagement can occur in other or distant communities. International volunteering has the potential to develop cosmopolitan forms of citizenship or to develop ethical citizens and, consequently, is often used by youth and/or faith groups to develop these forms of citizenship (Hopkins *et al.* 2010; Lorimer 2010). The association of citizenship with (local) community is particularly problematic given its (often misplaced) associations with inclusivity and communality (Lepofsky and Fraser 2003; Staeheli 2008a; Cheshire and Woods 2009). Community can be used as a catch-all term that brushes over a wide range of social characteristics and proclaims a cultural cohesiveness that is imagined or lacking.

Although community implies inclusion, it may also be the basis of exclusion (Valentine 2001; Staeheli 2008a). For example, local groups based on race, religion, gender, ethnicity or sexuality may limit membership to people who fit these categories. Robert Putnam (2001) associates strong participation in community activities (social capital) with the development of wider forms of economic, cultural and political capital and power (Bourdieu 1984). These perspectives echo communitarian views of citizenship that emphasize this link between community and citizenship, arguing that community is necessary to engage people with the actions, duties and rights associated with citizenship. He distinguishes between *bonding* capital, which is inward looking and bonds particular groups together to the exclusion of others (see, for example, Hubbard 2006), and *bridging* capital, which is outward looking and attempts to link different people, groups and communities together. While many state-based local initiatives have attempted to develop bridging capital, there is evidence that many people, groups and communities remain unwilling or unable to engage with these forms of active citizenship (Staeheli 2003b).

Sara MacKian (1995) argued that if people 'choose not to sit on committees or to shake boxes on flag days, we should not exclude them from citizenship or ignore their standing as citizens'. She suggested that most citizens act autonomously to help themselves rather than the wider community or, further still, the state or nation. She went on to say that only a minority of people might be considered 'active' citizens, with the vast majority 'living out daily lives as ordinary people'. Even Robert Putnam (2001), who places much emphasis on the value of community organizations, concedes that people are more likely to take individual rather than collective action. He points out that although 11 per cent of US residents took part in a community-based NW meeting, more took personal action to protect their property through the use of extra locks (41 per cent), a guard dog (15 per cent) or firearms (14 per cent). Perhaps greater academic attention should be paid to those whom Putnam describes as 'Schmoozers': people with an active social life that revolves around spending time with friends, going to bars and nights spots, holding barbeques, visiting relatives and so on.

Local participation emphasizes that citizenship is defined politically not only by the (central) state but also by a 'complex set of relationships and expectations knitting individuals into various political communities' (Kurtz and Hankins 2005). Many of the most successful forms of active citizenship have occurred where there is already strong social capital or community. The provision of welfare and services through voluntary participation in community is likely to produce a patchwork that reflects willingness to participate in (certain) forms of community action rather than need (Yarwood and Edwards 1995; Yarwood 2002).

In turn, the success of policies may be judged on the participation of place-based communities with implications for future relations with the state as well as funding and support (Desforges *et al.* 2005). Equally, funding will reflect what is seen to be worthy of support. Some groups and communities have been excluded from state-led volunteer programmes and have been forced to develop more autonomous actions. Brown (1997) documents how voluntary organizations emerged in Vancouver to provide welfare support for gay people with AIDS when the provincial government failed to respond. Phil Hubbard (1998) recounts an effective but exclusionary use of community action in the Balsall Heath area of Birmingham, UK in the 1990s. The area witnessed a growth in prostitution in the 1980s, achieving notoriety locally and nationally as Birmingham's Red Light District. Residents in the area made complaints against 'kerb crawling' (the practice of driving slowly around neighbourhoods and soliciting for sex), the use of private car parks by customers and a perceived decline in house prices. Despite some high-profile arrests and actions, the police were reluctant to act in case these activities were displaced elsewhere. From the 1990s onwards, residents organized themselves into groups that stood on the streets with protest placards and recorded the registration plates of cars driven by men considered to be soliciting for sex and passed these to the police. Although the police initially scorned this activity as vigilantism, these actions 'had more impact on the location of prostitutes in their respective cities than any police intervention over the last thirty years' (Hubbard 1998: 283), reducing kerb crawling by 80 per cent and reducing the number of sex workers by two-thirds (largely displaced elsewhere). In response, the police worked more closely with the community pickets and formalized the scheme as a kind of 'neighbourhood watch' in line with national active citizenship initiatives.

Officially sanctioned forms of active citizenship reflect a form of 'shallow citizenship' where citizens have their rights and responsibilities predefined for them (Parker 1999a). Although 'active' citizens engage below the scale of the nation-state, they nevertheless continue to engage with the state and, knowingly or otherwise, contribute to broader policies of social reform and welfare delivery. Chapter 5 considers forms of local action that challenge the nation-state and are led by activist, rather than active, citizens.

FURTHER READING

Nick Fyfe and Christine Milligan's (2003a) review of the geographies of voluntarism in *Progress in Human Geography* provides a good introduction to active citizenship. Milligan's (2009) entry on the voluntary sector in the *International Encyclopaedia of Human Geography* also provides a good summary of work in this area. Their empirical work on the voluntary sector (Fyfe and Milligan 2003a, 2003b; Milligan and Fyfe 2005) sheds light on the way that the voluntary sector has been shaped by the state. My own work on Neighbourhood Watch (Yarwood and Edwards 1995; Yarwood 2010b, 2011a, 2012), policing (Yarwood 2007a, 2007b, 2010a), higher education (Yarwood 2005) and mountain rescue teams (Yarwood 2010b, 2011a, 2012) provides further empirical examples of active citizenship. Paul Cloke, Sarah Johnsen and Jonathon May (2007) use voluntary work to support homeless people to posit the idea of 'ethical citizenship' as an alternative to state-regulated forms of active citizenship. For the official line on the Big Society see https://www.gov.uk/government/publications/big-society-faqs-and-useful-links (last accessed 6 August 2013).

5

CITIZENSHIP, NETWORKS AND ACTIVISM

FROM ACTIVE TO ACTIVIST CITIZENS

Chapter 4 examined ways in which citizens have been encouraged by the state to fulfil particular duties. 'Active' citizenship operates at spatial scales below the nation-state – neighbourhood, community and locality are emphasized – but generally in support of the state and its policies, conforming to what Parker (1999b) has described as 'good citizenship' (Figure 5.1). Citizens participating inside these frameworks may use them to press for greater self-determination or the delivery of particular services (see also Short 1993), but they have also been recognized as a form of 'government from a distance' that utilizes community and responsibility as a form of governmentality in order to achieve particular policy ends (Garland 1996; Rose 1996; Fyfe and Milligan 2003a; Lockie and Higgins 2007; Cheshire and Woods 2009). Thus a NW scheme may improve channels of communication between the public and police, allowing residents to demand improvements to local policing services, but it is also a way of making citizens responsible for their own policing.

These actions have been gaining more significance as a reliance on the free market (Goodwin and Painter 1996) has led to new forms of

'Deviant' citizen *'Protest'*	*Littoral zone*	'Good' citizen *'Participation'*
'Negative'	⟷	'Positive'
Outside	⟷	Inside
Direct action	⟷	Due process
Unstable	⟷	Stabilized
Illegal/not legitimized	⟷	Legal/legitimized
Visible	⟷	Obscured

Figure 5.1 Parker's (1999b) Continua of Citizen Protest and Action

governance (Rhodes 1996; Yarwood 2002; Woods 2006a; Goodwin 2009), an emphasis on duties over rights (Kearns 1992; Yarwood and Edwards 1995; Fyfe and Milligan 2003a; Mohan 2007; Skinner and Fleuret 2011; Skinner and Power 2011) and new ways of providing welfare and services through partnerships working between private, state and voluntary agencies (Edwards *et al.* 2001).

Yet it is also possible to trace a range of citizen actions (Saunders 1979; Short 1993) that extend from the types of conciliatory actions described above to forms of 'insurgent' (Holsten 1999) or 'deviant' (Parker 1999b) citizenship that challenge the state, its institutions and spaces in more radical ways (Figure 5.1). 'Deviant' citizens often mistrust the state and feel obliged to voice their concerns outside its formal apparatus using various forms of direct action that range in intensity, duration and legitimacy, from violent direct action to mundane acts of everyday consumption. Engin Isin summarizes these differences in citizenship aptly:

> we contrast 'activist citizens' with 'active citizens' who act out already written scripts. While activist citizens engage in writing scripts and creating the scene, active citizens follow scripts and participate in scenes that are already created. While activist citizens are creative, active citizens are not.[1]
>
> (Isin 2008: 38)

Activism is significant to the understanding of citizenship for three main reasons. First, by its very nature activism draws attention to the uneven terrain of citizenship. Actions are taken, amongst other things, in an effort to claim or demand rights, gain power, establish greater autonomy, support cultural difference, conserve nature or history or, quite simply, to defend personal interests and capital (Short 1993). A focus on the cause of conflict allows us to examine *de jure* and *de facto* inequalities in citizenship.

Second, citizen activism has the potential to transform space and, with it, what is understood by citizenship. Of recent interest, for example, has been the way in which some campaigns have been enacted above and beyond the level of the nation-state, gathering strength from global participation. Global movements, such as Fairtrade campaigns (Clarke *et al.* 2007b), aid agencies (Desforges 2004) or anti-capitalist protests (Routledge *et al.* 2006, 2007), seek to cross national boundaries and influence decision making at a global level (Khagram *et al.* 2002). These forms of action represent attempts to develop a global civic society and, with it, citizenry. It has been suggested that these actions draw upon and enforce a global or cosmopolitan sense of citizenship that challenges the conventional association of citizenship with the nation-state (Dower 2003; Mayo 2005; Isin and Nielson 2008; Miller 2010). These forms of citizenship find expression as *networks* that link and cross different spaces and boundaries.

Finally, activism raises questions about the nature of power and the ability of citizens to conclude genuinely transformative actions. Dissent, as Mitchell and Staeheli (2005) observe, can threaten the state, necessitating its regulation, incorporation and/or policing by those in authority. This chapter uses a range of citizen actions to consider these issues and question whether citizen action can extend or break the spatial and political boundaries of citizenship. It begins by considering tactical forms of protest before considering wider, more fluid movements that stretch beyond immediate localities.

FROM TACTICAL PROTEST TO TRANSNATIONAL CITIZENSHIP

Local actions by citizens are frequently triggered by issues that are deemed to impact negatively on their locality. Examples include unwelcome planning decisions (Rowley and Haynes 1990; Costello and Dunn 1994; Yarwood 2002; Gallent and Robinson 2011; Scott *et al.* 2012); the closure of local services (Ribchester and Edwards 1999; Brown 2003); the loss of power or self-determination (Pile 1995; Troy 2000; Cowell and Thomas 2002; Ellis 2004; Wood 2006); cultural threat (Woods 2003; Cohen 2007); environmental degradation (Valdivia 2008; Schelly and Stretesky 2009; Devine-Wright and Howes 2010); the loss of amenity (van Dijk and van der Wulp 2010); or perceived threats from social 'others' (Rowley and Haynes 1990; Hubbard 1998, 2005; D. Smith 2008). In response, citizen actions range from formal participation in the structures of civic and political decision-making through to protest, demonstration and direct action both within and outside the law.

Planning disputes are probably the most common form of citizen intervention at the local level. They usually fall within the boundaries of the law and reflect various forms of civic and political rights that allow, and indeed encourage, citizens to participate in formal decision-making processes (Box 5.1). However, these tend to reproduce the social and power relations inherent in local politics (Cheshire and Woods 2009). This is not least because planning frameworks have been developed to deal with land-use disputes rather than broader issues of social justice. Objectors are obliged to phrase their concerns within the language of land use, although this may disguise the social prejudices that may underpin these objections (Hubbard 2006). Many (but by no means all) objections to planning decisions *tend* to reflect parochial or 'not in my backyard' (NIMBY) standpoints that are concerned with change (or preventing change) in a particular locality (but see Wolsink 2006). Occasionally, resident groups, such as village preservation societies (Cloke and Goodwin 1992a; Murdoch and Marsden 1994), emerge from specific disputes to maintain the visibility of particular interests but, again, their goal is usually the maintenance of the status quo rather than radical change.

Citizens may resort to more direct forms of action if they feel that they are not served by formal systems of consultation or, indeed, if these are absent. The most moderate forms of action may involve petitioning, erecting banners and holding demonstrations, marches or rallies. Such actions usually take advantage of civil rights that allow people to assemble, protest and voice free speech. If these do not exist, or protestors feel their voices are still not being heard, more direct forms of action or civil

Box 5.1 TACTICAL PROTESTS

Civil and political rights allow citizens to participate in local decision making, for example a planning meeting, and to voice their concerns at developments in their local area. Rowley and Haynes' (1990) description of a dispute over a proposal to build a 'healing centre' in a public park in Stoke-on-Trent, UK provides a classic account of how civil and political rights are deployed to resolve local planning disputes. Local residents who opposed the scheme and the charitable trust that wanted to build it both deployed various and escalating types of civic engagement to support their cause, including the use of public petitions, protest marches, debates at planning meetings, writing to town councillors and votes at local and general elections. Both drew upon discourses of citizenship that variously championed rights to practise religion, access green space, participate in democratic processes and so on. Although the proposal to build a healing centre was eventually given planning permission, lack of funds prevented its construction.

Protests that use direct action rely on civic rights to be effective. For example, people chaining themselves to trees to prevent logging or lying in front of trucks transporting nuclear waste to protest against nuclear power rely on the right to life and the process of law to ensure their safe removal from danger. This is usually time-consuming and costly (for example requiring specially trained bailiffs to climb trees). As Marshall (1950) points out, such protests mobilize not only civic and political rights, but also social rights, such as an education, that allow people to articulate their concerns.

In countries where citizens have fewer civic and political rights, it is harder for people to express themselves in this way. In China, economic reform has increased social privileges for some, but corruption and the lack of democracy mean that civic and political rights remain limited (Cunningham and Watterstrom 2011). He (2012) traces how the process of gentrification in the city of Guangzhou revealed how few rights local residents have in their neighbourhoods. During the first wave, modest gentrification led to displacement and only sporadic struggles against authorities appropriating their property. A second, more sustained wave led to large-scale displacements and wider, more coordinated protests but, ultimately, revealed a lack of political power and, consequently, no rights to participate in local decision making.

disobedience may occur (Box 5.1). These may be non-violent and take the form of disruptive activities, often in symbolic, public places (Anderson 2010). In 1989, pro-democracy student protests in Tiananmen Square in Beijing, China were violently dispersed by the Chinese government using military force (Hsu 2008). In countries where criticisms of the government are curtailed in public spaces, protest must be more covert. In Zimbabwe, two anonymous forms of media – a satirical deck of playing cards and a 'Guide to Dangerous Snakes in Zimbabwe' – have used political cartoons and caricatures to criticize President Robert Mugabe's regime (Hammett 2011).

Isin (2008) argues that while radical acts of citizenship should be orientated towards achieving justice, their acts do not need to be founded or enacted in law itself. Some groups may resort to civil disobedience or even behaviour that is deemed criminal. Merriman and Jones (2009) chart how Cymdeithas yr Iaith Gymraeg (the Welsh Language Society) defaced English-language road signs as part of a campaign against English-only road signs in Wales. These non-violent but prominent actions contributed to the establishment of bilingual signs in Wales. In part, this was due to 'the very public support of hundreds of respectable Welsh professionals' (p.350) for the campaign. By contrast, John Short (1989) charted the growth of Class War's campaigns to 'mug a yuppie' and destroy their property as a response to economic and political changes wrought by gentrification and redevelopment in the London Docklands. This violence achieved little and represented 'the deathroes of a community undergoing marginalisation and eventual destruction' (p.187). The difference between the two actions and their outcomes reflected differences in the class and power of citizens supporting them. Often tactical protests reflect rather than significantly change existing power structures in society.

Some forms of local actions have the ability to 'jump scales' (Holsten 2008) and the potential to achieve more radical change, both to forms of citizenship and to social equality. These citizens are concerned less about local NIMBYism and more with *resistance* against forces of global changes (Cresswell 1996; Routledge 2000; Hubbard 2006). These kinds of actions are transnational in nature as they provide opportunities for citizens in diverse localities to act collectively to effect change on a global scale.

Khagram *et al.* (2002) classify transnational actions into three types: transnational advocacy networks, transnational coalitions and transnational social movements (Table 5.1). All have the potential to transform space and society, as the following sections reveal.

ADVOCACY NETWORKS

Khagram *et al.* (2002) describe advocacy networks as providing information that allows individual citizens to make personal decisions about lifestyle choices or to take actions in support of a cause. The potency of these networks has increased with the rise of internet fora and social media such as Facebook and Twitter that have allowed users to share

Table 5.1 Transnational networks (after Khagram *et al.* 2002)

Transnational movement	Primary features	Examples
Advocacy networks	Actors linked across boundaries and united by shared values and exchanges of information. Usually informal. No sustained coordinated use of tactics or actions of people.	Internet fora
Coalitions	Actors across countries that coordinate shared strategies to publicly influence social change. Formal agreements and coordinated action.	The Fairtrade Campaign
(New) social movements	Sets of actors with common purposes. Informal. Based on mobilizing actions concerned with disruption or protest.	Occupy movement

information across the world to establish campaigning and advocacy networks.

The influence of these networks was perhaps demonstrated in the series of uprisings that occurred in the Middle East from December 2010. The catalyst for action was the suicide of an educated, under-employed vegetable seller in Tunisia in response to police harassment, which was reported on social media. His death reflected a series of underlying grievances – inequalities in standards of living, rising living costs (especially food), disaffected youth, political corruption and authoritarian regimes – but relied on social media to forge the identities of protestors and formulate plans of action (Caprotti and Gao 2012). This prompted an uprising in Tunisia that led to the overthrow and exile of its president Zine al-Abidine Ben Ali and occasioned further protests across the Middle East (dubbed the 'Arab Spring' by the media) that brought about changes of regime in Egypt, Libya and Yemen (Smith 2011).

In Egypt protests centred on Tahrir (Liberation) Square, Cairo. This place is symbolically important as it had been associated with the liberation of Egypt from colonial rule at the start of the twentieth century. It provided a space for protestors to gather and reimagine a new Egyptian politics (Caprotti and Gao 2012). Despite violent confrontations in Tahrir Square, the movement succeeded in deposing President Mubarak and establishing Mohammed Morsi as an elected president. At the time of writing, Morsi has since been ousted as president following mass protest and action from the Egyptian army.

Protests occurred in other Arabian countries with varying measures of success, although many were met with further repression. In Syria, for example, protests have descended into civil war with the loss of many civilian lives.

Jeffrey (2013) noted that the uprisings of the 'Arab Spring' largely occurred outside formal political structures or institutions. Instead, he suggests that protests appeared to be leaderless and without formal plans for political alternatives. They were, instead, mobilized by web-based activism and internet traffic, which also reflected the youth of many protestors and their favour for these media (just as the British 'youth riots' of 2011 were, in part, motivated by social media). Jeffrey continues that the unplanned, flexible and spontaneous nature of these uprisings were their strength, perhaps highlighting the significance of global advocacy networks.

Not everyone has access to the World Wide Web (latest estimates suggest that only a third do (Gallup 2013)) and some states, notably China, have sought to regulate its use by citizens. During the Arab Spring, bloggers and users of the internet were prosecuted. Troops were also deployed from some Arab states to help suppress protests in others. So, despite the strength and potential of social media and global advocacy networks to transform society and space, they are not a panacea for social change. The use of technology must be buttressed with wider human rights that can affect longer-lasting change.

TRANSNATIONAL COALITIONS: ETHICAL CITIZENSHIP

Transnational coalitions involve formal agreements and coordinated actions that extend across countries to influence social change. This section uses the example of consumption practices to exemplify their operation. At first glance this might seem an unusual choice because there are, in principle, key differences between citizens and customers. Citizens are entitled to certain social, political and civic rights by virtue of their citizenship but, in contrast, customers only have an economic relationship with whoever provides their services or goods (Hill 1994; Parker 1999b):

> the concept of customer is very different from that of a citizen . . . If a customer is dissatisfied with a service transaction he or she normally can and should abandon, walk away from the service relationship and seek another supplier. If a citizen is dissatisfied, by contrast, he or she normally cannot or should not walk away but rather must work with other members of the community to seek improvement.
>
> (Heintzman, 1999 quoted in Clarke, 2002: 20)

However, the distinction between citizen and customer is becoming blurred. Thus, many neo-liberal governments have replaced state services with an array of private and voluntary providers (see Chapter 4), requiring citizens, with the help of charters and league tables, to act as customers seeking the best deal. It has been argued that these changes have led to a decline in 'public-spirited citizenship' that promotes 'collective action of strong-individuated, self-consciously committed citizens' (Dean 2003: 4).

The consumer-citizen is able to withdraw from politics and, instead, pursue strategies that promote their own, or at best, local concerns rather than those of the common good (Dagger 2002). This is aided by what Karl Marx (1990) referred to as the 'fetishism of commodity' that detaches consumers from the social relations that are needed to produce goods. While consumers value the latest electronic good, they show less concern about the exploitative labour relations that were used to produce it in another part of the world (Mansvelt 2005) and are less inclined to take political action to resolve them.

Yet there is growing recognition that practices of consumption *do* enrol citizens into networks that extend well beyond local spaces and *can* link them to people, places and conditions far beyond their immediate locality (Crewe 2003). Parker (1999b: 69) argues that 'consumption through material goods or other consumption practices provides a channel of communication for consumers to other members of society and to those in positions of power over them'. One way in which this finds expression is through campaigns to encourage ethical or moral consumption (Mansvelt 2008). Examples include 'Fairtrade' schemes (Whatmore and Thorne 1997; Clarke *et al.* 2007a; Malpass *et al.* 2007; Goodman 2010), the purchase of 'alternative' gifts as a form of charitable giving (Rutt 2011), the use of ethical banks (Buttle 2007), choosing to buy environmentally friendly and/or local produce (Clarke *et al.* 2008; Goodman *et al.* 2010) or, quite simply, stopping or reducing shopping (Klein 2001). Desforges *et al.* (2005: 442) argue 'the effect has not been to undermine the notion of citizenship per se but rather to change the ways in which people think about their sense of citizenship, their sense of belonging and their sense of responsibility'. This is exemplified by British academic and activist Noreena Hertz:

> Sunday morning. Central London, home. I wake up to the excesses of the night before. Washing up in piles. Open my bottle of Ecover and squeeze biodegradable liquid on to yesterday's plates crusted with GM-free organic pizza. Fill a cafetière with Fairtrade coffee and boil a free-range egg. Take a 'not tested on animals' Lush bubble bath. Pull on my 'child labour free' Reeboks, 'made by 100 percent union labour' Levis, and 'never use furs' Chloe T-shirt. Spray my hair with Wella non-CFC canister. Read the papers and learn about the latest McDonald's boycott. Remind myself to pick up a leaflet from the

> protestors on my next outing by jotting down a note on my pad of recycled paper.
>
> Nip down to Body Shop to get my 'fairly traded' moisturiser, read in-store leaflet on globalisation while paying for it with my 'investments only in ethical companies' Co-operative Bank credit card. Stop to fill up with unleaded petrol on the way home. Two petrol stations on either side of the road. Same prices, same petrol. Remember that the one on the left has been involved in an oil spill in Nigeria. Turn right with no second thought. Come home and log on. Check mail on 'we put social issues first' AOL. Send off a standard form e-mail to McDonalds, protesting at their activities in Argentina. Enter the UN hunger site, click my mouse and silently thank American Express for donating that day's bowl of rice and mealies. All the while snacking on Ben and Jerry's 'we don't cut down trees in the Amazon' ice cream.
>
> (Hertz 2001: 119)

In this example, consumption is consciously and contentiously linked to the rights and concerns of those well outside the consumer's community. Political concerns are expressed through the consumption of goods or participation in campaigns, rather than the formal channels of democracy. As Goodman *et al.* (2010: 1788) put it, 'buying organic and/or Fairtrade chocolate never tasted so politically nor subjectively good!' Clarke *et al.* (2007a: 234) state that these forms of consumption represent 'an emergent politics of choice distinct from a longer established politics of loyalty based on parties and elections' (and perhaps brand loyalties too). These forms of political engagement depend on 'repertoires' of cause-orientated expression that reflect ethical and political choices by the citizen to consume in particular ways, as well as actions of certain agencies, for example charities or campaign groups, that seek to influence this choice and campaign on behalf of consumers investing in their products (Box 5.2). Ethical consumption extends beyond local spaces, entwining local volunteers and consumers with aid agencies, NGOs and international regulators of trade (Micheletti 2003). It offers a chance to 'care at a distance' (Barnett and Land 2007) through participation in networks created and steered by NGOs.

These agencies seek to lay out the 'moral risks' associated with the purchase of goods connected with social, environmental or political harm (Barnett and Land 2007; Clarke *et al.* 2007a). Fairtrade networks

Box 5.2 THE FAIRTADE CAMPAIGN

Fairtrade emerged as a movement in the 1980s concerned with mitigating or balancing the effects of unfair neo-liberal trade policies on producers in the global South. It was driven initially by a number of charities including Oxfam, Christian Aid and Traidcraft that aimed to connect consumers closely with the producers of food through a discourse of 'fairness' (Whatmore and Thorne 1997). These agencies worked to develop non-exploitative trading relations that promoted sustainable development (Jaffee 2007). In brief, this is achieved by guaranteeing producers a minimum price for their goods that covers the cost of sustainable production. This is usually higher than market prices but, if the market price is higher, this is paid to the producer. In addition, Fairtrade organizations pay producers a separate premium to be 'invested in social, environmental and economic developmental projects' to be determined by a local committee or cooperative of producers (Fairtrade Foundation 2011). These costs are passed on to the consumer who will pay more for Fairtrade produce in the knowledge that producers are being paid a fair price and are benefiting from social development. The Fairtrade movement has gathered considerable momentum, evidenced by a significant increase in sales of fairly traded produce. Between 2011 and 2012 there were Fairtrade sales of €4.9 billion worldwide (Fairtrade International 2012).

Fairtrade networks enrol producers (often represented personally and pictorially on the packaging of products), consumers, charities, retailers and even celebrities (Goodman 2010) into networks that link 'distant others' with the 'local self' (Barnett *et al.* 2005; Herman 2010) (Figure 5.2). These networks are regulated globally by the umbrella organization Fairtrade International that, in turn, coordinates national bodies such as the Fairtrade Foundation in the UK. These organizations certify specific products that reflect the principles of Fairtrade and regulate the use of a widely recognized Fairtrade symbol to promote these products.

Figure 5.2 The site of a stall in a Fairtrade church allows ethical consumers to link into networks that connect them with 'distant others' (Photo: Author)

appeal to citizens who want to avoid these ethical pitfalls (Clarke *et al.* 2007a), offering an opportunity to turn what they 'ought to do' into something they 'can do' (Barnett *et al.* 2005). In doing so, citizens have been empowered to act and consume politically (Clarke *et al.* 2007a):

> there is a growing suggestion that 'voting with one's money' through the purchase of more ethical/moral alternative foods goes far beyond an economic vote to encompass an act that produces new political subjectivities, new forms of political representation, and new politics more broadly.
>
> (Goodman *et al.* 2010: 1787)

The concept of Fairtrade has been embedded into formal efforts to teach principles of national citizenship and global responsibility in schools (Pykett *et al.* 2010). The establishment of Fairtrade towns, organizations, retailers, cafés, churches, tourism ventures and shops committed to the use of Fairtrade produce has bound the principles of Fairtrade into local governance and decision making with important implications (Malpass *et al.* 2007). In some instances consumers have no choice but to buy Fairtrade produce. For example, it may only be possible to buy Fairtrade coffee in a 'Fairtrade university'. This renders the consumer subject to decisions made by governing bodies of the university rather than independent political or consumptive decision making (Malpass *et al.* 2007).

It is argued that ethical consumption practices are starting to have an impact on global production networks (Hughes *et al.* 2008). Many private businesses have adopted codes of corporate social responsibility (CSR) that suggest profits should also be accompanied by good citizenship (Sadler 2004). McDonalds, for example, stated:

> whether it's called 'good corporate citizenship' or 'social responsibility,' we take seriously our commitment to conducting our business in a way that respects the world around us and the issues that matter most to you.
>
> (McDonald's Corporation 2004)

CSR has become a key discourse within business and is seen as a good investment in a brand's image. A whole industry of advocates and consultants has emerged to advise firms on its principles (Sadler and Lloyd 2009). Critics argue that corporate efforts to meet the demands of ethical consumption are simply 'greenwash' (see Micheletti 2003 for a critique of these views; Goodman *et al.* 2010). Hartwick (1998: 443) considers that ethical campaigns are merely 'a simulated politics' that pretends to represent a popular struggle (Hartwick 1998: 433) or, at best, a 'conscience soother' for middle-class consumers (Crewe 2000: 283). Clarke *et al.* also suggest that consumptive practices could support rather than challenge neo-liberal politics:

> under so-called advanced liberal styles of government, the concept of the citizen is apparently transformed from one based on a notion of a subject with entitlement rights against a social state, to a 'responsibilised' citizen modelled on the consumer who activates personal preferences in the marketplace.
>
> (Clarke *et al.* 2007a: 235)

If new forms of citizenship are emerging through consumption practices, these are socially and economically uneven (Goodman *et al.* 2010). It reflects an ability to make consumption choices. Globally, over one billion people are undernourished (World Food Programme 2010). Many others are facing food poverty or living in 'food deserts' that offer little choice to consumers (Whelan *et al.* 2002; Wrigley *et al.* 2003). Although ethical consumption has increased in volume and scope, middle-class affluent consumers are more likely to pay the extra prices associated with it. Even then certain products, particularly coffee and bananas, are purchased more regularly then many others (Fairtrade International 2012). The choice not to consume certain goods is one that is held, ironically, by those who can.

On the positive side, citizenship through consumption may empower those women who are homemakers to make political decisions linked to everyday choices to purchase particular goods (Micheletti 2003). However, Goodman *et al.* (2010) caution that these people should not be held solely responsible for implementing socio-ecological change. Further, they suggest that a focus on ethical consumption highlights and privileges the consumer. By contrast, they argue, far less has been considered or written on the producers of ethical produce. Supporters of Fairtrade networks argue that such networks empower producers politically through, for example, decision making as part of a grower's cooperative as well as improving their social rights (such as improved education) and civic rights (for example, better employment practices) (Nelson and Pound 2009). Indeed, representation of these achievements to Western customers is an important part of encouraging ethical consumption (Herman 2012). Yet a study of south India (Neilson and Pritchard 2010) concluded that Fairtrade schemes did little to support those most in need, i.e. smallholders and workers on abandoned estates. While Fairtrade producers were becoming increasingly enmeshed into the complex networks of Fairtrade, those outside were regulated traditionally by state agencies and trade unions. Thus, two tiers of governance and empowerment seem to be emerging for citizen-producers. Elsewhere, farmers in Andhra Pradesh have been torn between Fairtrade and organic farming initiatives and driven in to new forms of agrarian capitalism (Makita 2012).

Ethical consumers negotiate a complex moral and ethical terrain (Herman 2010). The decision to buy Fairtrade goods may be a political choice but it is one that is often site- or product-dependent. Consumers may buy a Fairtrade product in one site, for example a chocolate bar at a Fairtrade stall in a school, and buy products from mainstream consumers elsewhere. Debates will continue as to whether consumption is a form of political engagement and whether it offers an alternative form of citizenship. Forms of ethical consumption may offer a 'proxy citizenship' (Desforges 2004) whereby members can choose to opt in or out of these networks on the basis of choice (and ability) to pay and consume. Gavin Parker (1999b: 69) refers to this as a form of hybrid 'consumer-citizenship' in which a 'mix of lifestyle, identity, belief and practice is brought to bear through market mechanisms'.

Political consumption and citizenship are not mutually exclusive, as Hertz (2001: 212) suggests:

> as consumers we must be both vigilant and active, as protestors we must force our politicians to realise the dangers of inaction and respond appropriately. And as citizens we must make it clear to government that unless government focuses on people as well as business . . . we will continue to scorn representative democracy, and will choose to shop and protest rather than vote.
>
> (Hertz 2001: 212)

The choice of citizens to consume ethically is often taken as *part* of a range of other actions and it is important to remember that Fairtrade and ethical consumption are transnational *coalitions* (Khagram *et al.* 2002) that use a particular strategy to achieve change. In comparison, transnational social movements use a *range* of strategies, tactics and actions to mobilize networks of citizen activists for collective action. The significance of these approaches is discussed in the following section.

TRANSNATIONAL SOCIAL MOVEMENTS

'New' Social Movements (NSMs) emerged during the 1960s in response to forms of global political decision making that were felt to be unaccountable, inequitable and exploitative. The label 'new' is used to distinguish from 'old' social movements that were more closely aligned with conventional politics. 'Old' movements were more formally organized and frequently took action to achieve particular tactical goals linked to working conditions or improvements in wages.

Of course, labels of 'old' and 'new' hide as much as they reveal and questions have been raised as to whether there are significant differences between the social movements of late modernity and previous ones (Mayo 2005; Melucci 2008). 'New' movements do not imply that 'old' ones have gone away (for example, trade unions remain an influential vehicle for wider social protest and themselves play a role within the networks of 'new' social movements) but a number of key features can be distinguished between the two.

NSMs frequently target transnational organizations, such as the World Trade Organization (WTO), and multinational corporations, the largest of which have more wealth and power than many nation-states. Given that these organizations are not directly accountable to citizens, NSMs are associated with non-conventional forms of politics, political actions and political organization (Jones *et al.* 2004). NSMs are not single, formal organizations but are, instead, characterized by fluid identities and memberships that cut across class lines and spatial scales. They form wide political alliances, operating outside conventional political channels, using direct action, protest or pressure to pursue their goals. Thus, NSMs consist:

> of networks sharing beliefs and solidarity, with commitments to collective action, including the use of varying forms of protest (whether violent or non-violent).
>
> (Mayo 2005: 55)

Consequently, NSMs have diverse participants rather than members (Della Porter and Diani 1999; Routledge 2003) and groups and individuals that constitute NSMs bear a 'family resemblance' rather than a formal relationship (Crossley 2002). There is a lack of a leadership hierarchy or a structured organization. In short, NSMs 'are not interested in assuming power, in taking over government: rather they seek to change political practice and policy' (Jones *et al.* 2004: 152). NSMs mobilize people with various identities, affiliations and motivation who find expression in a particular campaign or form of resistance. Thus, a protest against the use of child labour might be supported by faith groups practising religious teaching about social justice; trade unions concerned about worker rights; NGOs with an interest in protecting children's rights; Marxists seeking to resist neo-liberalization and so on. Groups may therefore desire the same outcome for different reasons. For example, indigenous people may campaign to preserve ecological niches to sustain their livelihoods, whereas a middle-class Western consumer may do so to maintain biodiversity and protect 'wildernesses from development'. Paul Routledge (2005) has identified four key areas in which NSMs intervene:

- Economic
  - Equitable access to resources
  - Struggles in workforce
  - New services in health and education
- Cultural
  - Material conditions and needs
  - Local tradition and integrity
- Political
  - Challenge neo-liberal political structures
  - Outside mainstream politics (but may form alliances with and include politicians)
- Environmental
  - Protection of ecological niches.

Given these goals, as well as the fluid and flexible nature of participation in NSMs, their actions are often symbolic moments aimed at influencing opinion, subverting hegemonic discourses or gaining media attention. They represent a 'new domain of cultural rights that involve the right to symbolic presence, dignifying representation, propagation of identity and maintenance of lifestyles' (Pakulski 1997: 1362).

NSMs occupy a range of spaces (Routledge 1997; Halfacree 1999). One tactic has been to protest visibly and disruptively at cities hosting meetings of transnational organizations such as the WTO or G8 Group of nations (Box 5.3). These types of actions provide 'another spectacle, another mediated moment of the emerging globalized networks of communication, solidarity and information sharing between social movements and other resistance formations' (Routledge 2003: 333) and, in doing so, offer an alternative vision to that represented by neo-liberal

Box 5.3 CASE STUDY OF THE BATTLE IN SEATTLE

The anti-globalization protest of 30 November 1999 in Seattle marked a significant point for NSMs (Wills 2005; J. Smith 2008). The action crystallized around a meeting of the WTO concerning inequalities that had arisen from the expansion of trade liberalization under previous WTO agreements (J. Smith 2008). Countries in the global South felt disadvantaged and disempowered by the scale and nature of liberalization that were seen to favour Western states and corporate interests.

The meeting was met by protests staged and organized by diverse groups with different concerns, interests and political motivations united by a desire to 'democratise and incorporate values other than profit making into global economic institutions' (J. Smith 2008: 317). These ranged from churches with a concern for global justice to groups, such as the 'Turtles', with environmental interests (Wills 2005) to trade unions opposed to the impact of neo-liberalization on workers' rights. Some participants were part of formal transnational organizations such as Greenpeace, while others were locally based, organized with no formal links to organizations beyond their locality (Table 5.2).

These loose, heterogeneous alliances attracted 40,000 people to Seattle. They sought to 'disrupt the meeting, damage the urban landscape of Seattle and consequently draw media attention to their protests and the economic and social consequences of WTO policies' (Painter and Jeffrey 2009: 84). These led to violent confrontations with the police and to the authorities establishing 'no protest' zones (Herbert 2007) to segregate protestors from delegates. The action disrupted the WTO's talks and contributed (along with major differences between the states concerned) to their postponement to another, more secure, location in Qatar. Similar scenes were repeated at further WTO meetings and those of other transnational organizations such as the World Bank.

Continued

Table 5.2 Organizations involved in Seattle and N30 demonstrations (Source: J. Smith 2008)

Nature of transnational (TN) connections	**Example of participants**	**Examples of other associated groups**
No formal ties	Local branches of social movement Organizations; Neighbourhood no-WTO committees; United for a Fair Economy	School groups; friendship networks
Diffuse transnational ties	Direct Action Network; Reclaim the Streets; Ruckus Society; Coalition for Campus Organizing	Union branches; some churches
Routine transnational ties	Public Citizen; Global Exchange; United Students against Sweatshops; Council of Canadians; Sierra Club	AFL-CIO; United Steel Workers of America; International Longshore and Warehouse Union; some churches
Formal transnational organization	Greenpeace; Friends of the Earth; International Forum on Globalization; Third World Network; People Global Action; 50 Years Is Not Enough; Women's Environment and Development Network	International Confederation of Free Trade Unions; European Farmers Union

actors. Keith Halfacree (1999) suggests that sites of occupation have neo-tribal qualities to them that are characterized by, amongst other things, fluid membership, celebrations of the earth, reflexive forms of non-hierarchical organization and 'saturated' politics that reflect 'a strong feeling amongst participants of the bankruptcy of conventional politics and politicians and a need to bypass this' (p.214).

More recently, the Occupy movement sought to occupy public spaces associated with global capitalism (Pickerill and Krinsky 2012). The action began at New York's Zuccotti Park, Wall Street in September 2011. The group's website proclaimed:

> Occupy Wall Street is a leaderless resistance movement with people of many colours, genders and political persuasions. The one thing we all have in common is that We Are The 99 percent that will no longer tolerate the greed and corruption of the 1 percent. We are using the revolutionary Arab Spring tactic to achieve our ends and encourage the use of nonviolence to maximize the safety of all participants.
> (http://occupywallst.org/ – last accessed 6 August 2013)

Similar actions developed across the world with Occupy protestors appropriating symbolic spaces including St Paul's Cathedral in London (when plans to camp at the Stock Exchange were thwarted). 'One per cent' referred to the concentration of wealth in an elite, rich (and growing richer) part of the world's population. The Occupy sites were well organized with press and visitor centres to publicize their activities within and beyond the spaces of occupation. Sites were linked electronically and via common branding (including the use of Guy Fawkes masks based on the *V for Vendetta* film), mirroring the global reach of the corporations and individuals they opposed. Support, as with many NSMs, came from a number of quarters including trade unions, activist groups, faith groups, politicians, academics (including geographer David Harvey who spoke at meetings and urged protestors to engage with anti-wealth rather than anti-poverty actions) and, inevitably, celebrities and musicians.

NSMs, such as Occupy, converge on particular spaces at particular times but they 'prosecute conflict on a variety of multi-scalar terrains that include both material places and virtual spaces' (Routledge 2003: 334), mirroring that global networks of power are also boundless 'both everywhere and nowhere, a non-place' (ibid.). Other activities include establishing shadow websites to counter corporate publicity (J. Smith 2008); 'ad busting' (Klein 2001) (defacing posters to provide alternative messages); buying a token amount of shares to allow participation in decision making; and boycotting of products.

Many commentators attest that actions by NSMs have done much to shape global politics by highlighting issues that have hitherto been neglected by transnational agencies (Naidoo 2000; Khagram *et al.* 2002; J. Smith 2008). However, the fluid nature of NSMs makes them susceptible to internal contradictions and differences that may threaten their long-term effectiveness. Although such actions may offer alternative forms of citizenship, they are often transitory and linked to the temporary occupation of a particular site. Efforts to cooperate at transnational scales can be disrupted when ideas that are assumed to be universal are challenged in particular places (Routledge *et al.* 2006; Routledge 2008). Prescribed gender roles, for example, may produce clashes between the different cultural, religious or ethnic groups that comprise a transnational movement. Paul Routledge's (2003) study of the People's Global Action (PGA) reveals how some of these issues are negotiated (Box 5.4).

NSMs are also threatened by those they are protesting against. Although 'the ability to dissent and to protest is a cornerstone of western liberal democracies . . . it always threatens to exceed its bounds and to become a threat' (Mitchell and Staeheli 2005: 813). Efforts to neutralize this threat have led to robust security measures that have sought to exclude protestors from certain spaces (Epstein and Iveson 2009). The WTO meeting that followed Seattle was held in Qatar behind a security cordon that kept protestors well away from the conference. Global fears over terrorism (Benton-Short 2007; Pain 2009) have led to a series of laws that, deliberately or otherwise, have impacted on the civic right to protest in public space. In the UK, the 2005 Serious Organised Crime and Police Act severely restricted protests within one kilometre of the Houses of Parliament and was used to evict a long-standing peace camp situated in Parliament Square. More widely, greater security and exclusion are associated with new phases of neo-liberal investment (Peck and Tickell 2002; Pain 2009). 'This emergent phase is witnessing an aggressive intervention by governments around issues such as crime, policing, welfare reform and urban surveillance with the purpose of disciplining and containing

Box 5.4 CASE STUDY OF PEOPLE'S GLOBAL ACTION (PGA)

PGA was formed in 1998 following meetings in Mexico and Spain by activists supporting the Zapatistas (the Zapatista National Liberation Army was itself created in response to the North American Free Trade Agreement that impacted unfairly on coffee and corn growers in the Chiapas region of Mexico) and other organizations opposed to neo-liberal capitalism. It aimed to provide a network to share information, coordinate actions and support activists (Routledge 2003). Those involved in the networks shared a collective vision to reject and resist 'capitalism, imperialism and feudalism' using civil disobedience and direct action where necessary. PGA's activities of communication, information-sharing, solidarity, coordination and mobilization were organized through a multilingual website, support groups situated in different countries and 'activist caravans', one of which participated in the Seattle protests outlined above. Indeed, involvement in protests such as these provided particular places where the PGA's ideals could be enacted and, in turn, contributed to the collective memory of the network.

Although it is not without organizational and political problems, Routledge (2003: 345) considers that the works of PGA illustrate a 'convergence space' or a 'world with many worlds' that allows activists to widen their spatial horizons and actions. Convergence spaces:

1. comprise diverse social movements that articulate collective visions, to generate sufficient common ground to generate a politics of solidarity, i.e. multi-scalar collective action;
2. facilitate uneven processes of facilitation and interaction;
3. facilitate multi-scalar political action by participant movements;
4. are comprised of contested social relations, because of the very different militant particularisms that are articulated by participant movements.

(Routledge 2003: 345–6)

those marginalized or dispossessed by the neoliberalization of the 1980s' (Routledge 2003: 334).

Appadurai (2008: 304) states that 'protest is not the key word associated with many of these movements, who frequently explore partnerships with multilateral agencies, with their own home states, with major global funders, and with other local and international civil society'. Parker (1999b: 72) also notes that 'an important strategy is for the state (or other powerful interests) to attempt to manoeuvre activists into positions where they can be enrolled into a more "participatory" stance; potentially where the state (or corporation) can control proceedings'. Dialogue, cooperation and partnership therefore characterize the actions of many pressure groups, with progress being made in the spaces of the boardroom as much as in the public spaces of the street (see Box 5.5). Although the intensity of initial action wanes, elements of it may become embedded in lifestyles, political systems and the growth of networks across different spatial scales (Halfacree 1999).

CRITIQUES OF TRANSNATIONAL CITIZENSHIP

The supposition that these actions equate to new forms of transnational citizenship has been contested. Three main arguments have been put forward. First, it is suggested that because there is no legitimate world state, one cannot be a global citizen in the strictest sense. Linklater (2002: 318) quotes this rumbustious comment from Michael Walzer:

> I am not a citizen of the world . . . I am not even aware that there is a world such that one could be a citizen of it. No one has ever offered me citizenship, or described the naturalisation process, or enlisted me in the world's institutional structures, or given me an account of its decision making procedures . . . or provided me with a list of the benefits and obligations of citizenship or shown me the world's calendar and the common celebrations and commemorations of its citizens.
>
> (Walzer 1994)

In response, one might point to the growing significance of bodies such as the United Nations (UN), World Bank or North Atlantic Treaty Organization (NATO) that make decisions and act at a global scale. However, they are not directly accountable to individual citizens who are unable to

Box 5.5 CASE STUDY OF THE JUBILEE 2000 CAMPAIGN

Jubilee 2000 campaigned for the cancellation of third world debt to mark the millennium. The name refers to an Old Testament concept of 'jubilee' associated with freeing slaves and cancelling debts. It 'mobilised people of all faiths and people of no faith, academics, pop stars, trade unionists and businessmen, sportspeople and artists, young and old, black and white, organising together on a global scale' (Mayo 2005: 173). The campaign comprised 69 worldwide coalitions that organized a petition of 24 million people from 60 countries, events (including a lobby of 70,000 people in Birmingham, UK when that country hosted the G7 meeting), publicity (based around a wrist band) and the lobbying of global political and financial leaders. Jubilee 2000 succeeded in engaging directly with political leaders (including UK Prime Minister Tony Blair) and achieved some reductions to the debts of the poorest countries, allowing resources to be channelled into social development (Mayo 2005). Since 2000, the campaign has split into various national or regional groupings that continue to lobby globally for debt relief (see www.jubileedebtcampaign.org.uk – last accessed 6 August 2013).

Mayo (2005: 175) argued that Jubilee 2000 exemplified themes of 'informal organisation . . . based upon shared beliefs and solidarity and engaging in collective action focusing upon conflicts, including the use of protest'. The movement gained its strength from solidarity rather than charity. Mayo provides evidence to demonstrate that this collectivity is developed through participation in the campaign. Although people may join as a result of personal beliefs that are shared with others, these can be strengthened through opportunities to participate or reflect on the campaign's activities. In doing so, people participated not only as activists but also as citizens through, for example, utilizing political rights to lobby their representatives or sign petitions (often for the first time) which, in turn, benefited from education initiatives that informed citizens of their civic, social and political rights in a national context as well as their responsibilities in a global one.

participate politically in their affairs (Bellamy 2008; Koenig-Archibugi 2010, 2011; List and Koenig-Archibugi 2010). Turner (2012) cautions that human rights that are championed by global bodies such as the UN do not equate to citizens' rights, which can provide some measure of accountability of a state to its people (see also Chapter 7). It is this lack of accountability that, perhaps, ironically, is often the focus for global protest movements (Klein 2001) and efforts to form new globalized forms of civic society.

Second, it is important to remember that nation-states remain the conveyors and arbiters of formal, *de jure* citizenship. Bryan Turner (1997: 9) notes that:

> 'generally speaking, it is rather unusual for people to acquire citizenship if they are not simultaneously members of a political community, that is a nation-state.

Thus, while it is possible to consider a global and cosmopolitan notion of human rights, Isin and Turner argue that those:

> that cannot be enforced by an authority are mere abstractions . . . In other words, a viable state is important as a guarantee of rights. Human rights abuses are characteristically a consequence of state tyranny, dictatorship, and state failure resulting in civil war and anarchy.
>
> (Isin and Turner 2007: 12–13)

International bodies such as the International Criminal Court (ICC), established in 2002, and the European Court of Human Rights (ECtHR) go some way to protecting rights beyond the state but still rely on individual nation-states being signatories to the conventions and treaties that empower them. The state and its apparatus, such as courts, are mainly responsible for upholding (or denying) both the human and particular rights of its citizens. Nation-states continue to play an important role in the regulation, definition and conferral of formal citizenship (Isin and Turner 2007). As Rubenstein (2003: 256) reminds us, 'while there has been considerable interest in the sociological, political and cultural aspects of citizenship, its legal foundations cannot be forgotten'. The bestowal of *de jure* citizenship, together with the rights and duties associated with it, is usually by birth within the territory of a state (*jus soli* or 'law of the soil') or through family or ethnic descent (*jus sanguinis* or 'law of the blood') (Samers 2010). Consequently, David Miller (2000, 2010) maintains that in the absence of a global government, cosmopolitan citizenship is a 'ghost concept' and that national forms of citizenship should be bolstered to provide 'the best way in which people of diverse beliefs and styles can live together under laws and institutions which they can endorse as legitimate' (Miller 2000: 96).

CONCLUSIONS

This chapter has traced a series of actions from the local, tactical protest to the emergence of NSMs. Many commentators suggest that the more radical of these have the potential to achieve lasting social change and establish new forms of citizenship that are associated less with the nation-state and more with transnational collective action (Ruggiero and Montagna 2008). These are far from utopian and, as some of the examples have sought to show, are often complex and contradictory.

Their impact may well be transitory. Halfacree, commenting on sites of occupations, points out that 'the short period of time in which these sites exist may be enough to undertake the symbolic challenge to the dominant order' (Halfacree 1999: 216). The extent to which they achieve lasting changes to citizenship and formations of citizenship is more contentious.

What is more certain is that these movements highlight inequalities in human rights, often considered the bedrock of citizenship, between and within places. Actions themselves also foreground the extent to which governments will tolerate dissent, reactionary movements or, quite simply, diversity and pluralism (Fyfe 1995; Sibley 1995; Parker 1999b). Arguably the most successful campaigns, such as Jubilee 2000, seek littoral forms of protest that fall between 'good' and 'bad' kinds of citizenship, performing a type of citizenship that the state finds difficult to eradicate or, indeed, oppose (Parker 1999b).

This chapter has also examined how ideas of citizenship are played out across networks that straddle national borders. The growing significance of these global connections contributes to speculation that the nation-state is no longer the only place that is significant to the formation of citizenship. New understandings of citizenship stress the significance of political spaces that simultaneously act above and below nation-states at simultaneous and multiple scales (Painter 2002, 2012). As the various actions in this chapter show, local spaces (be it the Fairtrade stand or Tahrir Square) continue to hold significance in the formation of citizenship, but perhaps of greater importance is to trace how these places are connected to others across the world. Although global in scope, participation in global politics is geographically uneven (Painter and Jeffrey 2009), itself reflecting differing human rights between states and the ability of citizens to cross state boundaries to make such protests. The state may attempt to cut some of these connections (for example, by regulating internet use or repressing national uprisings) but, despite these interventions and differences, it is clear that networks have potentially important roles in the formation of citizenship.

A final point to note is that these actions, however spectacular or effective, are usually undertaken by a minority of citizens. It is possible that their significance in the daily lives of most citizens has been overplayed, as Chapter 6 considers.

FURTHER READING

Engin Isin and Greg Neilson's (2008) edited collection *Acts of Citizenship* provides stimulating accounts of activism in many geographical settings. Naomi Klein's (2001) *No Logo* provides a classic critique of globalization and corporation that has inspired many transnational movements. Paul Cloke and his colleagues develop ideas of transnational ethical citizenship using the example of Fairtrade. Their article in *Antipode* provides a clear summary of their thinking in this area (Barnett *et al.* 2005).

The website http://www.occupy.com (last accessed 6 August 2013) publicizes the actions of the Occupy movement and highlights opportunities to engage with it. David Harvey provides a commentary on the movement at http://www.guardian.co.uk/commentisfree/video/2012/jun/04/david-harvey-occupy-movement-video (last accessed 6 August 2013) and there is footage of his speech to Occupy London on YouTube: http://www.youtube.com/watch?v=ht8W30gkVac (last accessed 6 August 2013).

NOTE

1 It might also be suggested that active citizens are created.

6

EVERYDAY CITIZENSHIP

INTRODUCTION

Many studies of citizenship have tended to emphasize the various ways in which people actively engage with the state or other political communities through democratic processes, active citizenship, local resistance and activism. Yet most people live out their lives without participating in these kinds of political or civic acts (MacKian 1995). W. H. Auden's poem 'The Unknown Citizen' (Box 6.1) charts some of the ways in which identity as a citizen is shaped (and lost) by various everyday practices, institutions and social relationships that, in turn, govern how he (or she) participates in different communities at various scales. Gender, employment, sexuality, cultural practices and consumption shape the daily life of the 'Unknown Citizen', as well as various local and state institutions. Written in 1939, the poem illustrates that 'our identities are not made in isolation, but are made in places, and are socially constructed and historically contingent' (Pykett 2010: 132).

Scholars are starting to pay greater attention to the ways in which cultural practices influence the experience and performance of citizenship on a daily basis (Stevenson 2001; Turner 2001; Miller 2002; Kabeer 2005a; Pykett 2010). Two very broad themes can be identified. First, attention has been given to the ways in which citizenship has been *socially constructed* in daily life and how these ideas impact on the lives of citizens. Here, the

Box 6.1 'THE UNKNOWN CITIZEN' BY W. H. AUDEN (1939)

(To JS/07 M 378 This Marble Monument is Erected by the State)

He was found by the Bureau of Statistics to be
One against whom there was no official complaint,
And all the reports on his conduct agree
That, in the modern sense of an old-fashioned word,
he was a saint,
For in everything he did he served the Greater Community.
Except for the War till the day he retired
He worked in a factory and never got fired,
But satisfied his employers, Fudge Motors Inc.
Yet he wasn't a scab or odd in his views,
For his Union reports that he paid his dues,
(Our report on his Union shows it was sound)
And our Social Psychology workers found
That he was popular with his mates and liked a drink.
The Press are convinced that he bought a paper every day
And that his reactions to advertisements were normal in
every way.
Policies taken out in his name prove that he was fully
insured,
And his Health-card shows he was once in hospital but left
it cured.
Both Producers Research and High-Grade Living declare
He was fully sensible to the advantages of the Instalment Plan
And had everything necessary to the Modern Man,
A phonograph, a radio, a car and a frigidaire.
Our researchers into Public Opinion are content
That he held the proper opinions for the time of year;
When there was peace, he was for peace: when there was war,
he went.
He was married and added five children to the population,

Which our Eugenist says was the right number for a parent of his generation.
And our teachers report that he never interfered with their education.
Was he free? Was he happy? The question is absurd:
Had anything been wrong, we should certainly have heard.

Auden's poem, published in 1939 after he emigrated to the USA, is a satire on conformity in people's daily lives. It is written from the perspective of a fictitious government department intent on surveying the life of a citizen through the technologies of statistics. Citizen JS/07 M 378 (his social security number) is celebrated (by means of a statue that alludes to the 'Unknown Soldier') for being a 'good citizen' by means of his 'civic virtue' that conforms to an expected set of 'moral behaviour, social practices and cultural beliefs' (Turner 2001: 11). As a result of his compliance he remains anonymous and 'unknown'.

The poem provides a thought-provoking introduction to everyday citizenship. It questions how people are identified as compliant citizens in ways that leave little room for emotive or affective behaviour ('Was he happy? The question is absurd') and mourns the loss of individual identity in modern society. Socio-cultural approaches to geographies of citizenship have attempted to place greater emphasis on individuality, which is sometimes lost in wider debates about citizenship (Staeheli 2011).

Auden's poem ends with a line that sinisterly implies action would be taken if the citizen did not conform to expectations of civic virtue, be it not complying with his union, not supporting the state in time of war, not consuming goods as expected and, more generally, fitting in with prevailing socio-economic trends. Given that many European countries were in the grip of or threatened by dictatorships at the time of writing, the threat of state action against non-conformity was very real. The state, however, is not the only agency that can shape behaviour. How would, for

Continued

example, the citizen's 'mates' behave if he was unpopular, what would his union do if they considered him a 'scab' and would his employers, Fudge Motors Inc., fire him if his work was not satisfactory? Citizens who do not conform to expected norms may also face *de jure* and *de facto* exclusion from places, especially public space (Painter and Philo 1995). Socio-cultural approaches to citizenship help to highlight the exclusionary nature of many daily practices.

work and role of institutions, landscapes and policies are important. Second, and more recently, citizenship and identity have been considered in *relational* terms. Citizenship is viewed as fluid rather than fixed, an identity that is created in relation to other people and places. Daily, often mundane, actions are important in reproducing these identities. Staeheli (2011: 399) asserts that: 'the practices of citizenship – the daily repetitions that are part and parcel of the relationships that construct and disrupt citizenship – are important to the lives of people. It feels unsatisfying to seem to overlook citizens in favour of citizenship.'

This chapter explores some of the daily geographies of citizenship. It begins by discussing how citizenship is socially constructed by and through different sites, institutions, policies, landscapes and bodies. The chapter concludes by highlighting how citizenship is performed on a daily basis and the importance of everyday actions to the understanding of citizenship.

CONSTRUCTING EVERYDAY CITIZENSHIP

The ways that citizen identities are socially constructed reflect different social and cultural practices and the power relations that shape them. The following sections examine the roles of institutions, education, bodies and landscapes in the production of citizenship.

Institutional geographies

An institution may be understood as 'a clearly delimited entity or agency with a more-or-less clear "mission", "internal structure", operational "rules and procedures", divisions, sub-divisions and personnel' (Philo and Parr 2000: 515). Their study allows geographers an opportunity of bridging the gap between macro-level theoretical statements and micro-level, empirical case studies (Flowerdew 1982; Philo and Parr 2000). In the case of citizenship, the study of institutions and institutional spaces sheds light on the way in which different views of citizenship are socially constructed and in turn how these constructions shape society and space.

Some community and voluntary organizations have the express purpose of training their members to be good or useful citizens according to particular ideals held by them. This is most clearly seen in youth organizations, which often consider young people as 'adults in the making' with a need to be trained as citizens (Mills 2013). The Scouting movement, for example, aims to develop 'responsible' citizens who can play a role in communities at different scales (Box 6.2). Cadet forces place importance on discipline through drill, ranks and uniform inspections, religious groups attend to spiritual development and sports clubs foster team work and good sportsmanship. In the inter-war period, the Scottish Youth Hostel Association (SYHA) encouraged outdoor recreation to foster an appreciation of landscape and, in turn, strengthen feelings of national identity and citizenship (Lorimer 1997: 42). The Duke of Edinburgh Award was founded in 1956 as a scheme for young people in Commonwealth countries. It evolved into a three-stage programme that requires candidates to undertake volunteering activities, participate in sport or physical education, pursue a skill such as a hobby or craft, take part in an overnight expedition in 'wild country' (see also Chapter 8) and, for the Gold Award, a residential activity. The scheme considers that participation in these activities 'builds confidence and develops self-esteem. It requires persistence, commitment and has a lasting impact on the attitudes and outlook of all young people' (DofE 2011). In turn, these qualities are seen to allow young people to achieve their full potential as citizens.

Other attempts have been made to treat young people as citizens in their own right and to involve them in civic participation and decision making. Thus, there have been efforts to establish youth councils (Matthews and Limb 2003) and to engage with marginalized young people in the planning and development of their cities (Hörschelmann and van Blerk 2012). Despite the potential of these structures, Matthews and Limb (2003: 189)

Box 6.2 CITIZENSHIP AND SCOUTING

The Scouting movement was founded by Robert Baden-Powell in 1907 and was based on his book *Scouting for Boys: A Handbook for Instruction in Good Citizenship* (Baden-Powell 1908, *emphasis added*). Citizenship was encapsulated by:

> duty to self, others and God – express[ing] a utilitarian concept of citizenship whereby Scouts are universalised as individuals working for the 'greater good' . . . I would also argue that there were two separate projects in action: firstly, to encourage Scouts to develop as self-regulated and duty-bound individuals; and secondly, to create a collective body of Scouts and unite them through a sense of belonging.
>
> (Mills 2013: 124)

These ideals were embodied through the notion of 'being prepared' (Mills 2011a) and performed through various rituals such as handshakes, collecting badges and striving to do a 'good turn' every day.

Baden-Powell's early articulation of citizenship was based firmly on national identity. His book (Baden-Powell 1908) included, amongst other things, a section on citizenship that gave advice to boys on how to behave as a good citizen in times of peace and war (Figure 6.1). During peace, good citizens were expected to know their place and work together for the good of the country. Military skills were also taught in preparation for war (Robinson and Mills 2012): 'I hope that before long every eleven, whether football or cricket, will also make itself good for shooting and scouting' (Baden-Powell 1908: 183–4).

Contemporary scouting takes a more internationalist view of citizenship and has also broadened its membership and concerns in terms of gender and religion (Mills 2011b, 2013). Twenty-eight million young people in 216 countries are involved in the movement, making it a significant receptacle of citizenship. It continues to encourage individual development, team-play and, following on from this, active citizenship by promoting:

> 'the development of young people in achieving their full physical, intellectual, social and spiritual potentials, as individuals, as *responsible citizens* and as members of their local, national and international communities'.
>
> (Scout Association 2011: 25, emphasis added)

The values of scouting espouse the virtues of communitarian citizenship. These include making an active contribution to society through the cultivation of skills, confidence and personal development in a range of sites, from the traditional campsite to volunteering in inner-city localities. This ability is not only taught to its young members but also reflected in the many adults who volunteer to run scout units.

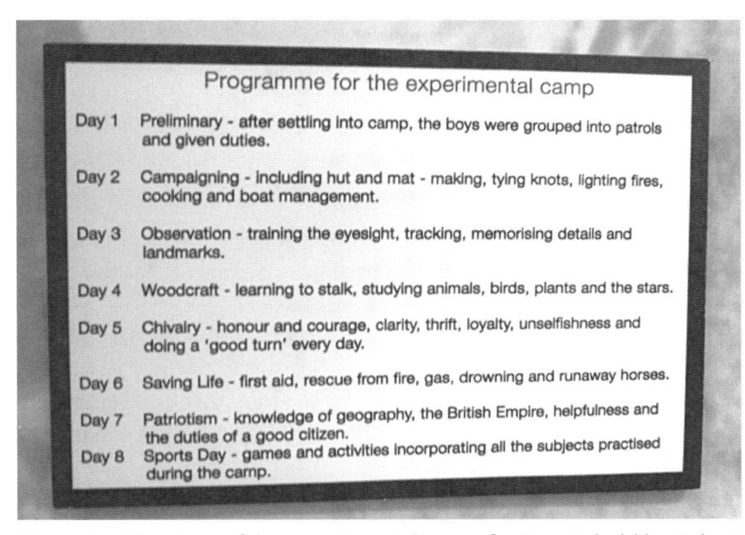

Figure 6.1 The aims of the experimental camp for Scouts held by Robert Baden-Powell at Brownsea Island, UK in 1907. Citizenship was linked to patriotism, a knowledge of the outdoors and skills seen as useful to the British Empire (Photo: Author)

conclude that 'the extent of young people's participation in local decision-making is modest and those who are taking part are not necessarily representative of their communities'.

The development of citizenship is not only confined to youth organizations as many adult groups also promote citizenship and, especially, active citizenship. The Women's Institute (WI), for example, was established in 1897 in Canada to teach domestic skills to rural women and developed as a national and international organization that provided a means for rural women to contribute to local politics and national campaigns and to take part in local voluntary activity, all seen as virtues of active citizenship (Stamper 2004). As Annie Hughes (1997) has shown, regular participation in the WI not only helps to confer identity as a 'countrywoman' but also provides a means for women to engage with their local communities in a particular, gendered way.

Robert Putnam (2001) advocates that these kinds of organization contribute to the development of social capital that leads to the growth of economic capital as well as inclusion, tolerance and even happiness. David Blunkett, the former UK Home Secretary, argued in a 2001 speech that:

> 'people who are active – who give – also tend, and all the evidence backs this up, to be more broadly engaged with civil and with political society'.

Thus a player in a football club whose pitch is threatened by developers may organize local petitions, attend planning meetings or write to his or her local councillor in an effort to block it.

Yet Putnam's work, and implicitly a focus on these kinds of institutions, has been criticized for fostering a particular, perhaps nostalgic, view of civic society. His book mourns a decline in participation of community organizations without noting new forms of social engagement that may be more important to new generations. This normative view prompted Amin to argue:

> Putnam's definition of civic virtue represents a kind of paradise on earth, with citizens, state and economic networks intertwined in civilised harmony and mutual regard. Putnam's good citizenship ends up, perhaps inadvertently, as a denial of civil society as an arena of social contestation.
>
> (Amin 1996: 327)

Certainly, as MacKian (1995) reminds us, not everyone takes part in local organizations and those who do are more likely to reveal biases in age, gender, race and social class that reflect the opportunity to participate (Munton and Zurawan 2003). While pursued with worthy intent, the kind of citizenship encouraged by the groups discussed is likely to be apolitical and unlikely, as Amin (1996) states, to include a wider social spectrum of society. By contrast, government policies have the potential to impact on a much wider range of people than voluntary organizations and have a greater potential to impact on how citizenship is used to shape society. This is explored in the following section that uses the example of education policy to examine how citizenship is constructed by policy makers.

Citizenship and policy: the case of education

Education has been viewed as both a right and an obligation (Marshall 1950 [1992]) in many nation-states and has therefore offered a way of influencing young citizens (Pykett 2009b). Although citizenship has been taught and developed through a wide range of curricula and extra-curricular activities, the discipline of geography has close associations with the concept (Driver and Maddrell 1996; Marsden 2001a; Anderson *et al.* 2008; Yarwood 2005). Schools have had a long-standing responsibility to prepare their pupils for citizenship. This occurs both implicitly and explicitly (Figure 6.2), through formal teaching and extra-curricular activity (Lambert and Machon 2001). Equally, in higher education, it has been advocated (Mohan 1995) that students should contribute to their local communities as active citizens (Figure 6.3). Geography has often been associated with the teaching of 'good' citizenship' although the ideas and practices of citizenship have changed significantly over time, reflecting how broader ideologies and beliefs have shaped education (Box 6.3). The formal teaching of citizenship has, though, been met with cynicism and criticism. Bill Marsden argues:

> the historical evidence in Britain and other countries, however, suggests that official imposition of education *for* citizenship has not been beneficial, whether in the context of any reasonable definition of what constitutes a genuinely liberal education or of what can practically be achieved in a democratic society.
>
> (Marsden 2001b: 270)

Figure 6.2 Posters drawn by primary school children exploring citizenship and human rights (Photo: Author)

Figure 6.3 Active citizenship is sometimes encouraged as part of school and university education (Mohan 1995; Yarwood 2005). Here university students are trained as part of the Royal Geographical Society's Student Ambassador programme to teach pupils in secondary schools about geography (Photo: Author)

Box 6.3 CITIZENSHIP, GEOGRAPHY AND EDUCATION IN THE UK

During the nineteenth and early twentieth centuries the teaching of geographical citizenship was most strongly associated with Imperialism and the British Empire. Often supported by Christian teaching, elite, male pupils were prepared for service as leaders of the British Empire, which included the study of classics and classical citizenship, while working-class children (those, at least, who had access to education) were taught to be diligent in labour and to obey superiors (Marsden 2001a). Education in the classroom was supplemented by games that were designed to teach teamwork, leadership and the ability to keep 'a stiff upper lip' in times of trial. The Duke of Wellington's apocryphal quotation that the Battle of Waterloo (1815) was 'won on the playing fields of Eton' reflected a belief that these values, instilled in public schools, were evident in British officers (even though most of the victorious soldiers were German (Hofschrer 1999)).

Geographical teaching was used to support British Imperialism and, significantly, service in Empire:

> We sometimes hear it said that Canada or New Zealand or some other country is 'ours' or that it 'belongs' to Britain. This is not true even if we are thinking of the land called Canada, and it is even less true if we understand that the Empire is not made up of land but of people. It is made up of the people of Britain and Canada and India and Australia and the rest. The Empire is not 'ours' but 'us'. And what keeps us together? Goodwill and knowledge. That is one reason why we learn geography.
>
> (Fairgrieve and Young 1927, quoted in Walford 1996: 440)

Avril Maddrell (1996) considers that the geographical curriculum sought to normalize colonization by favouring knowledge of countries of the British Empire rather those outside it. Thus:

> It is especially desirable in your examination of the fourth and higher Standards that attention should be given to the English

Continued

> Colonies and their productions, government and resources and to those climatic and other conditions which render our distant possessions suitable fields for emigration, and for honourable enterprise.
>
> (Committee of Council for Education 1885, quoted in Maddrell 1996: 379)

Maddrell notes the emphasis placed on *emigration* in the teaching of geography in the early twentieth century that 'valorised the settler Dominions over the tropical colonies and portrayed them as the good citizen's choice for emigration' (Maddrell 1996: 373):

> Properly taught, the leading facts relating to India and the colonies would greatly interest young people and in many cases the knowledge obtained at school would be of practical service in later life. Moreover the study could not fail to encourage the growth of a wholesome patriotism.
>
> (*Daily Graphic* 1893, quoted in Walford 1996: 440)

> English emigrants, in their own interest as well as in that of their native land, should prefer British settlements, or else the United States, to any foreign Countries.
>
> (Isbister 1883, quoted in Maddrell 1996: 382)

> Those who can today find work in Britain should stay here among their friends, but those who have no work should cross the ocean and make new homes for themselves in Canada, or Australia, or New Zealand, or South Africa. In all these lands they will remain the subjects of our King, Edward VII; the same flag will be there and they will not be among foreigners.
>
> (Mackinder 1906, quoted in Maddrell 1996: 382)

While undoubtedly jingoistic, some geographers at the time suggested that a better understanding of Empire would also contribute to a more global sense of citizenship:

> Geography is essential for the proper understanding of the problems of the different parts of the Empire and for the

> promotion of a sympathetic attitude towards the other nations, great and small, with whom our contact becomes closer every year. Its study should thus be utilised to give a true appreciation of the conditions and needs of the home region, and of its relations to the great world outside, and thus to develop first a local patriotism, then the larger patriotism of country and Empire, and, finally, as knowledge widens, and imagination and sympathy become more acute, the largest patriotism of all – that of citizen of the world.
>
> (Herbertson 1907, quoted in Marsden 2001a: 17)

This emphasis on internationalization became more apparent after the First World War. The Irish educator J. H. Cousins, an early advocate of internationalization, commented in 1918:

> Love of country will be inevitable, spontaneous and pure, and will stretch its hands towards the end of the earth in sympathy with all beings and beyond the earth in aspiration towards the Divine Power.
>
> (Cousins 1918, quoted in Nash 1996: 403)

The assumption was that a good national citizen would also be a good world citizen. Thus in 1935, Hayward suggested a sequence of five spatial 'celebrations' in the teaching of geography (quoted in Marsden 2001a: 17):

- home;
- city or region;
- country or nation;
- empire or Commonwealth;
- the League of Nations.

Marsden (2001a) cites several educators who viewed geography as a way of teaching this kind of citizenship:

> the fact of world independence and the actuality of modern economic co-operation, which is essential to modern civilisation, must be the basis of geography teaching.
>
> (Evans 1933, quoted in Marsden 2001a: 17)

Continued

> [Geography's greatest values are] the possibilities it offers for developing sympathy for the lives and problems of other peoples.
>
> (Dempster 1939, quoted in Marsden 2001a: 15)

Pupils should:

> try and imagine themselves in the place of other people to think how they would act and live if they were in that environment, to see things with their eyes, to look at the world from their point of view.
>
> (Unstead 1931, quoted in Marsden 2001a: 15)

In Britain, Professor H. J. Fleure considered geography as

> 'an instrument of humanist education providing a training in scientific observation and analysis and at the same time . . . a valuable influence in the enrichment of citizenship'
>
> (quoted in Gruffudd 1996: 417)

and worked closely with school teachers and the Geographical Association, which he helped to establish, to promote this view. This work, which including enrolling students into the Regional Surveys Movement, aimed to encourage an international view of citizenship that was embedded in the student's locality:

> ' . . . our region serves as a mirror, a miniature if you like, of the evolution of our civilisation. Let us spread the feeling that in addition to being citizens of our region we are citizens of civilization.
>
> (Fleure 1916, quoted in Gruffudd 1996: 418)

By contrast, the teaching of citizenship could also be used to promote national identity. Pyrs Gruffudd (1996) traces how the study of Welsh nature and folklore was used to foster national identity and citizenship in Wales during the inter-war period. Many of these efforts were cultural rather than political, emphasizing Wales' place in the British Empire and, later, the world (following internationalist visions).

In other places education was used to pursue nationalist agendas, notably in Nazi Germany (Marsden 2001b). The rise of fascism in Europe and the Second World War caused some to question internationalism as being well intended but naïve and, significantly, too broad to be effective. These critics called, instead, for more emphasis to be placed in educating children on 'the urgent and limited tasks which await them in private, working and public life' (Marsden 2001a: 18).

Following the Second World War and the apparent failings of internationalist thinking, the study of citizenship fell from favour in UK schools (Marsden 2001a). When referred to, history was seen as the main vehicle for teaching citizenship. Although citizenship was discussed in 'Social Studies' in other countries, this subject gained little credence in the UK. Instead, values associated with good citizenship, such as teamwork and stoicism, were taught implicitly in extra-curricular activities such as sport (with the emphasis on team games) or pastimes such as Scouting or youth hostelling, which were reinvigorated in this period (Matless 1996; Lorimer 1997; Mills 2011a), and charity work (Pykett *et al.* 2010).

Geographical education was seen to enhance these activities. David Matless (1996) traces how outdoor activities helped to teach young people to see, understand and, above all, appreciate the landscape, qualities that would, in turn, help in the reconstruction of post-war Britain. Matless notes that the aim of W. F. Morris's book *The Future Citizen and his Surroundings* (1946) was:

> the endeavour to make of the pupil a good citizen – ideally a citizen of the world, but in any case a citizen of his own country . . . [the child] . . . should be taught impatience with things unnecessarily drab or sordid, and should be infected with a desire to remove or improve them.
>
> (Morris 1946, quoted in Matless 1996: 433)

An appreciation of these qualities set youngsters apart from the 'anti-citizen' or those who were loud, vulgar and ignorant of

Continued

landscape and nature (Matless 1996; Brace 2000). Although these qualities were largely taught through youth organizations, Matless notes that in 1953 Jack Cox (Editor of *Boy's Own Paper*) thanked his geography tutors for teaching him 'the value of field studies of all kinds and the way in which studies could be carried out from bases under canvas or in youth hostels' (Cox 1953, quoted in Matless 1996: 428).

These issues aside, the teaching of citizenship in the UK was largely delegated to voluntary organizations following the Second World War. The introduction of a National Curriculum in 1990 saw citizenship referred to as a cross-cutting theme but, with no statutory weight, it was not formally taught and schools were being placed under greater pressures to audit and improve their performance in core parts of the curriculum (Pykett 2007).

Yet, more recently, the educational value of citizenship has been revisited as 'part of an agenda for "civil renewal", for common British values and against "yob culture" and voter apathy' (Geographical Association's Citizenship Working Group 2006: 1). In 1998 a report chaired by Bernard Crick (Qualifications and Curriculum Authority (QRA) 1998) led in 2002 to the introduction of citizenship to the National Curriculum, which emphasized three facets of citizenship: social and moral responsibility, community involvement and political literacy (Citizenship Advisory Group 1998: 40–1). As Pykett (2009b) points out, these are all explicitly linked to citizenship-formation rather than more philosophical issues and debates surrounding citizenship. She also argues they lack critical depth:

> the three strands of citizenship are each loaded with assumptions; social and moral responsibility, which fails to question to whom one is responsible; community involvement which fails to question the boundaries of community and the importance of belonging and identity; political literacy which fails to problematize the legitimacy of the nation-state and its political institutions.
>
> (Pykett 2009b: 311)

Any reading of policy (Box 6.3) implies a smooth transition, or transmission, from 'pedagogic state' to pupil via the site of the school (Pykett 2009b; Staeheli 2011). However, as Jessica Pykett (2007, 2009b, 2011) has demonstrated in a series of papers, this path is contested. Thus she argues that social inequalities impact on the way that citizenship is imagined by both staff and pupils. This is because both groups deploy 'place-based subjectivities' in discussions of what constitutes an 'ideal citizen' that, in turn, may reflect social inequalities and the location of the school:

> education is certainly the prime space within which to explore such ideas, but it is important to continue to question the legitimacy of fostering an education for citizenship amongst the very children and working teachers whose own entitlements to citizenship could be considered to be considerably lacking.
>
> (Pykett 2009b: 317)

Holloway and Pimlott-Wilson (2012) also argue that the workings of educational policies and housing markets combine to determine who gets access to good schools and, consequently, what kind of education and training for citizenship children receive in the UK. Further, they suggest that ideas about citizen workers are interpreted differently in different socio-economic neighbourhoods, which can also have a bearing on how education is delivered. Citizenship is, therefore, far from 'given' or 'neutral' but is shaped by the site of the school and the technologies of education (Bradley-Smith 2005). Views of citizenship are further shaped by:

> state-trained teachers who have been taught by non-state actors (university based teacher training lecturers), and in schools Citizenship Education is 'delivered' by a range of actors varying from non-governmental organisations, teachers, voluntary associations and educational consultants using a variety of texts, materials and resources produced by private publishing companies, NGOs, educational co-operatives, pressure groups and so on.
>
> (Pykett 2011: 628)

As Staeheli clarifies:

> the school can be thought of as an aggregation of the aspirations, ideals, values, and instrumentalities wielded by the gamut of social

> and political agents in society, who draw on different sources of power as they attempt to mould citizens capable of functioning in particular ways.
>
> (Staeheli 2011: 395)

Given this diversity, it is hardly surprising that a school is a place of contestation. This is reflected in the spatiality of schools, including the layout of classrooms, places that are 'in and out' of bounds and the way that these spaces are controlled and transgressed.

Although Pykett (2009b) outlines how citizenship education reflects various policy technologies that attempt to make citizens governable, she stresses that this does not reflect 'a done deal' as citizenship requires people to consider their own positionalities and viewpoints, many of which may challenge official discourses of taught citizenship.

Additionally, school life is strongly determined by children's everyday lives and activities, especially pressures to conform to peer groups and not to stand out as 'different'. Valentine (2001) identifies the significance of body shape and appearance in girls' identities and the importance of physicality in boys' school cultures. A combination of peer pressure, name calling, bullying and conformity leads to different friendship groups clustering in different parts of the school, some 'cooler' than others. Geographer Graham Gardner has explored some of these themes in his novel *Inventing Elliot* (Gardner 2003) which examines how a schoolboy reinvents himself to fit in with his peers. Drawing on themes of social control, identity and surveillance, the protagonist faces the dilemma of conforming with school bullies or rejecting them with the risk of being bullied himself. The story draws out who has power within school and the various ways this becomes manifest and spatialized in the daily life of the school. It illustrates that although schools attempt to shape children into adult expectations of 'good citizens', they are 'a hotbed of moral geographies' (Valentine 2001: 150) that challenge these expectations and enact different children's takes on citizenship and belonging.

Landscape

As the institution of the school reveals, the physical ordering of space is significant in the development and expression of citizenship. This is also the case in public spaces and landscapes. In France, the growth of the state after 1789 meant that a single, national identity was forced upon regions, such as Brittany, that had their own languages and cultures. This was achieved by the use of French as the universal language (Wise 2006) (in the mid-nineteenth century, only a quarter of the people in France could speak French), a national flag (the tricolour), landscape symbols such as the Gallic Coq, the construction of state buildings in prominent urban spaces (Figure 2.5) and national war memorials (Baker 2012). Elsewhere, key places, such as the Brandenburg Gate in Berlin or Capitol Hill in Washington, DC, are associated with national identity and the ideals of citizenship through the ordering of buildings, monuments, open spaces, vistas and views (Jones *et al.* 2004).

Memorials or statues, for example, help to focus citizens on key events, people or memories that are deemed important in the collective memory of the state (Storey 2001). Ceremonies, rituals or events carried out at these sites, such as Remembrance Day parades, reproduce these ideals through solemn performances that underscore the significance of these sites, the importance of what they signify and the place and role of individual citizens in memorializing them (Box 6.4).

These landscapes of memory often represent hegemonic visions of state and identity. For example, the commemoration of war dead through visible and numerous war memorials is a significant feature of Australian and New Zealand landscapes (Stephens 2007; Cloke and Pawson 2008) that is reinforced through solemn dawn service on ANZAC Day (Hall *et al.* 2010).[1] This service was initially adopted to mark the ANZAC dead of the Gallipoli campaign in the First World War but has since been broadened to commemorate those killed in later wars and, more recently, terrorist bombings (Seal 2011). These forms of memorialization have tended to reflect gendered and white visions of nationality (Reed 1999); in contrast there are very few memorials to aboriginal people killed in colonial conflicts, although some monuments do exist for white settlers killed in these confrontations (Pilger 2002). In 1998 the then Prime Minister of Australia, John Howard, dismissed the idea of a memorial to the 20,000 aborigines killed in 'frontier conflict' as, he argued, no conflict occurred.

Hegemonic visions of landscape can be contested or transgressed and used as places of resistance (Sibley 1994; Cresswell 1996; Anderson 2010).

ANZAC Day, for example, has been used for countercultural protests and events (Morton 2008). The Occupy movement also used symbolic spaces, such as Times Square, St Paul's Cathedral and the Mexican stock exchange, to challenge practices of capitalism.

Box 6.4 LANDSCAPE AND CITIZENSHIP ON PLYMOUTH HOE

The Hoe is an area of raised, open, public space in the English city of Plymouth that overlooks Plymouth Sound (the sea) and the city centre. Plymouth has long associations with military geopolitics (Sidaway 2009) and, in particular, the naval dockyard located in Devonport (Bartram and Shobrook 1998).

The landscape of the Hoe is dominated by many war memorials (Figures 6.4–6.6) that associate the city and its citizens with

Figure 6.4 The National Armada Memorial (foreground) and Naval War Memorial on Plymouth Hoe (Photo: Author)

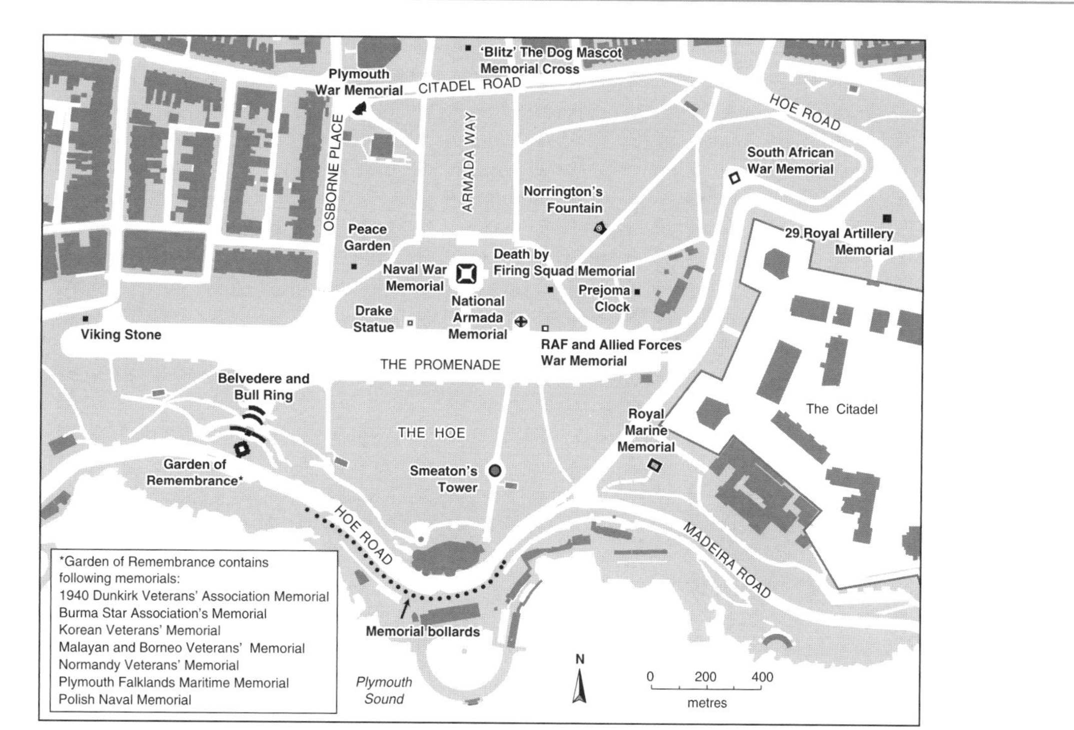

Figure 6.5 Memorials on Plymouth Hoe (Map drawn by Tim Absalom)

Continued

military history. While providing a fitting tribute to many lives lost in war, they also reflect a representation of the armed forces that celebrates the soldier-citizen as 'the heroic male figure striding commandingly through the sites and activities of public space' (Painter and Philo 1995: 114). Deborah Cowen (2005b, 2008) argues that this image of the Second World War soldier-citizen sits uncomfortably with the current realities of military service by what she terms 'welfare warriors'. She contends that at a time of state welfare cuts military service, with its access to service, training and housing, provides a form of welfare for work 'which require some form of service and sacrifice for access to "public" goods' (Cowen 2005b: 655). The statues also say little of the issues faced by some service personnel, including mental illness or problems of addiction, which can relegate them to marginal spaces in the city and oblige them to rely further on (reduced) state welfare or charitable support. These associations between places, military and citizenship are often hidden and demand greater scrutiny (Cowen 2005b; Woodward 2005; Cowen and Gilbert 2007; Pearson 2012).

The statues on the Hoe appear to confirm Bellamy's (2008) suggestion that masculine versions of citizenship are celebrated in public. Memorials to the 1,172 Plymouth civilians killed in the Second World War are absent from the Hoe although a peace garden has been planted on its western edge. In 2007, a statue was sculpted on the site of an air-raid shelter (located on what is now Plymouth University's campus) to commemorate 76 civilians killed there in 1941 (Figure 6.6).

In a further development the council commissioned a series of silver bollards along the edge of the Hoe that celebrate people associated with Plymouth. As well as admirals and soldiers, the names of entertainers, academics, sportspeople, business leaders and politicians are also inscribed there. This has broadened the range of citizen contributions that are celebrated on the Hoe, although achievement and fame, rather than everyday lives, are highlighted.

Figure 6.6 Portland Square Memorial Sculpture, Plymouth University, commemorating the deaths of 76 civilians in an air-raid shelter on the night of 22 April 1941. It is rare to see women and children portrayed in public statutes which more often portray male citizens and, especially, soldier-citizens

The body

Metaphors of 'the body politic' have long been used to describe the relationship between the state, its various components and its citizens (Rasmussen and Brown 2005) but, more recently, bodies themselves have also been recognized as a site of citizenship (Gabrielson and Parady 2010; Lorimer 2010) that can reveal processes, relations and experiences that can otherwise be obscured (Mountz 2004; Huq 2005). For example, bodies can be sold by people-traffickers, imprisoned or expelled by authorities or represented by different agencies for different political ends (Andrijasevic *et al.* 2012). The body, through biometric data, is enrolled into border crossings and access to territory (Amoore 2006), reflecting thinking that acknowledges the body's hybrid relationship with nature, technology and political spaces: 'determinants of citizenship do not fully rest on the individual body, but on the body's connections to other entities, the inter- and intra-active symbiotic condition of human–non-human living together' (Barker 2010: 350) (see also Chapter 8).

The growth of liberal paternalism reflects an effort by the state to affect, amongst other things, what goes into our bodies and how we use them. Thaler and Sunstein's (2009) concept of 'the nudge' has become an influential way of modifying people's daily lives in surreptitious ways. Attempts are made to 'nudge' or cajole citizens into 'doing the right thing' through persuasion rather than obligation (Jones *et al.* 2011a, 2011b). Drawing on research in psychology and behavioural economics, Thaler and Sunstein argue for what they term 'choice architecture'. Rather than banning or restricting behaviour, people are instead given information about the consequences of their actions in order to influence their decision making. For example, efforts to reduce smoking rely on graphic illustrations on cigarette packets to reveal the medical damage caused by smoking, rather than on a ban on tobacco products. Instead of a prohibition on 'junk' food, people are encouraged to eat healthily though 'five a day' campaigns that highlight the health benefits of eating fruit and vegetables. Changing default settings (for example, asking people to opt out rather than in to organ-donation schemes) may also prompt behavioural changes. Taken together, these approaches mean:

> a new kind of self-restricting governing has been emerging where people are 'nudged' in particular directions. This is not a 'nanny knows best' kind of paternalism, but a more avuncular spirit by which people are encouraged to govern their own temptations.
>
> (Pykett 2009a)

In everyday lives the nudge has manifested itself through macro- and micro-forms of engineering space that range from the designs of streetscapes, to the positioning of healthy food in canteens and, famously, using images of flies in urinals to encourage better aim (Jones *et al.* 2011b)! Nudge politics reflects the development of liberal paternalism that:

> 'is being justified on the basis of affording citizens greater choice in the co-production of personalised government service delivery'.
>
> (Jones *et al.* 2011b: 486)

This governmentality of the self has important implications for citizenship identities, according to Rhys Jones and his colleagues (Jones *et al.* 2011b). On the one hand, paternalistic or maternalistic (Pykett 2012) attempts to bypass independent decision making through the use of smart environments seem to position citizens as children and without the responsibility to make their own choices. On the other hand, some policies are empowering in their attempt to 'engage citizens in more reflexive and sustained considerations of their own behaviour' (Jones *et al.* 2011b: 16).

Either way, the example of 'the nudge' demonstrates how seemingly apolitical activities, such as eating or exercising, connect citizens to the state. 'Nudge' politics is a form of cultural governmentality that confirms Gavin Parker's (2006: 1) observation that:

> informal tools, as means of structuring citizenship and citizen behaviour, are in circulation, ranging from everyday signs, artefacts and warnings which structure behaviours and performativities . . . to a range of semi-formal tools, such as codes of conduct that may be viewed as attempts to construct citizenship.

DAILY PERFORMANCES

Socio-cultural approaches to citizenship have tended to 'emphasise the emotional and affective dimensions of citizenship rather than its strictly legal or political aspects' (Jackson 2010: 139). These emphasize the importance of understanding how citizenship is played out on a daily basis by people going about their daily lives rather than partaking in occasional political activities (MacKian 1995). The concept of performance focuses on the way in which identities are played out and reinforced through embodied actions (Woods 2010). Most obviously, performance can refer to staged events or scripted actions (Box 6.5) but it is important to consider how everyday performances are important to citizenship. These refer to:

> 'the ways of dwelling, working, socializing and relaxing in familiar space . . . largely unreflexive habits, quotidian performances that tether people to place, producing serial sensations via daily tasks, pleasures and routines'.
>
> (Edensor 2006: 491)

These repeated acts help to reproduce and reinforce ideas of citizenship and, in doing so, contribute to ways in which people are included or excluded from places.

Pine's (2010, 2011) study of Dominican immigrants in predominantly African American and Puerto Rican neighbourhoods of Philadelphia draws attention to the significance of these daily practices in the formation of citizenship. His research demonstrates how Dominican shopkeepers were able to overcome anti-immigration sentiments by providing services to more established citizens. These practices included flexible pricing, stocking 'boutique' services and allowing the shop to be used as a site of interaction between 'old' and 'new' groups of residents. Based on this evidence he argues that citizenship is not only negotiated with the state, but is also 'an identity created by the interactions between heterogeneous elements of the modern city' (Pine 2010: 1104). Likewise, female Kurdish immigrants to Istanbul, Turkey use both anonymity and visibility as they deem it appropriate to negotiate everyday places such as schools, neighbourhoods and workplaces (Secor 2004).

Sara MacKian uses the example of health care to argue for a less political approach to studying citizenship. Despite various reforms to the governance of health (see also Chapter 2), she points out that '85 percent of Britain's illness is managed without a professional consultation, and yet on any one day up to half of us are busy consuming some form of medication' (MacKian 1995: 211). Rather than focusing on the politics of health, most people are simply engaged with the business of getting better or feeling well so that they can participate fully in daily life. Citizenship is seen as something that is individualistic rather than communitarian. She continues that 'the proportion of patients engaging in the system laid out in the government's reforms and Patient's Charter, and realized through the hospital trusts and the fundholding GPs, is extremely small' (MacKian 1995: 211). A patient's '*own* active citizenship is something which blends imperceptibly into the life of the community' (MacKian 1998: 35), however he or she sees this, rather than the spatial and social structures imposed from the top. MacKian's work has explored the daily practices that people take to heal themselves, be it taking over-the-counter medicines, following lay advice, engaging with various communities of support groups or practising spiritual beliefs (MacKian 2012). These practices are seen as particularly important in enabling citizens to live fuller lives, especially if they are facing illnesses or

Box 6.5 CITIZENSHIP AS A SCRIPTED PERFORMANCE: FLASHMOBBING

As well as everyday actions, the idea of performance can refer to scripted actions or staged events. Events such as remembrance parades or festivals of celebration that are staged in places of local or national significance (Box 6.4 and Chapter 1) can be used to reinforce local or national identity. Other events represent expressions of cultural rather than national identity.

'Flashmobs' are apparently spontaneous but carefully preplanned (http://www.bbc.co.uk/news/uk-13598894 – last accessed 6 August 2013) acts that involve people appropriating a public space and performing an action or work of art, before vanishing again. Examples include mass pillow-fights in Toronto, silent discos on the London Underground and zombie attacks in various cities. Flashmobs have also occurred in schools (led by teachers to surprise students) and private stores. Flashmobs rarely seem to make political points although a recent zombie attack in Leicester was prompted by the council declaring that they were unprepared for such an eventuality in response to a question by a 'concerned citizen' under a Freedom of Information (FOI) request (http://www.bbc.co.uk/news/uk-england-leicestershire-13713798 – last accessed 6 August 2013).

Although acts usually lack any overtly political purpose, they might be considered as acts of citizenship which assert rights to make use of public space and gain (fleeting) recognition (Saunders 2008). Such performances may be uplifting and uniting as 'categories of citizen, stranger and outsider may become blurred through shared performance that interrupts conventional spaces and practices' (Saunders 2008: 296) in performance that reconsiders how subjects use the city and are defined by its spaces. Tellingly, some authorities are enacting by-laws or regulations to prevent, disrupt or police these gatherings; raising questions about how urban space is controlled and by whom.

using health practices that are not fully recognized by the medical establishment.

CONCLUSIONS

Although many writers have emphasized political forms of citizenship, for many people this simply does not matter. Indeed, the whole concept of citizenship is rarely thought about:

> 'It might only seem to matter at times of particular events (whether or not one's nation will go to war) or in particular places when proof of who you are can determine whether or not you can get home'.
>
> (Skelton 2006: 45)

For others, citizenship is considered as expressing a national identity rather than as something that is played out in daily life. This is illustrated by an exchange with an interviewee in Rasmussen and Brown's study of AIDS activism:

> 'Citizenship?' she cocked her head quizzically and looked beyond me, 'You mean like standing around on July 1 waving flags and saying "Yay Canada"?'
>
> 'No' I quickly replied. 'I mean how people are being political around AIDS – at various times and places in their daily lives . . . about claiming rights, duties, and membership in a political community.'
>
> (Rasmussen and Brown 2002: 175)

Nevertheless, as this chapter has shown, ideas of citizenship are influential in daily lives and help to shape how people define and play out their lives in relation to the wider communities in which they live. Citizenship provides a way of analysing daily practices and linking them to political and social structures. It is important, though, to recognize that not everyone is treated as an equal citizen in these places. As Painter and Philo articulate:

> If people cannot be present in public spaces (streets, squares, parks, cinemas, churches, town halls) without feeling uncomfortable, victimized and basically 'out of place', then it must be questionable

> whether or not these people can be regarded as citizens at all; or, at least, whether they will regard themselves as full citizens of their host community able to exist on an equal footing with other people who seem perfectly 'at home' when moving about in public spaces.
>
> (Painter and Philo 1995:195)

Chapter 7 examines some of the ways in which citizens can be excluded from various everyday spaces and some of the actions that have been taken to gain control of these spaces.

FURTHER READING

Sara MacKian's (1995) article in *Political Geography* made a forceful case to move the study of citizenship beyond the political and towards everyday experience. Nick Stevenson's (2001) book *Culture and Citizenship* (and subsequent editions) charts the development of interest in everyday citizenship. Sarah Mills (2013) provides a critical account of how the Scouting movement has shaped citizenship. A special issue of *Historical Geography* (1995, vol. 22.40) explores how education has been used over time to shape citizenship, while Jessica Pykett's work examines its introduction to the UK curriculum (2009b, 2012). It is also interesting to examine the ways in which the Geographical Association promotes the teaching of citizenship through geography: http://www.geography.org.uk/resources/citizenship/#top (last accessed 6 August 2013).

NOTE

1 ANZAC (Australia and New Zealand Army Corps) Day is held annually on 25 April to commemorate the war dead of Australia and New Zealand. It is marked by a solemn dawn service that includes a two-minute silence.

7

CITIZENSHIP AND EXCLUSION

INTRODUCTION

Chapter 6 illustrated some of the ways in which citizenship has been constructed and played out in different contexts. Implicitly or covertly, many of these approaches attempt to make people 'useful' citizens within wider communities. Yet Gill Valentine (2001: 306) has observed that 'despite the fact that the language of citizenship implies inclusion and universality, it is also an exclusionary practice'. She argues that citizenship tends to benefit selective groups of people, usually white, middle-class men, to the detriment of others who include 'women, ethnic, cultural and religious minorities, those with mental ill-health and indigenous people'. Indeed, there is a history of governments using 'gendered, racialized, religious, nativistic and other ascriptive categories to assign quite different civic statuses to different sets of people' (Smith 2002: 109). So, although American republicanism in the nineteenth century represented an ideal for some (de Tocqueville 2003 [1835–40]), its vision of citizenship was intra-racial rather than inter-racial, with black and Native American people excluded from the privileges and opportunities to participate in civic society.

Citizenship cannot, therefore, be mechanically associated with equality and, at the risk of reading an 'off-the-hip list' of marginalized groups (Cloke and Little 1997: 11), it is possible to identify many groups of people who continue to be excluded from full citizenship. Women, for example, may feel excluded from public spaces due to fear of assault (Valentine 1989; Pain 2000); gay people may hide their sexuality in order to participate in societies where heterosexuality is considered the norm (Bell and Binnie 2006); disabled people may be physically excluded from public space or service (Matthews and Vujakovic 1995; Chouinard 2001; Valentine and Skelton 2007); indigenous lifestyles have been repressed (Pant 2005); racism can impact on movement within and between nation-states (MacLaughlin 1998a; Tesfahuney 1998; Anderson and Taylor 2005); young people's opinions may be ignored (Hörschelmann 2008); and age can have a bearing on employment, residential preferences and lifestyles (Mansvelt 1997; Pain *et al.* 2000; Petersen and Warburton 2012).

Needless to say, this list hides as much as it reveals as it categorizes people along particular socially constructed faultlines rather than recognizing how identities are performed relationally and spatially (Pykett 2010). It also emphasizes exclusion from public space. However, as this chapter traces, some people have been excluded from full citizenship precisely because citizenship has tended to emphasize public over private space. The latter has often been ignored or hidden from discussions of citizenship.

Chapter 7 considers the relationship between citizenship, space and exclusion. It evaluates whether the very idea of citizenship is exclusionary or whether there is potential for citizenship to emancipate those on the margins of society. In doing so, it emphasizes how public, private and liminal spaces contribute to exclusion and inclusion from citizenship. It starts by reviewing how the language of rights has been deployed to identify and protect those who are socially, economically or culturally excluded from citizenship.

PROTECTING RIGHTS

Exclusion from citizenship can be articulated through the language of rights. As Chapter 2 highlighted, T. H. Marshall outlined some of the fundamental political, civil and social rights that he associated with contemporary citizenship. Although criticized for neglecting particular issues or people, his work nevertheless established the importance of rights to achieving full citizenship. One way to chart exclusion from citizenship is to monitor the extent of human rights and whether they have been granted, denied or abused in particular places (see Box 2.3). Equally, the concept of rights can be used to ensure that full citizenship is open to all. Formal international efforts have been made to enshrine the principles of universal rights into the political-judicial frameworks of different states (see Smith and van der Anker 2005 for a good introductory survey and discussion).

The United Nations (UN) sought to establish and safeguard universal human rights in its International Bill of Human Rights that drew together the 1948 Universal Declaration of Human Rights (UDHR), the 1966 International Covenant on Civil and Political Rights (ICCPR) and the 1966 International Covenant on Economic, Social and Cultural Rights (ICESCR). These have been enforced through various treaties at the international level as well as legislation and the judicial systems of individual states. In 2002, the International Criminal Court (ICC), was established to deal with war crimes and crimes against humanity.

The EU's Charter of Fundamental Rights contains 54 articles that outline the human rights of its citizens and draw together various pieces of legislation from the EU and its member states, as well as international conventions from the Council of Europe, the UN and the International Labour Organization (ILO) (Blackburn and Polakiewicz 2001) (Box 7.1). It was ratified by the 2009 Lisbon Treaty, although three countries, the UK, Poland and the Czech Republic, secured a protocol that limited the application of the charter. It is enforced by legislation of member states and the European Court of Justice (ECJ).

Although determined at a global level, these rights are implemented (or not) at the level of the nation-state using legislation and judicial apparatus (Turner 2012). For example, the UK's 2010 Equality Act drew together various pieces of legislation to ensure that age, disability, gender reassignment, marriage, civil partnership, race, religion or belief, sex or sexual orientation does not impact on employment or access to public services. Other laws are aimed at specific groups of people: the UN Convention on the Rights of the Child stresses the importance of children's participation, as well as their provision and protection in society (Skelton 2007).

Western countries tend to stress the rights of *individuals* 'independent of their social relations and place in society' (Kabeer 2005b: 11) (although these individual rights have often been achieved by collective demands). Arabic and African states place more emphasis on collective rights, often

Box 7.1 CHARTER OF FUNDAMENTAL RIGHTS OF THE EUROPEAN UNION

Chapter I: **Dignity**
Human dignity; the right to life; the right to the integrity of the person; prohibition of torture and inhuman or degrading treatment or punishment; prohibition of slavery and forced labour.

Chapter II: **Freedoms**
The right to liberty and security; respect for private and family life; protection of personal data; the right to marry and to found a family; freedom of thought, conscience and religion; freedom of expression and information; freedom of assembly and association; freedom of the arts and sciences; the right to education; freedom to choose an occupation and the right to engage in work; freedom to conduct a business; the right to property; the right to asylum; protection in the event of removal, expulsion or extradition.

Chapter III: **Equality**
Equality before the law; non-discrimination; cultural, religious and linguistic diversity; equality between men and women; the rights of the child; the rights of the elderly; integration of persons with disabilities.

Chapter IV: **Solidarity**
Worker's right to information and consultation within the undertaking; the right of collective bargaining and action; the right of access to placement services; protection in the event of unjustified dismissal; fair and just working conditions; prohibition of child labour and protection of young people at work; family and professional life; social security and social assistance; health care; access to services of general economic interest; environmental protection; consumer protection.

Chapter V: **Citizens' rights**
The right to vote and to stand as a candidate at elections to the European Parliament; the right to vote and to stand as a candidate

Continued

at municipal elections; the right to good administration; the right of access to documents; Ombudsman; the right to petition; freedom of movement and of residence; diplomatic and consular protection.

Chapter VI: **Justice**
The right to an effective remedy and to a fair trial; presumption of innocence and the right of defence; principles of legality and proportionality of criminal offences and penalties; the right not to be tried or punished twice in criminal proceedings for the same criminal offence.

Chapter VII: **General provisions**

(Source: European Union (2010).)

on the basis of kinship, community, caste and religion. Collective rights refer to cases where 'individuals meet their needs on the basis of a shared morality of claims and obligations and define their identities in relation to other members of their communities' (Kabeer 2005a: 12). In Pakistan, individual rights are applied in the economic sphere, with collective rights based on religion being more influential in the private sphere of the family. In Nigeria, rights are associated with ethnicity and only apply to areas of the country in which a person is indigenous (Kabeer 2005a).

Although practices, charters and laws aimed at ensuring human rights are well intended and lay valuable benchmarks for the delivery of social justice, they fall short of ensuring full citizenship. This is for three reasons.

First, there are gaps in the implementation of legislation. For example, although one review concluded that Britain was 'becoming a fairer place' as a result of various pieces of legislation, it also revealed that 'whatever progress has been made for some groups in some places, the outcomes for many people are not shifting as far or as fast as they should' (Equality and Human Rights Commission 2010: 5–6). It identified 15 'significant challenges' that impacted on equality and full participation in society that included the effect of socio-economic background on health and life expectancy, educational differences, employment and pay gaps, identity-based violence, discrimination and harassment and a need to give more people greater personal autonomy and civic power. International rights secured by international agreements are even harder to enforce and rely on the political will and resources of individual nations (Tonts and Larsen 2002).

Second, formal legislation can also overlook social and cultural inequalities that do not fit 'traditional' views of human rights (Blackburn and Busuttil 1997; Blomley and Pratt 2001). It has tended to focus on civic and political rights, with collective, gender and socio-cultural rights receiving less attention (Mutua 2002). It was not until 1979 that concerns about sexual or gender oppression were addressed by the UN through the Convention on the Elimination of All Forms of Oppression against Women (Tonts and Larsen 2002). Although the UN's Convention on the Status of Refugees offers asylum to those with 'well-founded fear of being persecuted for reasons of race, religion, nationality, membership of a particular social group or political opinion', sexuality is not specifically mentioned as a ground for protection.

Third, it is also clear that other forms of legislation impact unevenly on different types of people. For example, recent legislation has sought to remove 'undesirable people', including the homeless, young and prostitutes from some urban spaces, raising questions about universality of *de jure* rights and whether some people are treated as more as denizens than citizens (Mitchell 1995, 1997, 2005; Carr *et al.* 2009).

Although efforts to define and legislate for human rights are important, there is often a gap between *de jure* (legal) and *de facto* (actual) rights (Smith 1989, 2000). As the following section argues, the granting of *de jure* rights is not in itself enough to ensure full participation as citizens in society.

DE JURE AND *DE FACTO* EXCLUSION: THE CASE OF INDIGENOUS AUSTRALIANS

This section draws on the experiences of indigenous Australians to trace various forms of exclusion from citizenship. It starts by detailing how these people were denied any form of citizenship as a result of colonial oppression. Although *de jure* citizenship was won in 1967, aboriginal people have continued to be severely excluded from Australian society. While self-governance offered a new type of inclusionary citizenship, the 2007

Northern Territory National Emergency Response (NTNER) has raised questions about the status of indigenous people as full citizens of Australia.

De jure exclusion

Prior to colonization, aboriginal people lived nomadic lifestyles in Australia that were based on subsistence forms of hunting and gathering. As there were no permanent settlements, agriculture or evidence of territorial boundaries, the British claimed Australia as '*terra nullius*'. This allowed the peaceful occupation of unoccupied land under international law. In reality the land had been occupied for at least 50,000 years and indigenous people were numerous, especially in coastal areas where colonization occurred.

Indigenous, mobile lifestyles were replaced by enforced sedentarism. Aboriginal protectors were appointed in 1886 to organize the settlement of aborigines into remote reserves situated away from white society and the tribal territories which had supported nomadic lifestyles. Indigenous people were classed as wards, not citizens, of the state with few or no rights.

Their lives were controlled to an extraordinary degree. Indigenous people did not have the right to marry, work or travel without the permission of the state. Parents had no legal rights over their children (Grimshaw 1999). The sale of alcohol, land and property to aboriginal people was prohibited. Night-time curfews prevented aboriginal people entering towns at night and confined them to strongly policed settlements away from white towns. Although many aboriginal people were employed as stockmen or domestic servants, their wages (much lower than those for white Australians) were paid into state-controlled saving schemes that could only be accessed via aboriginal protectors. Others were paid rations, including 'grog' that contributed to high rates of alcohol dependency and disease.

The most insidious policy was the forced removal of children from their parents, superficially on assimilation and welfare grounds but in support of racist policies that aimed to prevent the development of a mixed-race population (van Krieken 1999). Children were confined in institutions that trained them for farm work or domestic service. It is estimated that between one in three and one in ten aborigine children were forcibly removed between 1900 and 1970; one in five of these children were abused in institutions and many suffered excessive physical punishment (Human Rights and Equal Opportunities Commission 1997). Over 100,000 people are thought to have been part of this 'stolen generation' who are unable to trace their parents. The actions contributed to the destruction of traditional kinship groups and, consequently, a raft of social ills including mental illness and alcoholism (ibid.).

Second-class citizens

Indigenous people were not granted citizenship until 1967 and they had few political rights in the face of this oppression. In 1957, non-European Australians, including indigenous Australians, were allowed to apply for citizenship of Australia if they were able to prove they could live as Europeans i.e. in settled rather than nomadic lifestyles (http://www.indigenousrights.net.au/section.asp?sID=2 – last accessed 6 August 2013). This freed them from the restrictions of wardship, granting them a degree of mobility that allowed them to move between states and into towns.

However, very few aboriginal people applied for citizenship. In part this was because some states banned citizens from socializing with aboriginals, so that indigenous people who were granted citizenship could not legally mix with their friends or even relatives. Albert Namatjira, the first aboriginal person to be granted full Australian citizenship, was jailed for supplying his kin with alcohol (Wells and Christie 2000). Definitions of aboriginality also varied between states so that an indigenous person moving between states could be variously defined as a citizen or ward, depending on state legislation (Andrews 1962). If, as Cresswell (2006a) argues, citizenship depends on the ability to travel, this was a very limited form (Chapter 3).

Following pressure from campaigners for indigenous rights, a constitutional referendum was held in 1967 in which 90 per cent of voters approved a change that effectively recognized indigenous people as citizens of Australia. With this came the right to vote and participate fully in Australian life and, for the first time, to be included in the Australian national census. The federal parliament was given power to legislate for aborigines, ending their diverse and unequal treatment by different states.

De facto exclusion

Although the 1967 referendum established *de jure* citizenship, aboriginal people still face a struggle to gain *de facto* rights as full Australian citizens. In everyday life aboriginal people continue to be socially, culturally and economically excluded from full participation in society. Indigenous Australians have a significantly lower life expectancy; are more likely to be arrested and imprisoned; achieve fewer qualifications; have worse health; are more likely to be unemployed or poor; have access to fewer basics; suffer from higher levels of domestic violence (especially women); and are more likely to be racially abused than white citizens (Gordon *et al.* 2002; Tonts and Larsen 2002; Yarwood 2007b). These issues reflect the legacy of colonial oppression and are common to indigenous people in many other settler countries (Cairns 2002; Perreault 2003; Castree 2004; Biolsi 2005; Walker and Barcham 2010; Andreasson 2011). Indigenous people often exist as 'shadow citizens' and 'as disempowered, dispersed subjects of a larger political entity' (Maaka and Fleras 2005: 114).

Mobile lifestyles, or the remnants of them, continue to clash with settled society. Indigenous groups view public, open-air spaces in towns as places to congregate, camp, negotiate kinship responsibilities and drink (White 1997; Cunneen 2001; Yarwood 2007b; Fisher 2012). These activities disrupt sanitized, suburban and white constructions of heritage and rurality that are being employed to reimagine Australian country towns (Tonts and Greive 2002). It is one reason why indigenous people are more likely to be arrested for public-order offences in public space.

Efforts to resolve these issues have rested on the development of self-governing communities that, in turn, relied on the recognition of aboriginal land rights. Following direct actions and legal cases, *terra nullius* was rejected in 1992 (Mercer 1993, 1997) and the 1993 Native Land Act recognized aboriginal ownership of land. Over half of land in Australia now has 'native title' (Davies 2003; Howitt *et al.* 2012) although disputes and legal challenges continue to occur with other land users or claimants. The recognition of land rights has paved the way for greater self-governance by indigenous communities. It was hoped that greater self-government (political rights) would help communities to tackle some of the social issues that prevented their full participation in society (Gibson 1998, 1999; Lane and Williams 2009;

Gibbs 2010; Hill 2011; Howitt *et al.* 2012). However, the 2007 NTNER demonstrates that the civic, social and political rights afforded by self-governance appear to be tenuous and vulnerable to withdrawal by the state.

The Northern Territory National Emergency Response (NTNER)

The Northern Territory National Emergency Response (NTNER) Act 2007 was passed in response to 'extreme disadvantage faced by indigenous peoples and issues of safety for children and women' (Anaya 2010: 2) identified in an official state enquiry into aboriginal child abuse (Anderson and Wild 2007). Included in the NTNER were measures to:

- prohibit the sale and consumption of alcohol;
- install filters on public computers to prevent their use for pornography;
- acquire compulsorily leases for over 65 aboriginal communities, effectively giving federal government direct control over them (Lea 2012);
- grant the Minister for Indigenous Affairs full control of the 'community service entities' of public and aboriginal agencies, including funding, assets and business structures;
- remove customary law or cultural practice as a mitigating factor when sentencing or applying for bail;
- require grocery stores to participate in the Income Management Regime (IMR) (see below).

(Source: Calma 2007)

Additionally, measures were taken to ban pornographic material, revoke the use of permits to enter aboriginal lands and strengthen federal legislation and policing. An Income Management Regime (IMR) was introduced requiring a proportion of all welfare payments to be spent on food, clothing or household goods (not alcohol). This was also extended to people on state-funded workfare employment programmes. Social security benefits were removed if a child was considered to be in need of protection, if the parents resided in specific areas, or if truancy was high (McCallum 2011). The NTNER was enforced by the deployment of military forces.

Given the extent and seriousness of child abuse identified in Anderson and Wild's (2007) report, there was a widely accepted need for intervention to fulfil Australia's international human rights obligations (Anaya 2010). However, the UN's special rapporteur, James Anaya (2010), criticized the NTNER for limiting the capacity of indigenous individuals and communities to control or participate in decisions affecting their own lives, property and cultural development and 'in a way that in effect discriminates on the basis of race, thereby raising serious human rights concerns' (Anaya 2010: 2).

Of particular concern was the suspension of the 1975 Racial Discrimination Act between 2007 and 2010 in areas covered by the NTNER, allowing indigenous people to be specifically targeted as part of NTNER's special measures. Thus, welfare reforms could be targeted on the basis of race rather than need. All indigenous people in NTNER areas were required to be part of the IMR, regardless of whether or not they had responsibilities over children or had been shown to have problems managing income in the past. By contrast, people living outside of the prescribed areas had income quarantining applied to them on a case-by-case basis (Anaya 2010). Blanket bans on alcohol and pornography were also felt to impinge on individual autonomy.

These measures were exacerbated by a lack of consultation with indigenous people and the use of excessive Commonwealth powers (including military force) to assert NTNER measures. The NTNER was also criticized for failing to address many of the issues and recommendations detailed in Anderson and Wild's (2007) report (McCallum 2011). In 2010, an amended Racial Discrimination Act was introduced that maintained compulsory income management and extended it to targeted non-indigenous welfare recipients, and NTNER was replaced by a 'Stronger Futures Programme' that continued to be criticized for its centralist approach.

Comparing the NTNER to liberal authoritarian responses of the past, McCallum (2011: 629) described it as paternalistic and an:

> 'overwhelmingly punitive response to a report which in fact highlighted the need for a series of ordered social policy responses that had been sought by Aboriginal communities for decades'.

Macoun (2011) goes further and argues that aboriginality was represented as something 'savage' and in need of settler-imposed control. Spatial and mobile constructions were important, with various communities and practices viewed alternatively as 'authentic' or 'threatening'. She concludes:

> The intervention is framed as extending settler authority over this troubling terrain, containing and redeeming Aboriginality through inclusion in the settler nation's moral order. This process involves a performance or enactment of settler sovereignty, a claim made over and through both the territory of Aboriginal people and the discursive terrain of nationhood.
>
> (Macoun 2011: 532)

Given this appraisal, forms of indigenous citizenship continue to be different and distant from that enjoyed by non-indigenous residents of Australia. The incident also highlights the need for self-government and to determine new, liminal forms of citizenship that allow aboriginal people to engage more closely in society. In the following section, ideas from feminist geographies are used to discuss how alternatives to traditional, exclusionary forms of citizenship may develop.

GENDER

Feminist scholars have argued that the theory and practice of citizenship have ignored the significance of gender to the detriment of women (Chouinard 2009). In the extreme, women in some countries have few or no civil or political rights, including the right to an education, freedom of speech or work (Lister 2002). This was highlighted in 2012, when Malala Yousafzai, a 14-year-old schoolgirl, was shot by the Taliban for going to school in the Swat Valley, Pakistan, and championing the rights of girls to be educated.

Patriarchal societies have a long history of using women as unpaid, domestic labour, often enforced through law, domestic violence and cultural expectation, which ensured men were positioned as the 'head of household' with greater economic, political and social freedoms (Bellamy 2008). Economically, women have often been expected to be the primary carers or, at best, make a choice between being carers or earners (Lister, 2003). Women are still more likely to take part-time work and lose opportunities for promotion, leading to occupational and fiscal inequalities. Women may lose benefits if they do not comply with male-employment patterns (Lister 2002). In the UK, the 1975 Sex Discrimination Act was a landmark piece of legislation that prevented, in *de jure* terms, sexual discrimination in the workplace and in the provision of public services. However, in *de facto* terms, there remains a significant pay gap between men and women (Equal Opportunities Commission 2005); occupational segregation is widespread and many women still face discrimination and loss of earnings or even jobs through pregnancy (ibid.).

In terms of political citizenship, women are under-represented in formal politics (Bellamy 2008) and other forms of governance (Little 2002). This reflects the fact that women won the right to vote far later than men in many Western countries and have been 'allowed' to enter male-dominated political institutions on terms that have often been set by men.

Women are widely excluded from social citizenship. For example, a woman can be excluded from participation in public spaces due to fears of sexual harassment or assault. This can be exacerbated by poor urban design (Bowlby 1984) and patriarchal policing that tends to overlook domestic violence (Valentine 1989; Pain 1997b).

One reason for these exclusions is that citizenship has often been rooted in the public sphere (see Chapter 2) and so private practices, which have dominated or repressed women, have largely gone unnoticed (Isin and Wood 1999). In order to gain more rights in the private sphere, such as outlawing rape within marriage or the right to apply for loans without a male guarantor, campaigning has often had to occur in the public sphere through political channels that have been male-dominated and reluctant to countenance change. Many abuses of women's rights continue to go unnoticed in private spaces. Migrant domestic servants, for example, can suffer harsh working conditions that go unseen, unregulated and unpoliced as they occur in private homes (Pratt 2005).

Despite hard-fought campaigns and equal-opportunity legislation in many countries, many structures of citizenship continue to favour men and have treated women as second-class citizens in *de facto*, if not *de jure*, terms (Lister 2002). These levels of exclusion have led some feminist scholars to question whether the whole idea of citizenship has any relevance for women (McEwan 2005).

Yet in Ruth Lister's (2003) opinion, citizenship not only is relevant for women but can be used as a powerful analytical and campaigning tool to empower women and improve their lives. But to do so, citizenship needs to be reconceptualized. In part, this means challenging the divide between public and private space in ways that involve 'the disruption of its gendered meaning; recognition of the ways in which it is socially and politically constructed . . . and acknowledgment of how in practice each side impacts on each other' (Lister 2003: 197). There is widespread evidence to support these ideas.

Ruiz (2005) charts how indigenous women in Chiapas, Mexico, work long hours, suffer domestic violence and are prevented from speaking in public meetings. In the context of wider social change and legal demands for more indigenous rights, women have used their daily activities to improve participation in society. This has centred on cooperatives of female artisans that have been able to provide a platform for women to voice their concerns and turn individual and private problems 'into public and collective ones' (Ruiz 2005: 138). These collective activities have helped to give women a more powerful voice in community affairs and to find 'their own solutions and construct alternative forms of family, community and social relations' (ibid.). These daily practices are as important as formal political structures to these women and their ability to participate politically in society.

Moon (2012) examines the role of a women's organization, the People's Friendship Society (PFS), in articulating citizenship in South Korea. This work highlights how the organization fosters the idea of citizenship as something that is based on community identity and care for others. Interviewees stressed how private concerns led them to become more widely engaged in the public sphere. For example, concern about food safety in the home led one mother to join a food co-operative and engage in actions in the public sphere. Others saw household management as a way of initiating change in society through consumption choices that affected the environment (see also Chapter 5). In most cases, women wanted a closer continuity between public and private life, challenging more established ideas of masculine citizenship that were based on military service and employment.

Numerous studies have revealed how important women are to the negotiation of citizenship by immigrants (Al Sharmani 2010; Elmhirst 2011; McIlwaine and Bermúdez 2011). In particular, their interactions in schools, homes, shops, nurseries and community groups help to establish them and their families as visible and valuable citizens in wider society. By way of example, Bosco *et al.*'s (2011) study of Latina immigrant women in southern California is instructive. They trace how women and children work in a Neighbourhood Action Group (NAG) to access health care and enhance their neighbourhoods. Their three main activities are providing support for NAG members to improve themselves (perhaps by gaining US citizenship), advocating community needs and providing community services through various projects. As the authors point out, their position as citizens is contradictory: they are pushed out of public space as a result of their uncertain status as immigrants, yet they choose to participate in community affairs. These actions support the idea that citizenship is participatory and based on a politics of solidarity, rather than something that is defined by a state-imposed identity.

As these studies of international migrants suggest, women, and other excluded groups, draw strength not only from local communities but also from international connections. Indeed, Lister (2003) advocates global citizenship as a valuable way of linking women's concerns in different countries and focusing on the responsibilities held by affluent nations to support women's rights. As Chapter 5 examined, many transnational movements have been established and supported by women to support other women in other places. Women Working Worldwide (WWW) is one example of an NGO that provides solidarity and support for female workers in the global South (Hale and Wills 2007). WWW used transnational networks to highlight the needs and voices of female workers and to pressure companies to act ethically in the employment of women and sourcing of products. Their involvement in the Clean Clothes Campaign, Labour Behind the Label and the Ethical Trading Initiative highlights how different local organizations in different parts of the world can work together with each other to produce transnationally coordinated projects (see also Chapter 5).

Rather than dismissing the idea of citizenship, it is important to consider how new formations of citizenship can be used to analyse power relations and empower those who have been excluded from full participation in space and society. Although this section has examined women, these ideas can also be used to support other minority groups. The next section examines how ideas of citizenship provide new perspectives on sexuality and inclusion.

SEXUALITY

According to Bell and Binnie (2000: 10) 'all citizenship is sexual citizenship'. They argue that many foundations for citizenship are based on ideas of sexuality and, usually, heterosexuality (Valentine 1993; Hubbard 2000, 2001). By contrast, other forms of sexuality that are not concerned with 'monogamous, heterosexual, procreative sex' (Hubbard 2001: 51) may be viewed as less appropriate, especially in public space, restricting the sexual citizen's right to be sexual (Brown 2006; Hubbard 2012). Bell and Binnie (2000: 142) assert: 'we may all be sexual citizens, but we are not all equal sexual citizens'. They observe (2006: 870): 'the contours of sexual citizenship are heavily heteronormative, for example the centrality of the opposite-sex couple or family as the legitimate form of adult relationship, on which are built whole infrastructures such as those of social welfare'. For example, Oswin (2010) demonstrates that colonial heteronormative ideals of (small) families have been used to drive the regeneration of Singapore through, first, the building of new apartment blocks and, then, determining who can buy or live in them. She reports:

> to purchase an HDB [Housing and Development Board, the government's housing agency] flat, the applicant must be 21 years of age and 'form a proper family nucleus', which is defined as: the applicant and fiancé′(e); the applicant, spouse and children (if any); the applicant, the applicant's parents and siblings (if any); if widowed/divorced, the applicant and children under the applicant's legal custody; and, if orphaned, the applicant and unmarried siblings.
>
> (Oswin 2010: 257)

She argues that such narrow definitions of hetronormativity exclude not only gay and lesbian people but also those who are unmarried, widowed, divorced or single parents. Single, male foreign workers are, for example, housed in dormitories that are 'buffered' from family flats.

Much work on sexual citizenship has focused on identifying and addressing these inequalities. Although some work has centred on sexual practices (Bell 1995), the majority has revolved around sexuality and how sexual minorities are placed within heteronormative society: 'access to public space concerns not the performance of sexual acts but the right to participate in public spaces even if that sexuality is homosexuality' (Isin and Wood 1999: 85). Particular attention has been given to the legal status and rights of gay people to participate fully in society. These include, amongst others, the rights to marry or form civil partnerships (Baird 2006; Stychin 2006); practise religion (Andersson *et al.* 2011; Vanderbeck *et al.* 2011; Valentine and

Waite 2012); work, including service in the military (Isin and Wood 1999); migrate (Binnie 1997; Coleman 2008; Simmons 2008; Sandell 2010) or travel (Baird 2006; Waitt *et al.* 2008); adopt children; participate in public events (Marston 2002; Jakobsen 2004); and express national identity (Waitt 2005). As with the case of gender, sexual minorities have frequently had to assert their rights to privacy through the public sphere, often through 'carnivalesque transgression' (Weeks 1998), such as the Australian Mardi-Gras festival, or radical direct action (Andrijasevic *et al.* 2012). Hubbard (2001: 62) continues:

> the idea that sexual dissidents can define themselves as sexual citizens by occupying public space on their own terms thus offers a tantalizing vision of a situation where a wide range of individuals are granted rights, recognition and respect, irrespective of their sexuality. In effect, they would have no need to hide their sexuality and to confine its expression.
>
> (Hubbard 2001: 62)

The intended outcome, however, 'increased public legitimacy for their own privacy' (Hubbard 2001: 65)

This often reflects a desire to access 'mainstream culture' through demanding equal rights of citizenship (Richardson 2005). While valuable, this approach has been critiqued and developed in a number of ways. Despite many *de jure* gains in the rights of sexual minorities in many Western countries, gay people may still experience *de facto* discrimination or exclusion in everyday public environments that are often constructed as 'heteronormative' (Box 7.2). As Hubbard (2001: 57) argues, sexual minorities 'feel free to express their sexuality only in certain (and principally private) spaces, with the streets being experienced as exclusionary spaces where heterosexuality is aggressively asserted as the norm'. There is still a need to consider how sexuality and citizenship are performed on a daily basis and the extent to which many feel 'out of place' or intimidated in particular spaces. Such exclusion from public space, as Painter and Philo (1995) argue, falls well short of an inclusive model of citizenship.

Thus, while Baird (2006: 983–4) celebrates that legislation has 'made legible . . . the space of gay tourism, gay home ownership, gay rights, gay benchmarks, gay investment and limited rights as parents' in Tasmania,

Box 7.2 KISSING GATEKEEPERS

Phil Hubbard (2012) discusses an incident in 2011 in which two gay men were ejected from a pub in Soho, London for publicly kissing despite legislation passed in 2010 to outlaw discrimination on the grounds of sexuality in the provision of public services. Drawing on press and social media coverage, Hubbard recounts that a kiss from the two men drew complaints from another patron and, when the act was repeated, they were asked to leave. Despite the 2010 Equality Act, it seems that the landlord was able to invoke the 2003 Licensing Act which states that the landlord of licensed premises commits an offence if 'he (*sic*) knowingly allows disorderly conduct on the premises'. This gives the landlord discretion (and indeed the duty) to manage his or her premises in a way that maintains orderliness. In this case, given complaints by another patron, the landlord ruled same-sex kissing to be disorderly. Certain sexual rights appear to be overruled at the local level by an appeal to the public good and the maintenance of order. Hubbard concludes that the equalities landscape is not always evident at the local scale and that national laws can only partially determine rights and responsibilities.

she also argues that it continues to distinguish and regulate what is deemed acceptable and unacceptable in public space.

It has also been questioned whether incorporation into 'mainstream culture' is desirable. Campaigns for the right of sexual minorities to participate fully in society have raised questions about the normative assumptions of citizenship. Bell and Binnie (2006: 869) suggest that in order to gain rights, gay citizens are also required to become 'responsible' citizens as a 'pay-off for the granting of formal rights by the state'. Michael Brown (2006) has engaged with this critique in a study of public health (often an arena in which sexual practices and obligations are debated) and, drawing on feminist thinking, argues that political obligation is more positive than Bell and Binnie suggest. He considers that obligations are not imposed by the state but, instead, are defined relationally, ethically and on ideas of care. He argues (Brown 2006: 893) that 'rather than relying on a tacit consent or a moral economy between rights and obligations, it suggests we ground obligation in an ethic of care and connection, where obligations are contested and negotiated, and grounded in everyday life'.

Sexual citizenship has been used to transform and promote space. On the one hand, Baird (2006) illustrates how the legalization of lesbian and gay relationships in Tasmania has been used as part of a wider regeneration strategy to promote the state as 'new', global and neo-liberal. Likewise, other places have marketed themselves as gay-friendly tourist destinations (Waitt *et al.* 2008), using sexuality in place promotion. Some places, such as the Castro District in San Francisco or Brighton in the UK, have been branded a 'homonormative space'. This not only provides a visible, safe and, above all, public territory for sexual minorities (Storey 2012) but can also be used in the promotion of urban space on a global stage (Bell and Binnie 2004). Diane Richardson (2005: 523) notes that greater visibility of lesbians and gay men as consumer-citizens has led to an 'expanding lesbian/predominantly gay "business community" that has become increasingly "professionalised"'. Although consumption can shape identity and citizenship (Mansvelt 2008), Evans (1993) argues that there has also been a commodification of sexual identities. This has helped to make sexual minorities more visible but reflects the interests of neo-liberal capital. Evans notes that this frequently leads to the exploitation of private pleasure for corporate profit, a practice that treats people as consumers rather than citizens.

Although the lives of gay and lesbian people have often been a focus for this work, subsequent work has sought to recognize that sexuality is wider, and often more blurred, than binary hetero/homosexual classifications suggest (Browne and Lim 2010). Cooper (2006) noted that the expansion of sexual citizenship to bisexual and transsexual people proved problematic in UK local authorities. Questions still remain about what forms of sexual practice and culture are accepted within discourses of citizenship and 'what kinds of sexual citizen is it possible or desirable to become' (Bell and Binnie 2006: 870). Some of Bell's earlier work has explored these issues. Drawing on the label of 'the citizen-pervert', Bell (1995) examines how sexual practices challenged the extent to which the state could or should (or should not) regulate these activities in private spaces. Through an analysis of Operation Spanner, a police action to arrest same-sex sadomasochists, he demonstrated that the state was willing to invade private spaces and, through prosecution, make them public. Bell also argued that these actions reflected broad contradictions and conflicts over citizenship, namely a blurring between what was seen as 'sinful and criminal', acceptable or illegal: 'the state and law's somewhat arbitrary and contradictory ruling on what kinds of sex are scary marks one limit of the spaces open to the citizen-pervert' (Bell 1995: 150). Other authors have noted that urban architecture and surveillance have been used to shape what sexual practices are deemed acceptable or otherwise by the state and where these should occur (Hubbard 1998, 2000, 2001; Brown 2006; Jeyasingham 2010).

As a point of observation, literature on sexuality has tended to assume that citizens are *sexually active* citizens and, by contrast, little attention has been given to those who are celibate, be it through choice or obligation, or to those who are asexual. Sexual health campaigns, for example, have an implicit assumption that adults are sexually active. Although this may be the norm, people may choose to abstain from sexual practices and partnerships for a range of reasons including religious belief or cultural practice. These people may also face *de jure* exclusion, perhaps through being unable to adopt or foster children, or face economic disadvantage with tax breaks and differential payments (for example, membership of clubs) frequently offered to couples. In terms of daily life, these people may feel excluded from events or spaces where partners are the norm or face jibes, questions or inferences about their lack of sexual activity.

CONCLUSIONS

This chapter has considered how some people are excluded from citizenship and has sought to demonstrate how various ideas of citizenship can be used to identify exclusion and, more significantly, provide ways of empowering minority groups. It has argued that traditional forms of citizenship that have relied on formal and political engagement in public spaces often fall short and fail to include those at the margins of society. There needs to be a reconceptualization of citizenship in order to strengthen the participation of these groups in civil and political society.

Four key issues emerge. First, greater attention should be given to private space in the study of citizenship. This has often been neglected in research, but is important in the formation and practices of citizenship.

Ruth Lister (2003: 197) calls for an end to the binary that has associated private space with 'particularity, care and dependence' and public space with 'universalism, justice and independence'. As the examples in this chapter have shown, grass-roots organizations (be they for women, gay people, indigenous people) offer opportunities to mix these ideas and spaces.

Second, therefore, informal groupings of people should be taken seriously as they point to a different, more fluid and accessible way for a wide range of people to engage as citizens in their localities. Rather than dismissing citizenship as an elite, exclusionary ideal, theories of citizenship need to be reconceptualized in order to understand new and emerging forms of political and civic engagement. Feminist and post-colonial perspectives on citizenship are in valuable as they point to some of the new possibilities offered by these theorizations. They also highlight the importance of moving beyond the formal, public spaces of citizenship. As some of the examples in this chapter have demonstrated, private and communal spaces provide liminal places that can empower excluded groups and allow them to engage more fully in society.

Third, the examples in this chapter develop and support arguments that citizenship can be transnational rather than national (see Chapter 5). The evidence in this chapter points to citizens' identities being more readily associated with non-territorial groupings based on race, ethnicity, sexuality, religion, physical traits, personality, interests and local places than with an imposed national identity (Painter 2002; Lister *et al.* 2005; Phillips and Ganesh 2007; Pykett 2010). It is also clear that global movements, such as women's organizations, are capable of linking and uniting people and actions in different parts of the world for common causes. It might be stated optimisitically that such actions might lead to a sense of gobal citizenship.

Finally, this chapter has drawn on specific examples of exclusion and in doing so has neglected other groups of people in this analysis. Many spaces and forms of citizenship have been ignored as a result of academic practices or cultures (Isin 2012b). It is possible to identify many 'other' groups (Philo 1992, 1997) and doubtless many 'other others' continue to go unnoticed by academics (Cloke and Little 1997). Spaces of rurality and nature, for example, have often been overlooked as citizenship has usually been associated with the city, as Chapter 8 considers.

FURTHER READING

Isin and Wood's (1999) *Citizenship and Identity* was an agenda-setting book that highlights how many groups have experienced exclusion from different forms of citizenship. Ruth Lister's (2003) *Citizenship: Feminist Perspectives* is another powerful piece of work that questions women's relationship with citizenship. David Bell and Jon Binnie's (2000) book *The Sexual Citizen: Queer Politics and Beyond* placed sexuality on the agenda of citizenship studies and has been followed up in a series of publications. A 2006 special issue of *Political Geography* (vol. 25.8) edited by Bell and Binnie presents and critiques current directions in this research. Cheryl MacEwan's (2005) work on women and citizenship in South Africa challenges the white, male, Western view on citizenship.

8

CITIZENSHIP, RURALITY AND ENVIRONMENT

INTRODUCTION

The etymology of citizenship refers to the inhabitants of urban areas and, more precisely, the city-states of the ancient world (Woods 2006a; Cheshire and Woods 2009). Over time the meaning of the word has broadened to include those who do not live in cities but, predominantly, studies of citizenship have tended to focus on *urban* citizenship. Recently, *rural* citizenship warranted entries in the *International Encyclopaedia of Human Geography* (Cheshire and Woods 2009) and *The Handbook of Rural Studies* (Woods 2006a), suggesting, perhaps, that it is somehow distinguishable from more general forms and geographies of citizenship. This reflects wider debate about the distinctiveness of rural society and whether it is significantly different to urban life (Woods 2011b).

The following section examines the emerging literature on rural citizenship and considers the relationships between rurality and citizenship. In doing so, it highlights the importance of understanding how the imagination and performance of space contributes to formations of citizenship. Following this analysis, the chapter broadens out and considers the relationships between citizenship and the wider environment.

RURAL

Rurality and rural change

It is widely accepted that rurality per se does not shape social relations in areas of low population density (Hoggart 1988), but it is also recognized that distinct forms of economic development in the countryside, together with ways in which rural places have been portrayed and imagined (Mormont 1983; Cloke and Goodwin 1992b; Halfacree 2006; Woods 2006a, 2006b, 2010), have an important bearing on the way that rural society has been shaped. Over time, rural society in the West has moved away from local, patriarchal foundations and has become much more closely linked to national and international patterns of change. These changes in rural society have had a strong bearing on the nature of citizenship in the countryside (Woods 2006b).

At the start of the twentieth century rural politics in the West was strongly equated with land ownership and agriculture. This reflected the 'combined influence of the local agrarian elites, farm unions, rural-leaning political parties and agricultural ministry officials [who] not only controlled the direction of agricultural policy but also ensured the primacy of agricultural interests in the rural political sphere' (Woods 2006b: 581). Local landowning elites provided welfare and employment in paternalistic ways that stressed community coherence and ensured a compliant apolitical workforce (Newby 1978). Participation in politics, unionized activity or protest by the rural working classes was rare and this hegemony went largely unchallenged (but see Mingay 1989; Mawby and Yarwood 2010). Needless to say, not all landlords supported their workers, meaning that the provision of welfare was patchy, reliant on charity and did little to empower local people. Intervention by local authorities, such as in the provision of social housing, was far lower than in urban areas with local landowners seeing to the welfare of their workforce through, for example, tied housing or local almsgiving (Cresswell 2009). Where state services were provided, they were often a side effect of wider modernization programmes to support the exploitation of rural resources and space (Woods 2006b).

As the twentieth century progressed, rural places were subject to significant changes that challenged and replaced localized paternalism with new political structures and conflicts (Woods 2005, 2006b). The economic and social significance of agriculture declined as new forms of economic investment and employment, often in the service and manufacturing sectors, gained dominance in many rural places of the developed world. With this, the countryside became populated with new people, often from the middle classes who were seeking idealized rustic living. Consumption rather than production dominated rural lifestyles, economies and politics. Finally, there were higher levels of state intervention in the provision of welfare and housing although, as the twentieth century wore on, the decline of services (deemed inefficient by the state and private sector) became the dominant theme. The nature and impact of these changes varied over space (Murdoch and Marsden 1994) so the countryside was lived, experienced and governed in different ways in different places (Cloke and Goodwin 1992b; Woods 1997). These new social formations had a significant impact on rural citizenship, as the following section examines.

Rurality and duties

Chapter 4 examined how citizens in the West are now expected to be 'active' members of their local communities with a duty to undertake voluntary work. These policies have deeper roots in rural areas as there has always been an expectation that rural communities will help themselves (McLaughlin 1986, 1987). The whole concept of community has been 'celebrated, encouraged, nurtured, shaped and instrumentalized in the hope of producing consequences desirable for all and for each' (Rose 1996: 335) so that they were seen as the solution and cause of the problems facing rural places (Lockie *et al.* 2006). For example, the DETR 2000 White Paper 'Our countryside: the future. A fair deal for rural England' assumed that 'rural areas often have a strong sense of community and a valuable network of voluntary groups' that could be nourished and supported to provide local services. In England, parish councils are democratically elected to provide a forum for local decision making and community representation (Tewdwr-Jones 1998; Yarwood 2002). Similar bodies, such as *Maires* in France or town councils in the USA, provide important local platforms for citizens to participate actively in local decisions that are missing from urban areas.

As the state made rural communities more responsible for the management of their localities (Rose 1996; DETR 2000), partnership and voluntary working increased significantly in rural places (for some empirical examples and discussions see Edwards *et al.* 2001; Higgins and Lockie 2002; Barnett and Barnett 2003; O'Toole and Burdess 2004; Lockie *et al.* 2006; Yarwood 2007b). However, its uptake varies considerably. The adoption of rural crime prevention schemes in England and Australia, for example, has changed substantially at the local level, reflecting the attitudes of local people and the way rural crime has been represented by state authorities (Yarwood and Edwards 1995; Yarwood 2007b, 2011b; Gilling 2011). This variation reflects the micro-politics of partnership working (Parker 1999a; Woods and Goodwin 2003) and the 'bargaining games' played by different actors within and between networks (Rhodes 1996, 2007). These have the potential to draw upon particular ideas of rurality (Woods and Goodwin 2003: 256) that, in turn, may strengthen (Herbert-Cheshire 2000) or weaken (Woods 2006a) community involvement.

The idea of rural community is, however, problematic (Liepins 2000b; Staeheli 2008a, b) with a tendency to obscure diversity beneath the banner of communal identity. Schemes that purport to represent 'community views' may in fact be reflecting elite or powerful interests. In Australia, the farming agenda continues to dominate rural governance, with an assumption that what is beneficial for farmers is beneficial for the rural community (Herbert-Cheshire 2000). Alternatively, in places where traditional rural community relations have been weakened, efforts to re-engage rural citizens may lead to new forms of local power relations developing that seek to protect or enforce different ideals of non-agrarian rurality (Woods 2006a). Here, citizen-based participation tends to favour the preservation of the countryside, rather than the needs of those marginalized in rural society. Examples include:

> small-scale disputes over barn conversions, blocked footpaths, streetlighting or tree-felling, to large-scale conflicts over new roads, windfarms, waste dumps and major housing developments, [in which] the appropriateness of the development to the rural setting and the impact on the rural character of the locality are commonly evoked alongside issues of environmental impact, pollution, noise disturbance, traffic, property devaluation and so on.
>
> (Woods 2006b: 584)

In the UK, for example, efforts to involve communities in the provision of affordable housing have led to a tortuously slow way of (under-)

providing homes in places where there is the political will (or lack of political will to oppose house building), rather than where there is the most need (Yarwood 2002; Satsangi *et al.* 2010).

Those who do not share or are unlikely to benefit from 'community' interests are likely to find themselves excluded from any potential benefits that active citizenship may bring to a rural locality. Local social and economic structures, together with the way rurality is imagined and contested, impacts on the way that communities are governed.

Yet, far from being autonomous, rural communities are subject to scrutiny and management by government agencies (Lockie and Higgins 2007) that seek to shape conduct in particular ways (Foucault 1991). Community represents a way that the state can govern 'from a distance' (Higgins and Lockie 2002) by empowering but regulating communities to behave in certain ways (see also Box 4.2). Given these problems, other commentators have focused on the rights rather than the duties of rural citizens.

Rurality and rights

Just as in cities, rural areas have been the focus for actions and protests over citizen rights. Until recently, protests associated with rights in the countryside were perceived as coming from *outside* rural areas 'primarily by urban-based participants whose transgression, politics and lifestyles threatened established rural interests' (Woods 2011a: 111). Examples include protests over access rights, the right to nomadic lifestyles and environmental concerns. Social constructions of the countryside and 'rural people' are central to many of these contests. While some activities and people are seen as complicit with idyllic or traditional visions of the countryside, others are very much 'out of place' (Cresswell 1996; Woods 2011a).

In a series of publications (Parker 1996, 2001, 2006; Parker and Ravenscroft 2001), Gavin Parker uses the example of public access to the British countryside to explore how the language of citizenship has been deployed 'to "see off" challenges to interest-based positions and rural imaginations' (Parker 2006: 11). Debates over rights to the countryside (ostensibly between the 'right to roam' and the property rights of landowners) draw not only upon the law but upon various historic, environmental and social contingencies. Drawing specifically on the example of the 'Countryside Code', a set of guidelines written to encourage responsible behaviour when visiting the countryside, Parker (2006) suggests that it represents semi-formal ordering of contingent rural citizenship based on what is deemed acceptable behaviour in the countryside. This is enforced through daily performances of visiting the countryside, with those conforming to the code viewed as 'good citizens' in comparison with irresponsible, anti-social or even criminal people who trespass, leave gates open or drop litter (Yarwood and Gardner 2000). As the code is aimed at visitors, Parker argues that it delineates separate countryside citizenship for 'rural' and 'non-rural groups'.

Quite who is viewed as 'rural' or 'non-rural' is, however, open to debate that goes to the crux of rural citizenship. Hunting with hounds and 'raves' were subject to much public scrutiny in Britain in the 1980s and 1990s. Both were pursued by minorities, were disruptive to others and caused widespread outrage, yet the 1994 Criminal Justice Act outlawed the latter and strengthened the former by criminalizing protest on private land (Sibley 1994). The same Act also limited the ability of Travellers to camp and move about the countryside (Halfacree 1996a, 1996b). The Act reflected the right of people to practise legitimate rural sports (DETR 2000), but not the right to peaceful protest against these sports; equally it privileged an idyllic view of the countryside free from inappropriate intrusion and noise (rave music was famously described as being a 'succession of repetitive beats'). As Parker (2001) argues, these reflect a view of country citizenship that is contingent on certain hegemonic and historic rural values. The idea of (rural) 'citizenship is both defined and enforced downwards by the state and claimed upwards by individuals and groups' (Woods 2006a: 459). As a consequence some activities may be viewed as 'rural' and worthy of rural citizenry, others are not.

The subsequent ban on hunting led to demonstrations that came from *within* rather than *outside* rural places (Woods 2011a). Protests by rural citizens in favour of hunting adopted the language of rights to argue for both hunting and the wider status of rural areas. Specifically (Woods 2006a) it was demonstrated that these protests centred on three sets of rights: the decline of rural services and the social rights associated with them (Box 8.1); the political right to demand state intervention to protect rural interests, especially the livelihoods of farmers; and, conversely, the social, cultural and civil rights to follow particular lifestyles, such as hunting, without regulation from the state.

Box 8.1 CITIZENSHIP, RIGHTS AND RURALITY

Tonts and Larsen (2002) have used a human rights perspective to critique service provision in rural Australia (Figure 8.1), arguing that 'as governments withdraw, or fail to provide, certain services . . . the human rights of rural people are diminished' (2002: 132). They note that geographies of human rights have tended to examine differences between countries, an approach that has neglected variance at the sub-national scale. Remote areas of rural Australia have high levels of socio-economic disadvantage that has been exacerbated by service decline and rationalization due to cuts in government funding. Further, towns lose political power as they are subjected to centralized decision making (Gray and Lawrence 2001). These assertions are supported by an examination of housing, education and health using the framework of the UN's International Covenant on Human Rights (ICHR). In terms of housing, they contend that the quantity and quality of public housing in rural areas is worse than in urban areas. In 1998 (Tonts and Larsen 2002), between 1,200 and 1,800 aboriginal people in the Northern Territories were accommodated in only 183 houses and 70 tin sheds. In terms of health, there is a chronic shortage of doctors, hospitals and other medical facilities in remote areas; consequently male death rates in capital cities were 6 per cent lower than in 'small rural centres' and 17 per cent lower than in 'remote' communities (Figure 8.1). Poor resourcing of rural schools, especially in information technology, has meant that 'rural children perform less well in basic competencies, have fewer subject options and experience more limited career options than those living in metropolitan areas' (Tonts and Larsen 2002: 138; see also Ribchester and Edwards (1999) for a UK context).

In all three areas, inequalities are detrimental to the universal language of the ICHR. Consequently Tonts and Lawson (2002: 139) argue that these disparities might be 'constructed as human rights issues' and, in this light, people living in remote rural

Figure 8.1 Roebourne, a remote settlement in Western Australia. (Photo: Christina Birdsall-Jones)

areas may be seen to lack full status as citizens. The authors suggest that the language of rights might be used to prompt better provision of rural services. In the UK, 'rural proofing' was introduced in 1999 as a mandatory part of the policy process, which means that, as policies are developed, policy makers should systematically:

- consider whether their policy is likely to have a different impact in rural areas, because of particular rural circumstances or needs;
- make proper assessment of those impacts, if these are likely to be significant;
- adjust the policy, where appropriate, with solutions to meet rural needs and circumstances.

Continued

More recently the Department for Agriculture, Food and Rural Affairs (DEFRA) clarified that:

> While rural proofing requires policy-makers to adjust their policies to take due account of rural impacts, it does *not* require exactly the same outcome or the provision of exactly the same level of service in rural as in urban locations. This would not be practical in many cases, as the costs would be prohibitive and in any case rural communities do not necessarily expect this. They do, however, rightly expect that policies should be sufficiently flexible to apply fairly in their areas and to deliver quality services that meet their everyday needs. It is the job of policy-makers to design policies that are capable of achieving this.
>
> (DEFRA 2012)

This gives policy makers some scope to deliver different, perhaps voluntary services, according to the needs of a rather nebulously defined 'rural community'. The term 'community' can be used to brush over the diverse experiences and needs of rural citizens but probably represents the loudest, most powerful voices.

Indeed, many issues of inequality between rural citizens reflect broader social differences. Hogg and Carrington (1998: 167) note 'race, not rurality, is the touchstone of local experiences' in Australia and, as Tonts and Lawson (2002) reveal in their analysis, it is not just rural Australians, but rural aboriginal Australians who are excluded most from health, education and services. Indigenous people living in urban places also suffer disproportionately from poor housing, health, education and employment opportunities. As Hoggart (1990) urges, it is important to look through the veneer of the rural setting and examine the social and economic factors that shape it and the experiences of citizenship in remote places.

Some pressure groups have used the language of rights to argue that rural citizens and places should have the same access to services and opportunities as people living in urban areas (Woods 2006a) and, just as in urban politics, a wide range of citizen actions have been undertaken to pursue these rights, ranging from formal political participation to direct action:

> 'some, like the Countryside Alliance, combine mainstream lobbying with law-abiding mass demonstrations; others—the Confederation Paysanne, Farmers for Action, the Rural Rebels—engage in non-violent direct action that pushes the boundaries of legality'.
>
> (Woods 2003: 315–16)

Differences in tactics and actions reflect the diversity found across any social movement (see Chapter 6) but what is shared between these approaches, and is perhaps unique to rural movements, is that rural identity is used as a cohesive force (Woods 2003, 2006a). Organizations such as the Countryside Alliance have positioned themselves as 'The Voice' of the countryside and an excluded minority in respect to the largely urban population of the UK (Figure 8.2). Closer analysis, though, reveals that particular views of rurality and rural identity are privileged in their campaigns (Cloke 2005). Woods (2006a: 464) notes that in defending liberty and livelihood the organization 'subverts the conventional association of citizenship with the city by positioning the countryside as the repository of a more elemental citizenship' that is linked to land and soil.

The idea that rural citizenship is somehow more 'natural' means that rural places can also provide spaces for new or alternative forms of society and citizenry (Valentine 2001). In part, this is due to isolation but, more significantly, because the countryside is widely imagined, rightly or wrongly, as a counter to consumerist and impersonal urban lifestyles (Short 1991, 1996; Halfacree 1993, 2006; Bunce 1994). Consequently, rural places have formed the basis for separatist communities with their own forms of membership, structures of decision making and, by implication, forms of communitarian citizenship that have been based on, amongst other things, counter-cultural ideas (Halfacree 2006, 2009); religion (Philo 1997; Tonts 2001); gender and sexuality (Valentine 2001; Browne 2011); political extremism (Woods 2006a); sustainable living (Halfacree 2007; Bailey *et al.* 2010); and nomadic lifestyles (Halfacree 1996b). Although these groups have been capable of achieving a degree of autonomy, they are often temporary in nature and prone to disintegration due to internal tensions, state legislation and a loss of intensity (Halfacree 1999) and perhaps fail to offer a lasting alternative to conventional structures of citizenship.

Figure 8.2 Rural pressure groups such as the UK's Countryside Alliance have positioned rural citizens as a cultural minority whose rights are threatened by an urban majority (Photo: Author)

In a series of studies, Woods (1998, 2003, 2006b, 2008) highlights the complexities of associating a particular form of rural identity with broader notions of rights and citizenship. Despite the rhetoric of groups that purport to campaign for a 'single rural voice', it is clear that 'models of rural communities as stable, hierarchically structured, paternalistic societies are no longer sustainable' (Woods 2006a: 468) and consequently citizens identify with many types of rurality and rural identity.

Landscapes

Rural landscapes have frequently been connected to identity (Storey 2001) and have also been used to instil citizenship through various forms of outdoor recreation and education (Lorimer 1997). Gruffudd (1996) reveals that in the inter-war period an emphasis was placed on nature studies and rural folklore in the teaching of citizenship in Wales:

> the genius of rural life, with its wealth of local knowledge, local history, local sentiment, and its cultivation of individual tastes and

> imagination, needs something more than the application to it of cast-iron and artificial methods evolved largely from our town life and town civilisation.
>
> (Welsh Department 1922, quoted in Gruffudd 1996: 416)

Geographers such as H. J. Fleure called for a greater understanding of local regions:

> 'our region serves as a mirror, a miniature if you like, of the evolution of our civilisation. Let us spread the feeling that in addition to being citizens of our region we are citizens of civilisation'.
>
> (Fleure 1916, quoted in Gruffudd 1996: 418)

He put this into practice by calling for children to engage actively with the Regional Survey Movement led by Patrick Geddes to:

> help foster social renewal, inculcate citizenship, and generate a spiritual awareness of place and its historical development . . . the development of a 'loving familiarity' with, and an objective understanding of, the home region, and an awareness of the networks that combined to create it and the individual's place within them.
>
> (Gruffudd 1996: 417–18)

While focused on British regions, the project was aimed at developing 'world citizenship' by furthering understanding of the ways in which local places were connected to the world (see also Marsden 2001a) through field enquiry.

Similarly, after the Second World War, active exploration and understanding of the countryside was seen as a way of teaching citizenship and national identity. David Matless (1996, 2001) reveals how planners such as John Dower (who in 1945 chaired the Standing Committee on National Parks in the UK) and W. J. Morris who, in his 1942 publication *The Future Citizen and his Surroundings* with its cover picture of children on a nature ramble, argued that an appreciation of landscape and rural history was part of:

> the endeavour to make of the pupil a good citizen – ideally a citizen of the world, but in any case a citizen of his own country . . . [the child] . . . should be taught impatience with things unnecessarily drab or sordid, and should be infected with a desire to remove or improve them.
>
> (Morris, quoted in Matless 1996: 433–4)

A reinvigoration of Scouting, youth hostelling (see also Lorimer 1997) and other outdoor pursuits, enabled young people to access rural places and develop the kind of appreciative citizenship envisaged by Morris and others (Matless 1996). Those who did not have the eye or ear to appreciate landscape ('day trippers') were often positioned as the loud, ignorant antithesis of these citizens, enforcing the importance of an educated engagement with rurality (Matless 1997; Brace 2000; Parker 2006). These values are reflected in Arthur Ransome's (1934) novel *Coot Club* where a group of young people concerned with the protection of bird habitats are drawn into a conflict with noisy 'Hullabaloos' or day trippers who are ignorant of local wildlife.

The countryside is still used as a training ground for citizenship. Many organizations, such as the Scouts (Mills 2013), use rural places to prepare young people for citizenship through country activities including camps or hikes (see also Chapter 7). The Duke of Edinburgh's (DoE) Award, for example, is a three-stage voluntary award undertaken by young people in Commonwealth countries that aims 'to inspire, guide and support young people in their self-development' (www.dofe.org – last accessed 6 August 2013). To achieve these goals, participants undertake physical, voluntary and skill-based activities but, for many participants, the highlight of the award is a hiking and camping expedition made in 'wild country'. Here the challenge of walking and living in an unfamiliar, rural environment, often a considerable distance from support, is used to test skills such as teamworking, leadership, self-sufficiency, fitness, enquiry, resolve and confidence, all seen as valuable in the self-development of future citizens. The annual Ten Tors Challenge also uses a rural environment to challenge young people and develop skills needed to be soldier-citizens (Box 8.2).

Rurality to nature

The sections above have considered how ideas of rurality have influenced citizenship. In common with other studies of citizenship, the major focus has been on *people* and their social, cultural or political relationships with various *human* communities. Human associations with and within 'natural' communities have often been ignored within conceptualizations of citizenship. Yet geographers have taken an increasing interest in the relationship between humans and nature (Anderson 1995; Wolch and

Box 8.2 THE TEN TORS CHALLENGE

The Ten Tors Challenge is organized by the British Army and is a challenging two-day walking expedition across Dartmoor National Park in the south-west of the UK. Teams are required to complete a 35-, 45- or 55-mile course and, in doing so, visit checkpoints located on ten of Dartmoor's tors (granite outcrops of rock). They are also required to camp overnight and carry all the equipment they need to do this and to walk safely and independently on Dartmoor. The event was initially organized as a training exercise for junior leaders in the army but was opened to civilian teams (or patrols) of 16–18-year-olds in 1960. Today, the Ten Tors Challenge attracts 2,400 entrants aged between 14 and 19 who walk in teams of six that are drawn from schools, colleges, cadet forces, Scout or Guide troops and other youth groups (Figure 8.3).

Figure 8.3 Teenagers undertaking the army's Ten Tors Challenge across Dartmoor National Park, UK (Photo: Emma Quigley)

Continued

The walk occurs in challenging terrain and conditions (Yarwood 2010b, 2012b) and so young people must draw upon navigation skills, fitness, teamwork, endurance and determination. Although most Ten Tors participants do not go on to join the military, these qualities are also valued in soldier-citizens (Woodward 2004) and the event gives the opportunity for young people to test themselves in the same way as soldiers in difficult rural terrain. It should also be pointed out that the nature of the landscape means that the event requires a high level of support to run successfully and safely. This is largely provided by many civilian volunteers who train teams, assess their progress and provide safety cover through, for example, mountain rescue teams (Yarwood 2010b). The rural setting of the Ten Tors therefore provides many opportunities for active citizenship.

Emel 1998; Philo and Wilbert 2000; Castree 2005) with many commentators questioning how ideas of citizenship can be extended to non-humans (Turner 1986; Anderson 2000; Delaney 2001; Dobson 2003; Bullen and Whitehead 2005; Leach *et al.* 2005; Barker 2010). The second part of the chapter engages with this challenge and considers how these ideas have been manifest in ideas of environmental citizenship.

ENVIRONMENTAL CITIZENSHIP

'Environmental citizenship' has been recognized as a distinct form of citizenship by some commentators (Hawthorne and Alabaster 1999; Dobson 2003, 2010; Dobson and Saiz 2005; Fletcher and Potts 2007). This idea emphasizes:

> 'pro-environmental behaviour, in public and private, driven by a belief in fairness of the distribution of environmental goods, in participation, and in the co-creation of sustainability policy'.
>
> (Dobson 2010: 2)

The emphasis here is on a form of active citizenship that seeks to change personal behaviour and to influence policy makers towards sustainable living and development (Dobson 2010). Dobson goes on to suggest that an environmental citizen:

> believes that environmental sustainability is a common good; is moved by other-regarding motivations; believes that ethical and moral knowledge is as important as techno-scientific knowledge; believes that other people's environmental rights engender environmental responsibilities; believes that these responsibilities are due not only to one's neighbours or fellow nationals but also to distant strangers; is aware that private environmental-related actions can have public environmental-related impacts.
>
> (Dobson 2010: 3)

A number of studies have attempted to focus on environmental behaviour and what prompts citizens to adopt this kind of conduct (see, for example, Fletcher and Potts 2007; Barr *et al.* 2011a, 2011b; Evans 2011; Harris 2011; Mazzarino *et al.* 2011; Reid *et al.* 2011; Green *et al.* 2012). Hawthorne and Alabaster (1999) used multivariate statistical analysis to model the factors that influence an individual's decision to act as an environmental citizen. They conclude that:

> an environmental citizen is therefore likely to be a member of an environmental group . . . be emotional about environmental issues, have a religious affiliation, be a middle-class parent, have an internal LOC [locus of control] and a sense of personal responsibility for the solution of environmental problems.
>
> (Hawthorne and Alabaster 1999: 41)

For some authors, the environmental citizen is someone who acts within 'the context of the state's environmental policy' and 'is focused on achieving the environmental goals determined by a state' (McKinley and Fletcher 2012: 840). While many citizens, and probably many of those described by Hawthorne and Alabaster (1999), would no doubt fall into this category, these kinds of actions align the environmental citizenship with models of citizenship that view the nation-state as the key determinant of citizenship (Smith 2000).

Certainly, such a focus makes it possible to examine the relationships between the state and environmental citizens, be it efforts of the state to regulate, educate (Hawthorne and Alabaster 1999; Dobson 2003; Bullen and Whitehead 2005) or 'nudge' (Jones *et al.* 2011a) the environmental behaviour of its citizens. It makes it possible to examine how decisions are made through emerging systems of environmental governance that enrol state, private and voluntary actors and to consider the ways in which the state responds to environmental campaign groups.

The figure of the responsible sustainable citizen has been adopted by many international and state bodies to support environmental policy. Bullen and Whitehead (2005) go on to argue that such actions reflect a 'post-cosmopolitan' citizenship that recognizes the importance of global dialogue and international obligations as well as the significance of formal state and international mechanisms such as Agenda 21 (an international agreement that encourages environmental initiatives at international, national and, significantly, local levels) that can be acted upon by citizens in their own localities to achieve global environmental change ('think globally, act locally').

Dobson (2003) also suggests that post-cosmopolitan, ecological citizenship is characterized in four ways. First, its obligations are non-reciprocal. He argues that globalization reflects imbalances of power that allow some (usually first world) nations and political bodies to inflict harm on other places, often at a distance (for example, greater emission of carbon dioxide from developed countries leads to global warming and greater impacts on poorer countries). The burden of ecological citizenship should, therefore, fall on the nations and political formations that do most ecological harm. Second, he argues that ecological citizenship emphasizes justice and, in order to achieve this, 'secondary virtues' of care and compassion. Third, as these virtues can be learnt and applied in the domestic arena (for example, recycling waste), ecological citizenship applies to private as well as public places. Finally, Dobson stresses that post-cosmopolitan citizenship goes beyond the state, even though the state can contribute to the creation of liberal, ecological citizens through, for example, formal education.

Yet, for some, this concept of environmental citizenship does not go far enough (Parker 1999b; Leach *et al.* 2005). Bullen and Whitehead (2005) argue that these forms of citizenship, which often rely on active individuals or voluntary groups doing their bit for the environment, reflect an extension of the shadow state to encompass environmental as well as welfare provision (see Chapter 4 for a discussion of the latter). Given that the shadow state has encouraged middle-class volunteers to participate in providing welfare services, it is hardly surprising that the environmental citizen described by Hawthorne and Alabaster is also middle class, well educated and empowered. It goes without saying that local involvement in environmental issues by some of these citizens often reflects a desire to maintain power and property rather than a commitment to green politics, as reflected, for example, in NIMBY protests against the construction of wind farms in rural places (Walker *et al.* 2007; Munday *et al.* 2011). Two main criticisms have been levelled at this form of environmental citizenship.

First, it may be argued that these forms of environmental or ecological citizenship do little to encourage meaningful citizen participation in environmental affairs. Instead, some environmental campaign groups, often in opposition to state policy, have established new ways of making decisions and acting together in order to achieve sustainable outcomes (Box 8.3).

One tactic has been to act as consumer-citizens (Parker 1999b) and to use the marketplace to register protest or concern and, in doing so, to influence the outcome of market-based processes that impact on the environment. These have included ethical consumption (see Chapter 5) as well as buying shares in companies (allowing protestors as shareholders to attend annual general meetings (AGMs), ask questions and vote as shareholders) or targeting companies in order to persuade them that their contracts were environmentally unsuitable (Parker 1999b). These moves help to position protestors as 'good', law-abiding citizens but suggest that responsibility for environmental governance rests with the marketplace and private companies rather than the state. In other instances, the occupation of space has been used not only to challenge state environmental policies and actions but to establish new spaces of citizenship and participation (Halfacree 1996b, 1999, 2006; Routledge 1997; Woods 2003).

A second challenge to state-centred visions of environmental citizenship comes from the way that society and nature are conceptualized. Rather than viewing nature and society as two distinct elements, many geographers are seeking to understand them in hybrid terms (Whatmore 2005). A cow, for example, is a 'natural' being but also something that has been bred to meet human needs and is managed by farmers who draw upon different technologies, knowledge and practices (Sellick and

Box 8.3 TRANSITION TOWNS: NEW FORMS OF ENVIRONMENTAL CITIZENSHIP?

The Transition Network was established in response to concerns about climate change and reaching peak oil production (Hopkins 2008). Drawing on an intellectual and activist tradition of permaculture movements and global environmental perspectives (Bailey *et al.* 2010), its aim is to develop pathways that enable communities to move away from consuming high levels of fossil fuel and towards futures based around relocalization, low energy consumption and better community resilience. In order to achieve these aims, Transition Towns are encouraged to identify issues that are of pertinence to their community (Table 8.1; Bailey *et al.* 2010). The first 'Transition Town' was established in Totnes, Devon, UK in 2005 and since then the initiative has spread globally to nearly 450 sites, mainly in first world countries (Transition Network 2012). These initiatives have dispersed in a 'rhizomic' fashion (Woods 2007), characterized by 'a spontaneously-forming international network of re-localisation initiatives combined with strong embedding in host communities through the use of participatory methods, voluntary involvement, mass communications, and psychological persuasion tactics' (Bailey *et al.* 2010: 596).

Local steering groups are a key part of the establishment and management of Transition Towns. Brangwyn and Hopkins (2008), cited in Bailey *et al.* (2010), identify 12 stages in this process:

1. Set up a steering group and design its demise from the outset.
2. Raise awareness.
3. Lay the foundations.
4. Organize a great unleashing.
5. Form sub-groups.
6. Use open space.
7. Develop visible practical manifestations of the project.
8. Facilitate the great reskilling.
9. Build a bridge to local government.
10. Honour the elders.

11. Let it go where it wants to go.
12. Create an energy descent plan.

(Brangwyn and Hopkins 2008, cited in Bailey *et al.* 2010: 600)

Although groups aim to build bridges with existing government (stage 9), this is some way down their list of actions. The intention is that these groups are grass-roots organizations that operate outside rather than within existing government structures. As such, they may offer the potential to create new platforms of governance and citizen participation on the basis of environmental concern

Table 8.1 Activities in Totnes Transition Town (Source: Bailey *et al.* 2010)

Working group	Main activities
Building and housing	Eco-construction Co-housing
Economics and livelihoods	Local currency: the Totnes pound ATMOS: sustainable business park Oil vulnerability audits with local companies
Education	Transition tales with local schools to create vision of powered-down society Public future scenario workshops
Health and well-being	Directory of complementary health practitioners Collections of illness-to-wellness stories Discussion group on NHS and sustainability
Heart and soul	Meetings to discuss events and experiences Meditation meetings
Local government	Building of links with town, district and county council to support and encourage inclusion of climate change and peak oil in decision making
The arts	Events utilizing the arts to explore peak oil, climate change and transition
Transport	Totnes cycling group Totnes Rickshaw Company

Continued

and action. They attempt to maintain an apolitical approach but, equally, to build up sufficient momentum and support that, when it is necessary to negotiate, they have a strong voice that becomes difficult for government to ignore. According to Bob Jessop (2003: 146–7) self-governing, autonomous groups are required to behave in four ways to be successful:

> 1. adopt practices that reduce the complexity of the world, are congruent to real world practices and are relevant to the goals of actors;
> 2. develop capacities for social learning, responsibility and action;
> 3. build methods that coordinate actions across a wide social and spatial spectrum;
> 4. establish a common world view to regulate individual action and to develop a system of governance to control key players' actions and expectations.
>
> (Jessop 2003)

It is possible to identify several ways in which these steering groups have achieved these principles. They include the use of psychological models aimed at modifying behaviour and setting up 'Parallel Public Infrastructure' to provide

> shadow economic, social and technological infrastructures in readiness for the failure of existing systems. These include infrastructure to support locally-produced products, energy storage, public transport, currencies, seed storage, grains, reforestation, general municipal services, information sharing, and shortened supply chains.
>
> (Bailey *et al.* 2010: 599)

These, in turn, rely on the ability of activists to develop a common world-view that is based on 'spatial constructions of re-localisation that use selective readings of evidence about peak oil to posit a homogenised view of global resource scarcity alongside encouraging each initiative to develop its own vision of a post peak-oil world' (Bailey *et al.* 2010: 596).

These views have helped to establish and spread Transition initiatives in a 'rhizomic' manner (Woods *et al.* 2013). Currently the Transition Movement runs independently of big business and local government, imbuing its membership with a sense of local empowerment and global citizenship. Despite its early successes, questions have been raised about whether it can maintain a position outside the political, or indeed corporate, mainstream and whether the various discourses it seeks to unite may, as Halfacree has noted in occupation sites (Halfacree 1999), challenge and unravel the movement (Bailey *et al.* 2010).

Recently the political accountability of the Transition Town movement has been questioned in Totnes, where the movement was founded. In 2012, the multinational company Costa Coffee withdrew plans to establish a café in the town in face of opposition from some local shopkeepers and the Transition Town Totnes (TTT). However, the media also reported that some people wanted the chain in the town and felt that TTT was acting as an unelected representative of the town and ignoring wider opinion. To counter this, 'Take Back Totnes' has been established to counter TTT's apparent (and unelected) influence in the town. Shove and Walker (2007) argue that more analysis is needed as regards on whose authority and behalf these citizens act.

Yarwood 2013). According to this ontology, it is hard to separate nature from society. Instead, people, animals, nature, technology and knowledge are part of intricate, interdependent networks (Thrift 1994; Philo and Wilbert 2000; Latour 2005; Allen 2011).

Bullen and Whitehead (2005) argue that citizenship should also be conceptualized in these terms. Rather than being viewed separately from nature, people should be recognized *in relation* to it. Consequently they call for an 'open or hybrid form' of citizenship, which recognizes the interdependence of these different elements. They argue that 'it is not simply that we are responsible for the non-human world but that it is this world that makes citizenship possible' (p.508).

This challenges us to consider citizenship beyond the traditional notion of political or social communities and to consider citizens' relations with much wider communities of nature (Rose 2007). These relationships may be played out through existing political structures and therefore be contested (Box 8.4) (Leach *et al.* 2005: 5). In South Africa, for example, former President Mbeki's questioning of conventional science meant that is was difficult for citizens to access anti-retroviral drugs to treat AIDS. This led to groups, such as the Treatment Action Campaign (TAC), deploying arguments about human rights to mobilize grass-roots support in working-class, black communities to gain access to medicines (Robins 2005). Their court victories were about 'a struggle for poor people to access drugs but it was also a campaign to assert the rights of citizens to scientific knowledge; a post-apartheid expression of health citizenship' (Robins 2005: 128).

It also challenges us to take seriously the role of non-human actors in networks of citizenship. This is not only in the ways that they impact

Box 8.4 BIOCITIZENSHIP

Kezia Barker (2010) argues that citizenship is shaped by a person's biology and the organisms and viruses that affect it:

> this political co-shaping encompasses those viruses that thrive in the moisture in our throats and lungs, the subject of biosecurity concerns over SARS, avian- or swine-flu. It extends to those entangled entities that cling on outside the epidermis of the human body: in our hair, the creases of our skin and clothes, caught up in our material possessions, the corners of our luggage, the warmth of our gardens, all those non-humans with which we, knowingly or unknowingly, have relationships.
>
> (Barker 2010: 353)

Rose (2007) refers to these relations as a form of 'biocitizenship'. One way of illustrating their significance is to consider some of the measures that states take to ensure biosecurity.

In New Zealand, strict measures have been taken to prevent unwanted species or organisms entering the country (Barker 2010) to conserve native species that, in turn, contribute to fostering national identity (Genus and Rogers-Hayden 2005; Turner 2007; Henry 2011): 'native species – including our national icons (the kiwi, silver fern, and koru) – and their supporting habitats and ecosystems help define us as a nation' (Biosecurity Council 2002: 15, quoted in Barker 2010: 355). Particular care is taken at customs to ensure that unwanted organisms do not cross into the state on the bodies of travellers. Checks, for example, are made to ensure that footwear or camping equipment is clean and unlikely to harbour spores or viruses. The import of food is prohibited and passengers, as is the case in most countries, are observed for signs of illness. These symbiotic relationships have also led to obligations for people to act responsibly as biosecure citizens to maintain biosecurity by, for example, reporting organisms 'not normally seen or otherwise detected in New Zealand' (Barker 2010: 354). Yet, as Barker goes on, these ideas are contested and she notes that while some people harboured illegal, non-native plants in their private gardens, others offered to take part in voluntary spraying to eradicate crops.

upon citizenship but also how they are placed as citizens in hybrid networks. Foxes, stags, hounds and horses have been enrolled into different political networks that have opposed or supported hunting (Woods 1998). Pictorial or statistical representations of these animals have been used to support their place within the practices of hunting. Some commentators consider such actions to be a form of *post-citizenship* that goes beyond concern for solely human rights (Lowe and Ginsberg 2002; Verdonk 2012). It opens up consideration of animal *rights* and offers the exciting prospect of enrolling animals and other non-human actors more closely into advocacy and action networks. This presents a radically different view of citizenship and, as Chapter 7 also suggested, demonstrates that the idea of citizenship has undergone profound change to embrace all elements of society and, now, nature.

CONCLUSIONS

In some ways rural and environmental citizenship mirror wider debates about other forms of citizenship discussed in this volume and it could be argued that they just happen to occur in rural areas or be about environmental issues (Woods 2006a: 466). Seen in these terms, this chapter provides a fitting illustration of many of the issues already discussed elsewhere in this book. Yet two broader points emerge from the discussion of these themes.

First, terms such as rural, sustainability, nature and environment are used widely in an effort to fix the identity of and mobilize citizens. Thus people who consider themselves 'rural people' may be coerced to engage with a variety of issues and rights that are broadly associated with the countryside. Similarly, concepts of environment or sustainability motivate a range of issues from recycling household waste to the occupation of sites. Recognizing the diversity of identities and actions under the banner of 'rural' or the 'environment' contributes to understandings of citizenship as multilayered and fluid (Woods 2006a). Understanding how these ideas are socially constructed and performed, both in a daily context and at specific events or actions, will contribute to wider understandings of citizenship and space. There is a need to expand the scope of this work for, as this chapter has reflected, most of the literature on citizenship and rurality has been written in a Western context. Clearly perspectives from other parts of the world would be valuable in developing these ideas.

Second, perspectives from post-human geography have the potential to significantly extend the remit of citizenship studies. This work draws attention to the way in which citizenship is co-constructed relationally by nature and society. Significantly, these understandings impact on many areas of political, civic and social life:

> The politicisation of symbiotic individuality has implications beyond the domain of biosecurity, as our post-human condition is increasingly the focus for identity construction and subject to governance in diverse arenas such as xenotransplantation, genetic modification and food consumption, biotechnology, and domestic animal husbandry.
>
> (Barker 2010: 353)

Practices such as forensic policing, bio-tattooing and bio-profiling offer new opportunities for political control, spatial regulation and the development of 'enclave spaces' that exclude citizens and strangers (Sidaway 2007; Turner 2007).

FURTHER READING

Gavin Parker has written widely on citizenship in a rural context, especially in regards to access (2001, 2006). His article on consumer-citizens (1999b) in *Space and Polity* provides a helpful model that distinguishes between active and activist citizens. Mike Woods' work has also explored themes of rurality and citizenship, focusing on rural politics and governance. His (2006) chapter in the *Handbook of Rural Studies* provides a critical commentary on these themes and sets an agenda for continuing research. Andrew Dobson's (2003) *Citizenship and the Environment* and subsequent work examine how individual citizens engage with the environment through personal actions and political networks. Kezia Barker's (2010) study of biosecurity in *Transactions of the Institute of British Geographers* exemplifies how post-human approaches are contributing to knowledge and debate in this area.

9

W(H)ITHER CITIZENSHIP?

This book has attempted to draw together work on the geographies of citizenship. It has explored what is meant by citizenship and why understandings of place and space are important to changing conceptions of citizenship. In doing so, it also set out to demonstrate why citizenship is a key concept in geography.

It has viewed citizenship through different spatial lenses and has variously critiqued, dismissed, supported and modified the whole idea. Within the confines of this volume alone, the study of citizenship has drawn upon diverse topics that range from apathy to Zapatista. This book has described ethical citizens, ethnic citizens, global citizens, excluded citizens, activist citizens, active citizens, sexual citizens, to name but a few. Box 9.1 charts *some* of the ways that geographers and other social scientists have understood citizenship. It is this sheer diversity of topics and ideas that makes citizenship exciting and relevant to geography. Citizenship is no longer just a term used to describe the relationship of somebody to a nation-state. It has been variously viewed 'as a legal category, as a claim, as an identity, as a tool in nation building and as an ideal' (Staeheli 2011: 393).

Yet, the book does not claim to be a comprehensive survey of geography and citizenship. Doubtless many areas have been missed. There is certainly a need to move beyond the largely Western ideas that have shaped citizenship. The book has nevertheless brought to the surface a rich vein of theoretically and empirically rich material that has sometimes been overlooked by geographers.

Box 9.1 A GLOSSARY OF CITIZENSHIP

Citizenship is fluid, contested and rarely static. It is therefore difficult and unhelpful to try and categorize people as particular kinds of citizen. Nevertheless many authors have used different terminologies of citizenship in order to analyse particular social, political and cultural issues. Needless to say, the following list is not exhaustive but it tries to summarize some of the ways in which citizenship has been used by geographers and other social scientists in this book.

Active citizenship: implies that citizenship must be actively sought or performed (Ghose 2005) rather than passively accepted. Duties are emphasized over rights and, consequently, the term has been used in policies that have encouraged people to engage in local state-led voluntary activity (Kearns 1995; Fyfe and Milligan 2003a). The terms 'public' and 'communitarian' citizens have also been used to describe those who engage in these activities (Mullard 2004).

The anti-citizen: a term used by David Matless (1996) to describe those who do not share hegemonic views of citizenship.

Biocitizenship: recognizes the symbiotic associations between citizenship, people and non-human actors such as animals, plants, bacteria and viruses. These are often played out in debates about biosecurity (Barker 2010).

The consumer citizen: can refer to a withdrawal from politics and the use of consumption to maintain privileges (Dagger 2002) but, more widely, is applied to people who use consumptive practices, such as buying Fairtrade goods, to achieve political goals (Hertz 2001; Klein 2001; Clarke *et al.* 2007a).

Cosmopolitan citizenship: recognizes that political and cultural identities extend beyond the formal borders of the state (Heater 2002; Linklater 2002). This idea focuses on the emotional and affective dimensions of citizenship rather than its legal aspects (Jackson 2010), but also recognizes the significance of political actions at a global level (Desforges 2004; Routledge *et al.* 2007).

Continued

Denizenship: is used to refer to non-national residents of a country. They may have social and civil rights in that state, but no political rights (Hammer 1990). Shearing and Wood (2003) have expanded the term to describe how people may be affiliated to different forms of governance (e.g. a member of a club, a customer of a shopping centre).

Dual or plural citizenship: holding or acquiring formal rights of citizenship from one or more nation-states at the same time (Samers 2010).

Environmental citizenship: a form of citizenship 'based on the active participation of citizens in moving towards sustainability' (Dobson 2010: 2) either via the state (Fletcher and Potts 2007) or through more radical channels (Bullen and Whitehead 2005).

Ethical or moral citizenship: a willingness, often shaped by religious or political principles, to engage in society through a sense of 'what is right' rather than duties prescribed by the state (Cloke *et al.* 2007).

The independent citizen: is one committed to 'rational individualism' through market forces. Neo-liberal capitalism, rather than state intervention, is viewed as the best determinant of choice, expression and decision making. Self is prioritized over society (Mullard 2004).

Insurgent citizenship: new forms of citizenship and citizens that challenge established power structures, often through forcible opposition to lawful authority (Holsten 2008; Painter and Jeffrey 2009).

Multilevel/layered citizenship: citizens are simultaneously members of different political communities that operate at different spatial scales (e.g. local, regional, national, etc.) (Painter 2002). It also acknowledges that citizens can have multiple memberships of different social groups (based on, for example, gender, ethnic identity, etc.). It has also been referred to as 'flexible citizenship' by some commentators (Lepofsky and Fraser 2003). Desforges *et al.* (2005) argue this leads to 'multi-scalar' rights and responsibilities that span spaces from the local to the global.

Passive citizenship: the citizen is the passive receiver of the benefits and privileges of citizenship. The receipt of rights is emphasized over the fulfilment of duties (Desmoyers-Davis 2001). Mullard (2004) refers to the 'entitled' citizen as one who has access to particular formal and informal rights.

The prosthetic citizen: a term coined by Tim Cresswell (2009) to acknowledge that citizens are reliant on features (or prosthetics) of the urban environment (such as transport) to be functioning citizens.

Rural citizenship: refers to the ways in which social constructions, performances or structures of rurality impact on ideas of citizenship (Cheshire and Woods 2009). It has also been applied to discuss issues specific to rural areas, including hunting (Woods 2008) and access (Parker 2001).

Sexual citizenship: focuses attention on the sexual, usually heteronormative, foundations that underpin citizenship and can exclude citizens who do not conform to them (Bell and Binnie 2000, 2006). Bell also uses the notion of the 'citizen pervert' to describe someone who not only practises 'scary sex' but also transgresses the boundaries of private and public space (Bell 1995).

Transnational citizenship: recognizes that citizenship crosses the borders of the state and shifts attention away from the container of the nation-state and towards flows of people, material and technologies that circulate across and through different national spaces (Favell 2001).

Although it is difficult to pin a single definition on citizenship, this very ambiguity makes the concept valuable to academics and activists. While citizenship has often been associated with gendered, Western visions of society (McEwan 2005), it can also be deployed to understand how those with little power or living in non-Western countries forge relationships with other people in other places (Isin 2012b). Geographical understandings of citizenship have become crucial to understanding these new and emerging relationships.

THE VALUE OF GEOGRAPHY TO CITIZENSHIP

Geographical theorizations of spatiality are leading to a greater appreciation of the role of space and place in the formation, contestation and performance of citizenship (Desforges *et al.* 2005; Staeheli 2011). This book has attempted to identify how different spaces are important to ideas of citizenship. Territories, regions, localities, networks, sites, bodies, ruralities, mobilities, landscapes, homes, public and private spaces all have important associations with the way that citizenship is given meaning, reproduced, contested and played out on a daily basis. It is important, though, to remember that these spaces are not mutually exclusive.

Citizens are simultaneously members of different political communities that operate across different spatial scales (e.g. local, regional, national, etc.) and spaces. People may be part of many different networks that cross or weave between different spaces. For example, immigrants who have recently been awarded citizenship may live in a *neighbourhood* where they must negotiate the bureaucracy of the wider state, gain support from *networks* of volunteers from across the city, feel trapped by hostility to asylum seekers in the *local and national* media, read *internet* reports about their *countries* of birth and reach out to their family in other parts of the *world* through letters, emails or phone calls (Cowen and Cizek 2012). Citizenship is '*decentred* along a multitude of networks rather than *centred* (or at most only ever partially and temporarily centred) in a set of territories' (Lee 2008: 4).

Joe Painter (2002) has stressed that citizenship should be understood in a 'multi-scalar' way, as Luke Desforges and his colleagues (2005: 441) elaborate:

> citizenship is defined and articulated by engagement with different scales of political authority and with a range of other social identities. Alongside this, it may be argued, are multi-scalar responsibilities of citizenship, expressed both through the different responsibilities felt by individuals towards the different contexts in which their citizenship is defined (nation, locality, faith and so on), and through the ways in which citizens are exhorted to act out the responsibilities of citizenship at different scales – for example, through connecting household practices with global environmental problems in the model of the sustainable citizen.
>
> (Desforges *et al.* 2005: 441)

This is not to underestimate the continuing power of the nation-state to shape identity and action. Rather, there should be a greater appreciation of how citizenship is framed by the state and in *relation* to wider spaces, networks and scales of citizenship that cross above and below it.

A PLACE FOR CITIZENSHIP IN GEOGRAPHY

Citizenship also deserves a more central role in the discipline of geography. Susan Smith (2000: 83) argues that, it 'marks a point of contact between social, cultural and political geography'. Certainly, evidence from key textbooks in political geography (Short 1993; Jones *et al.* 2004; Goodwin 2005; Painter and Jeffrey 2009; Storey 2009), social geography (Valentine 2001; Del Casino 2009; Samers 2010) and, to a lesser extent, cultural geography (Anderson 2010) suggests that citizenship is a key part of these subdisciplines. Review articles and special issues of journals have regularly commended the study of citizenship to geographers (Smith 1989; Staeheli 1994; Painter and Philo 1995; Driver and Maddrell 1996; Desforges *et al.* 2005; Kurtz and Hankins 2005; Bell and Binnie 2006; Leitner and Ehrkamp 2006; Anderson *et al.* 2008; Chouinard 2009; Staeheli 2011; Closs Stephens and Squire 2012a) but, despite these efforts, citizenship has often remained in the background of geography (Painter and Philo 1995). This may be because citizenship has been viewed as a concept rather than a theory (Smith 2000); an idea to be investigated, rather than a means of studying people and places. As a key idea for geographers, it is probably not on a par with some of the others that have been discussed in this series, such as scale, mobility, nature, landscape, urban or rural. Yet it should be. Citizenship has immense value in helping to draw together various strands of geographical thinking in a coherent and helpful manner.

Paul Cloke (2006: 26) argues that there is a need for 'theoretical hybridization which can combine, for example, the concerns of the cultural turn with those of political and economic materialism', one that is 'less totalizing, less judgemental, less certain, more fluid' in nature. Theorizations of citizenship provide such an approach. The idea of citizenship underpins concerns between individual identity and performance and understandings of broader political structures that shape, and are shaped by, these contexts. It offers a chance to bridge the personal and performative aspects of the cultural turn with the structural and institutional foci of political and social geography within various and fluid spaces and places.

Its conceptual strength is its ability to draw together different, and sometimes diverse, theoretical ideas. While citizenship theory discusses formal political structures, it also reveals that they are enforced and contested through a range of informal mechanisms, including 'everyday signs, artefacts and warnings which structure behaviours and performativities' (Parker 2006: 1). It offers ways of analysing 'the interface between political arrangements and social structure' (Smith 1989: 148; see also Lewis 2004a).

Citizenship offers ways of drawing together the personal and the political; the performative and the structural; the imagined and the material; the national and transnational; the included and excluded; and the local and the global. All have been enrolled into understandings of citizenship that, in turn, reflect and affect how people live their lives in particular places (Smith 1989; Painter and Philo 1995; Isin and Wood 1999; Desforges *et al.* 2005; Kurtz and Hankins 2005; Cheshire and Woods 2009; Mitchell 2009). The value of citizenship to geography is also underlined in its potential to effect change.

Citizen geographers

Isin and Turner are correct to argue that the study of citizenship is 'ultimately not about books and articles but is about addressing injustices suffered by peoples around the world . . . thus bringing about fundamental changes' (Isin and Turner 2002: 2–3). There have been growing voices calling for geographers to move beyond the academy and make a difference on the ground (Cumbers and Routledge 2004). As a collection by Fuller and Kitchin (2004) demonstrates, geographers have been motivated by their own politics, moralities, ethics, faith and altruism to engage as activists in a wide range of campaigns and actions.

Teaching also plays a significant role in linking citizenship and geography. As Chapter 6 revealed, there has been a long history of using geography to engage students with ideas of citizenship outside the lecture hall. These have often attempted to use geography to create a particular type of citizen with disastrous results (Marsden 2001b).

This does not mean, however, that the teaching of geography should be removed from citizenship. Recently, a working party of academic geographers collaborating with the UK's Geographical Association (Box 9.2) concluded that geography contributes best to citizenship education by emphasizing the value of critical reflection rather than citizen formation (Anderson *et al.* 2008). This is a view shared by Lyn Staeheli:

> We try to use our research to help students think critically about issues facing our cities. It is through helping students question their assumptions and to look at the processes shaping cities and societies that we may have the greatest impact . . . having students share our politics is not necessarily our goal; helping them understand the array of possibilities that face our cities should be.
>
> (Staeheli 2005: 198)

Box 9.2 GEOGRAPHY AND CITIZENSHIP

Chapter 6 outlined how past efforts to use geographical education to make and shape citizens have been problematic. Nevertheless, the introduction of citizenship into the UK's National Curriculum prompted renewed speculation on the place of geography in the teaching of citizenship. In 2006, the Geographical Association established a working group to consider how ideas of citizenship could be incorporated into the geography curriculum (Anderson *et al.* 2008). It rightly concluded that:

> Geography as a discipline, then, cannot make citizens, but it can create the language and intellectual space for explorations of the meaning, spatiality and contextualisation of what citizenship is, where it plays a role and what future citizenship rights might or might not entail.
>
> (Anderson *et al.* 2008: 39)

Continued

> Rather than trying to mould citizens, the discipline should provide its students with a critical geographical imagination that allows them to consider their citizenship in relation to other people and places. Five elements were identified by the working group:
>
> 1. political identities are often assumed to spring naturally from territorially bounded places, but nation-states are spatial devices resulting from and constantly modified by political struggles – placing people beyond their boundaries as 'other';
> 2. an alternative geographical imagination can better demonstrate how citizenship is relationally and globally formed through increasingly de-centred networks;
> 3. geography can create a language and intellectual space for exploring the meaning, spatiality and contextualisation of what citizenship is, the creation of belonging and connectedness, the injustices of citizenship and non-citizenship;
> 4. geography can challenge the notions of identity based on the presumption of territorial politics by pointing out how 'self' and 'other', 'us' and 'them', 'here' and 'there' are both the same and different;
> 5. a geographical imagination of citizenship can be developed through a culture of argument and an education for conversation. This should equip pupils with an 'adaptive expertise' which will help them to recognise and better understand important new connections in the future.
>
> (Geographical Association's Citizenship Working Group, 2006: 2)

I hope that the book has made the reader consider not only the academic relevance of citizenship but also the relevance of the concept to his or her life and the lives of others. Whether or how this is expressed in study or beyond the classroom is a matter for the individual. I do not try to prescribe what citizenship should mean, only that it should mean something.

FURTHER READING

The Geographical Association's Citizenship Working Group examined the contribution of geography to understandings of citizenship. Its online document (http://www.geography.org.uk/download/ga_aucwgviewpointsjan07.pdf – last accessed 6 August 2013) includes thoughtful and varying contributions from many leading geographers on the relationship between geography and citizenship (Anderson *et al.* 2006, 2008).

BIBLIOGRAPHY

Adey, P. (2010) *Mobility*. London: Routledge.

Advisory Group on Citizenship (1998) *Education for Citizenship and the Teaching of Democracy in Schools. Final Report of the Advisory Group on Citizenship*. London: Qualifications and Curriculum Authority.

Al Sharmani, M. (2010) 'Transnational family networks in the Somali diaspora in Egypt: women's roles and differentiated experiences', *Gender, Place and Culture*, 17: 499–518.

Alexander, A. and Klumsemeyer, D. (2000) *From Migrants to Citizens: Membership of a Changing World*. Carnegie Endowment for International Peace: Washington, DC.

Allen, C. (2011) 'On actor-network theory and landscape', *Area*, 43: 274–80.

Amin, A. (1996) 'Beyond associative democracy', *New Political Economy*, 1: 309–33.

Amnesty International (2010) *Annual Report 2012*. London: Amnesty International.

Amnesty International (2012) *Amnesty International Report 2012*. London: Amnesty International.

Amoore, L. (2006) 'Biometric borders: governing mobilities in the war on terror', *Political Geography*, 25: 336–51.

Anaya, J. (2010) *Observations on the Northern Territory Emergency Response in Australia*. Kingston: United Nations Information Centre for Australia, New Zealand and the South Pacific.

Anderson, J. (2010) *Understanding Cultural Geography: Places and Traces*. London: Routledge.

Anderson, J., Askins, K., Cook, I., Desforges, L., Evans, J., Fannin, M., Fuller, D., Griffiths, H., Lambert, D., Lee, R., MacLeavy, J., Mayblin, L., Morgan, J., Payne, B., Pykett, J., Roberts, D. and Skelton, T. (2006) *What is Geography's Contribution to Making Citizens?* Available online at http://www.geography.org.uk/download/ga_aucwgviewpointsjan07.pdf (accessed 9 July 2012).

Anderson, J., Askins, K., Cook, I., Desforges, L., Evans, J., Fannin, M., Fuller, D., Griffiths, H., Lambert, D., Lee, R., MacLeavy, J., Mayblin, L., Morgan, J., Payne, B., Pykett, J., Roberts, D. and Skelton, T. (2008) 'What is geography's contribution to making citizens?', *Geography*, 93: 34–39.

Anderson, J. and Tresidder, J. (2008) *A Review of the Western Australian Community Safey and Crime Prevention Partnership Planning Process*. Perth: Australian Institute of Criminology.

Anderson, K. (1995) 'Culture and nature at the Adelaide Zoo – at the frontiers of human geography', *Transactions of the Institute of British Geographers*, 20: 275–94.

Anderson, K. (2000) '"The beast within": race, humanity, and animality', *Environment and Planning D: Society and Space*, 18: 301–20.

Anderson, K. and Taylor, A. (2005) 'Exclusionary politics and the question of national belonging – Australian ethnicities in "multiscalar" focus', *Ethnicities*, 5: 460–85.

Anderson, P. and Wild, R. (2007) *Ampe Akelyernemane Meke Mekarle 'Little Children are Sacred' Report of the Northern Territory Board of Inquiry into the Protection of Aboriginal Children from Sexual Abuse*. Darwin: Northern Territory Government.

Andersson, J., Vanderbeck, R., Valentine, G., Ward, K. and Sadgrove, J. (2011) 'New York encounters: religion, sexuality, and the city', *Environment and Planning A*, 43: 618–33.

Andreasson, S. (2011) 'Confronting the settler legacy: indigenisation and transformation in South Africa and Zimbabwe', *Political Geography*, 29: 424–33.

Andrews, S. (1962) *The Australian Aborigines: a Summary of their Situation in all States in 1962*. Adelaide: Adelaide Federal Council for Aboriginal Advancement.

Andrijasevic, R., Aradau, C., Huysmans, J. and Squire, V. (2012) 'European citizenship unbound: sex work, mobility, mobilisation', *Environment and Planning D: Society and Space*, 30: 497–514.

Appadurai, A. (1990) 'Disjuncture and difference in the global cultural economy', *Theory, Culture and Society*, 7: 295–310.

Appadurai, A. (2008) 'Grassroots globalisation', in V. Ruggiero and N. Montagna (eds) *Social Movements*. London: Routledge, 303–6.

Askins, K. and Fuller, D. (2006) *Citizenship and Geography – the 'Geographies of Citizenship'*. Available online at http://www.geography.org.uk/download/ga_aucwgviewpointsjan07.pdf (accessed 9 September 2013).

Atkinson, R. (2003) 'Domestication by cappuccino or a revenge on urban space? Control and empowerment in the management of public spaces', *Urban Studies*, 40: 1829–43.

Australian Government (2012) *Australian Citizenship: Our Common Bond*. Canberra: Department of Immigration and Citizenship.

Baden-Powell, R. (1908) *Scouting for Boys: A Handbook for Instruction in Good Citizenship*. London: Horace Cox.

Bailey, I., Hopkins, R. and Wilson, G. (2010) 'Some things old, some things new: the spatial representations and politics of change of the peak oil relocalisation movement', *Geoforum*, 41: 595–605.

Baird, B. (2006) 'Sexual citizenship in "the New Tasmania"', *Political Geography*, 25: 964–87.

Baker, A. (2012) 'Forging a national identity for France after 1789: the role of landscape symbols', *Geography*, 97: 22–8

Balibar, E. (2012) 'The "impossible" community of the citizens: past and present problems', *Environment and Planning D: Society and Space*, 30: 437–49.

Banister, D. and Norton, F. (1988) 'The role of the voluntary sector in the provision of rural services – the case of transport', *Journal of Rural Studies*, 4: 57–71.

Barbero, I. (2012) 'Orientalising citizenship: the legitimation of immigration regimes in the European Union', *Citizenship Studies*, 16: 751–68.

Barbulescu, H. (2012) 'Constructing the Roma people as a societal threat: the Roma explusions from France', *European Journal of Science and Theology*, 8: 279–89.

Barker, K. (2010) 'Biosecure citizenship: politicising symbiotic associations and the construction of biological threat', *Transactions of the Institute of British Geographers*, 35: 350–63.

Barnett, C., Cloke, P., Clarke, N. and Malpass, A. (2005) 'Consuming ethics: articulating the subjects and spaces of ethical consumption', *Antipode*, 37: 23–45.

Barnett, C. and Land, D. (2007) 'Geographies of generosity: beyond the "moral turn"', *Geoforum*, 38: 1065–75.

Barnett, P. and Barnett, R. (2008) 'New time, new relationships: mental health, primary care and public health in New Zealand', in D. Conradson and C. Milligan (eds) *Landscapes of Voluntarism: New Spaces of Health, Welfare and Governance*. Bristol: Policy Press, 73–90.

Barnett, R. and Barnett, P. (2003) '"If you want to sit on your butts you'll get nothing!" – community activism in response to threats of rural hospital closure in southern New Zealand', *Health and Place*, 9: 59–71.

Barr, S., Gilg, A. and Shaw, G. (2011a) 'Citizens, consumers and sustainability: (re)framing environmental practice in an age of climate change', *Global Environmental Change: Human and Policy Dimensions*, 21: 1224–33.

Barr, S., Shaw, G. and Coles, T. (2011b) 'Sustainable lifestyles: sites, practices, and policy', *Environment and Planning A*, 43: 3011–29.

Bartram, R. and Shobrook, S. (1998) 'You have to be twice as good to be equal: "placing" women in Plymouth's Devonport Dockyard', *Area*, 30: 59–65.

Beaumont, J. and Baker, C. (eds) (2011) *Postsecular Cities*. Continuum: London.

Beaverstock, J. (2011) 'Servicing British expatriate "talent" in Singapore: exploring ordinary transnationalism and the role of the "expatriate" club', *Journal of Ethnic and Migration Studies*, 37: 709–28.

Beck, U. (1992) *Risk Society: Towards a New Modernity*. London: Sage.

Bell, D. (1995) 'Pleasure and danger: the paradoxical spaces of sexual citizenship', *Political Geography*, 14: 139–53.

Bell, D. and Binnie, J. (2000) *The Sexual Citizen: Queer Politics and Beyond*. Oxford: Polity Press.

Bell, D. and Binnie, J. (2004) 'Authenticating queer space: citizenship, urbanism and governance', *Urban Studies*, 41: 1807–20.

Bell, D. and Binnie, J. (2006) 'Geographies of sexual citizenship', *Political Geography*, 25: 869–73.

Bellamy, R. (2008) *A Very Short Introduction to Citizenship*. Oxford: Oxford University Press.

Bennett T., Holloway, K. and Farrington, D. (2008) *The Effectiveness of Neighbourhood Watch*. Oslo: The Campbell Collaboration.

Benson, M. (2011a) *The British in Rural France: Lifestyle Migration and the Ongoing Quest for a Better Way of Life*. Manchester: Manchester University Press.

Benson, M. (2011b) 'The movement beyond (lifestyle) migration: mobile practices and the constitution of a better way of life', *Mobilities*, 6: 221–35.

Benson, M. (2011c) '"We are not expats; we are not migrants; we are Sauliacoise": laying claim to belonging in rural France', in C. Trundle and B. Bönisch-Brednich (eds) *Local Lives: Migration and the Politics of Place*. Aldershot: Ashgate, 67–84.

Benton-Short, L. (2007) 'Bollards, bunkers, and barriers: securing the national mall in Washington, DC', *Environment and Planning D: Society and Space*, 25: 424–46.

Bergeon, C. (2010) 'Romanian Roma in France: between migration and exclusion policies', *Revue d'Etudes Comparatives Est–Ouest*, 41: 197–211.

Beveridge, W. (1942) *Social Insurance and Allied Services*. London: HMSO.

Beveridge, W. (1948) *Voluntary Action*. London: HMSO.

Binnie, J. (1997) 'Invisible Europeans: sexual citizenship in the new Europe', *Environment and Planning A*, 29: 237–48.

Biolsi, T. (2005) 'Imagined geographies: sovereignty, indigenous space, and American Indian struggle', *American Ethnologist*, 32: 239–59.

Biosecurity Council (2002) *Guarding Pacific's Triple Star: Draft Biosecurity Strategy for New Zealand*. New Zealand: Biosecurity Council.

Blackburn, R. and Busuttil, J. (1997) *Human Rights for the 21st Century*. Pinter: London.

Blackburn, R. and Polakiewicz, J. (2001) *Fundamental Rights in Europe: the European Convention on Human Rights and its Member States, 1950–2000*. Oxford: Oxford University Press.

Blomley, N. and Pratt, G. (2001) 'Canada and the political geographies of rights', *Canadian Geographere Géographe Canadien*, 45: 151–66.

Bluewater Shopping Centre (2013) *Guest Conduct* (http://www.bluewater.co.uk/content/cu_guestconduct last accessed 6 August 2013).

Bosco, F., Aitken, S. and Herman, T. (2011) 'Women and children in a neighbourhood advocacy group: engaging community and refashioning citizenship at the United States–Mexico border', *Gender, Place and Culture*, 18: 155–78.

Bottomore, T. (1991) 'Citizenship and class, forty years on', in T. Bottomore (ed.) *Citizenship and Social Class*. London: Pluto, 55–93.

Bourdieu, P. (1984) *Distinction: a Social Critique of the Judgement of Taste*. London: Routledge and Kegan Paul.

Bowlby, S. (1984) 'Planning for women to shop in post-war Britain', *Environment and Planning D: Society and Space*, 2: 179–99.

Boyer, K. (2012) '"The way to break the taboo is to do the taboo thing": breastfeeding in public and citizen-activism in the UK', *Health and Place*, 17: 430–7.

Brace, C. (2000) 'A pleasure ground for the noisy herds? Incompatible encounters with the Cotswolds and England, 1900–1950', *Rural History*, 11: 75–94.

Bradley-Smith, P. (2005) *The Challenges of Teaching Global Citizenship through Secondary Geography*. Canterbury UK: Citized.

Brangwyn, B. and Hopkins, R. (2008) *Transition Initiatives Primer: Becoming a Transition Town, City, District, Village, Community or Even Island*. Totnes: Transition Network.

Brown, G. (2000) 'Speech to the Children and Young Person's Unit Conference', Paper presented at Children and Young Person's Unit Conference, Islington, 15 November 2000.

Brown, M. (1997) *Replacing Citizenship: AIDS Activism and Radical Democracy*. London: Guilford Press.

Brown, M. (2006) 'Sexual citizenship, political obligation and disease ecology in gay Seattle', *Political Geography*, 25: 874–98.

Brown, T. (2003) 'Towards an understanding of local protest: hospital closure and community resistance', *Social and Cultural Geography*, 4: 489–506.

Browne, K. (2011) 'Beyond rural idylls: imperfect lesbian utopias at Michigan Womyn's music festival', *Journal of Rural Studies*, 27: 13–23.

Browne, K. and Lim, J. (2010) 'Trans lives in the "gay capital of the UK"', *Gender Place and Culture*, 17: 615–33.

Bryson, J., McGuiness, M. and Ford, R. (2002) 'Chasing a "loose and baggy monster": almshouses and the geography of charity', *Area*, 34: 48–58.

Bullen, A. and Whitehead, M. (2005) 'Negotiating the networks of space, time and substance: a geographical perspective on the sustainable citizen', *Citizenship Studies*, 9: 499–516.

Bulmer, M. and Rees, A. (1996) 'Conclusion: citizenship in the twenty-first century', in M. Bulmer and A. Rees (eds) *Citizenship Today: the Contemporary Relevance of T. H. Marshall*. London: UCL Press, 269–84.

Bunce, M. (1994) *Countryside Ideal: Anglo-American Images of Landscape*. London: Routledge.

Burchell, D. (2002) 'Ancient citizenship and its inheritors', in E. Isin and B. Turner (eds) *Handbook of Citizenship Studies*. London: Sage, 89–104.

Bushin, N. and White, A. (2010) 'Migration politics in Ireland: exploring the impacts on young people's geographies', *Area*, 42: 170–80.

Buttle, M. (2007) '"I'm not in it for the money": constructing and mediating ethical reconnections in UK social banking', *Geoforum*, 38: 1076–88.

Cabinet Office (2010) *Building the Big Society*. London: The Cabinet Office.

Cairns, A. (2002) 'Citizenship and Indian peoples: the ambiguous legacy of internal colonialism', in E. Isin and B. Turner (eds) *Handbook of Citizenship Studies*. London: Sage, 209–30.

Calma, T. (2007) *Social Justice Report 2007*. Sydney: The Aboriginal and Torres Strait Islander Social Justice Commissioner.

Caprotti, F. and Gao, E. (2012) 'Static imaginations and the possibilities of radical change: reflecting on the Arab Spring', *Area*, 44: 510–12.

Carr, J., Brown, E. and Herbert, S. (2009) 'Inclusion under the law as exclusion from the city: negotiating the spatial limitation of citizenship in Seattle', *Environment and Planning A*, 41: 1962–78.

Castles, S. and Davidson, A. (2000) *Citizenship and Migration: Globalization and the Politics of Belonging*. Basingstoke: Macmillan Press.

Castles, S. and Miller, M. (2009) *The Age of Migration: Population Movements in the Modern World*. New York: Guilford Press.

Castree, N. (2004) 'Differential geographies: place, indigenous rights and "local" resources', *Political Geography*, 23: 133–67.

Castree, N. (2005) *Nature*. London: Routledge.

Chang, K. and Turner, B. (eds) (2011) *Contested Citizenship in East Asia: Developmental Politics, National Unity and Globalization*. London: Routledge.

Chang, K. (2012) 'South Korea's condensed transition from class politics to citizenship politics', *Citizenship Studies*, 16: 1–12.

Cheshire, L. and Woods, M. (2009) 'Citizenship and governmentality, rural', in R. Kitchen and N. Thrift (eds) *International Encyclopedia of Human Geography*. London: Elsevier, 113–18.

Chouinard, V. (2001) 'Legal peripheries: struggles over disabled Canadians' places in law, society and space', *Canadian Geographer/Le Géographe Canadien*, 45: 187–92.

Chouinard, V. (2004) 'Making feminist sense of the state and citizenship', in L. Staeheli, E. Kofman and L. Peake (eds) *Mapping Women, Making Politics: Feminism and Political Geography*. New York: Routledge, 227–4.

Chouinard, V. (2009) 'Citizenship', in R. Kitchen and N. Thrift (eds) *International Encyclopedia of Human Geography*. London: Elsevier, 107–12.

Clark, J., Dobbs, J., Kane, D. and Wilding, K. (2009) *The State and the Voluntary Sector: Recent Trends in Government Funding and Public Service Delivery*. London: National Council of Voluntary Organisations.

Clarke, C. (2002) 'Between a rock and a hard place: RCMP organizational change', *Policing and Society*, 25: 14–31.

Clarke, N., Barnett, C., Cloke, P. and Malpass, A. (2007a) 'Globalising the consumer: doing politics in an ethical register', *Political Geography*, 26: 231–49.

Clarke, N., Barnett, C., Cloke, P. and Malpass, A. (2007b) 'The political rationalities of fair-trade consumption in the United Kingdom', *Politics and Society*, 35: 583–607.

Clarke, N., Cloke, P., Barnett, C. and Malpass, A. (2008) 'The spaces and ethics of organic food', *Journal of Rural Studies*, 24: 219–30.

Cloke, P. (2005) 'The country', in P. Cloke, P. Crang and M. Goodwin (eds) *Introducing Human Geographies*, second edition. London: Hodder Arnold, 451–71.

Cloke, P. (2006) 'Conceptualising rurality', in P. Cloke, M. Goodwin and E. Mooney (eds) *Handbook of Rural Studies*. London: Sage, 447–56.

Cloke, P. (2011) 'Emerging postsecular rapprochement in the contemporary city', in J. Beaumont and C. Baker (eds) *Postsecular City*. London: Continuum, 237–53.

Cloke, P. and Goodwin, M. (1992) 'Conceptualising countryside change – from Post-Fordism to rural structured coherence', *Transactions of the Institute of British Geographers*, 17: 321–36.

Cloke, P. and Little, J. (1997) 'Introduction: other countrysides?', in P. Cloke and J. Little (eds) *Contested Countryside Cultures: Otherness, Marginalisation and Rurality*. London: Routledge, 1–18.

Cloke, P. and Pawson, E. (2008) 'Memorial trees and treescape memories', *Environment and Planning D: Society and Space*, 26: 107–22.

Cloke, P., Johnsen, S. and May, J. (2005) 'Exploring ethos? Discourses of "charity" in the provision of emergency services for homeless people', *Environment and Planning*, 37: 385–402.

Cloke, P., Johnsen, S. and May, J. (2007) 'Ethical citizenship? Volunteers and the ethics of providing services for homeless people', *Geoforum*, 38: 1089–101.

Closs Stephens, A. and Squire, V. (2012a) 'Citizenship without community?', *Environment and Planning D: Society and Space*, 30: 434–6.

Closs Stephens, A. and Squire, V. (2012b) 'Politics through a web: citizenship and community unbound', *Environment and Planning D: Society and Space*, 30: 551–67.

Cohen, S. (2007) 'Winning while losing: the apprentice boys of Derry walk their beat', *Political Geography*, 26: 951–67.

Coleman, M. (2008) 'US immigration law and its geographies of social control: lessons from homosexual exclusion during the Cold War', *Environment and Planning D: Society and Space*, 26: 1096–114.

Coles, A. and Walsh, K. (2010) 'From "trucial state" to "postcolonial" city? The imaginative geographies of British expatriates in Dubai', *Journal of Ethnic and Migration Studies*, 36: 1317–33.

Collins, D. and Kearns, R. (2001) 'Under curfew and under siege? Legal geographies of young people', *Geoforum*, 32: 389–403.

Committee of Council for Education (1885) *Revised Instructions* London: Committee of Council for Education.

Conradson, D. (2003a) 'Doing organisational space: practices of voluntary welfare in the city', *Environment and Planning A*, 35: 1975–92.

Conradson, D. (2003b) 'Geographies of care: spaces, practices, experiences', *Social and Cultural Geography*, 4: 451–4.

Conradson, D. (2003c) 'Spaces of care in the city: the place of a community drop-in centre', *Social and Cultural Geography*, 4: 507–25.

Conradson, D. (2006) 'Values, practices and strategic divestment: Christian social service organisations in New Zealand', in D. Conradson and C. Milligan (eds) *Landscapes of Voluntarism: New Spaces of Health, Welfare and Governance*. Bristol: Policy Press, 153–72.

Conradson, D. (2008) 'Expressions of charity and action towards justice: faith-based welfare provision in urban New Zealand', *Urban Studies*, 45: 2117–41.

Cooper, D. (2006) 'Active citizenship and the governmentality of local lesbian and gay politics', *Political Geography*, 25: 921–43.
Costello, L. and Dunn, K. (1994) 'Resident action groups in Sydney – people power or rat-bags', *Australian Geographer*, 25: 61–76.
Cousins, J. H. (1918) *The Kingdom of Youth: Essays towards National Education*. Madras: Ganesh.
Cox, J. (1953) *Camping for All*. Ward Lock: London.
Cowell, R. and Thomas, H. (2002) 'Managing nature and narratives of dispossession: reclaiming territory in Cardiff Bay', *Urban Studies*, 39: 1241–60.
Cowen, D. (2005a) 'Suburban citizenship? The rise of targeting and the eclipse of social rights in Toronto', *Social and Cultural Geography*, 6: 335–56.
Cowen, D. (2005b) 'Welfare warriors: towards a genealogy of the soldier citizen in Canada', *Antipode*, 37: 654–78.
Cowen, D. (2008) *Military Workfare: the Soldier and Social Citizenship in Canada*. Toronto: University of Toronto Press.
Cowen, D. and Gilbert, E. (eds) (2007) *War, Citizenship, Territory*. Routledge: New York.
Cowen, E. and Cizek, K. (2012) 'Extended intimacies: digital citizenship in the global suburb', Paper presented at International Conference 'Opening the Boundaries of Citizenship', Open University, Milton Keynes, 6 February 2012.
Crack, S., Turner, S. and Heenan, B. (2007) 'The changing face of voluntary welfare provision in New Zealand', *Health and Place*, 13: 188–204.
Cresswell, T. (1996) *In Place/Out of Place: Geography, Ideology and Transgression*. Minnesota: University of Minnesota Press.
Cresswell, T. (2001) *The Tramp in America*. London: Reaktion Books.
Cresswell, T. (2006a) *On the Move*. London: Routledge.
Cresswell, T. (2006b) 'The right to mobility: the production of mobility in the courtroom', *Antipode*, 38: 735–54.
Cresswell, T. (2009) 'The prosthetic citizen: new geographies of citizenship', *Political Power and Social Theory*, 20: 259–73.
Cresswell, T. (2010) 'Towards a politics of mobility', *Environment and Planning D: Society and Space*, 28: 17–31.
Cresswell, T. (2011) 'Mobilities I: catching up', *Progress in Human Geography*, 35: 550–8.
Crewe, L. (2000) 'Geographies of retailing and consumption', *Progress in Human Geography*, 24: 275–90.
Crewe, L. (2003) 'Geographies of retailing and consumption: markets in motion', *Progress in Human Geography*, 27: 352–62.
Crossley, N. (2002) *Making Sense of Social Movements*. Milton Keynes: Open University.
Cumbers, A. and Routledge, P. (2004) 'Alternative geographical imaginations: introduction', *Antipode*, 36: 818–28.
Cunneen, C. (2001) *Conflict, Politics and Crime: Aboriginal Communities and the Police*. Crows Nest, NSW: Allen and Unwin.

Cunningham, M. and Wasserstrom, J. (2011) 'Interpreting protest in modern China', *Dissent*, 58, 13–18.

Dagger, R. (2002) 'Republican citizenship', in E. Isin and B. Turner (eds) *Handbook of Citizenship Studies*. London: Sage, 145–58.

Daily Graphic 2 January 1893, 4.

Dajani, D. (2012) 'Telling tales, performing justice: the political subject of the Hikaya', *Citizenship Studies*, 16: 673–88.

Darling, J. (2011) 'Giving space: care, generosity and belonging in a UK asylum drop-in centre', *Geoforum*, 42: 408–17.

Dean, K. (2003) *Capitalism and Citizenship: the Impossible Partnership*. London: Routledge.

Delaney, D. (2001) 'Making nature/marking humans: law as a site of (cultural) production', *Annals of the Association of American Geographers*, 91: 487–503.

Delanty, G. (2002) 'Communitaianism and citizenship', in E. Isin and B. Turner (eds) *Handbook of Citizenship Studies*. London: Sage, 159–73.

Delanty, G. (2003) *Community*. London: Routledge.

Del Casino, V. (2009) *Social Geography*. Oxford: Wiley Blackwell.

Della Porter, D. and Diani, M. (1999) *Social Movements*. Oxford: Blackwell.

Dempster, J. (1939) 'Training for citizenship through geography', in Association for Education in Citizenship, *Education for Citizenship in Secondary Schools*. London: Humphrey Milford, Oxford University Press.

de Nanclares, J. (2011) 'Reflections regarding European Union law compliance risks: on the repercussions of the French expulsion of gypsies', *Revista Espanola de Derecho Constitucional*, 31: 11–40.

Desforges, L. (2004) 'The formation of global citizenship: international non-governmental organisations in Britain', *Political Geography*, 23: 549–69.

Desforges, L., Jones, R. and Woods, M. (2005) 'New geographies of citizenship', *Citizenship Studies*, 9: 439–51.

Desmoyers-Davis, T. (2001) *Citizenship in Modern Britain*. London: Cavendish Publishing.

de Tocqueville, A. (2003 [1835–40]) *Democracy in America*. London: Penguin.

Devine-Wright, P. and Howes, Y. (2010) 'Disruption to place attachment and the protection of restorative environments: a wind energy case study', *Journal of Environmental Psychology*, 30: 271–80.

DETR (Department of the Environment, Transport and the Regions) (2000). Our countryside: the future. A fair deal for rural England. London: HMSO.

DETR (2012) *What is 'Rural Proofing'?* Available online at http://www.defra.gov.uk/corporate/about/how/policy-guidance/rural-proofing/ (accessed 15 August 2012).

Dobson, A. (2003) *Citizenship and the Environment*. Oxford: Oxford University Press.

Dobson, A. (2010) *SDRN Briefing 5: Environmental Citizenship and Pro-environmental Behaviour*. London: Sustainable Development Research Network.

Dobson, A. and Saiz, A. V. (2005) 'Special issue: citizenship, environment, economy. Introduction', *Environmental Politics*, 14: 157–62.

Dower, N. (2003) *An Introduction to Global Citizenship*. Edinburgh: Edinburgh University Press.

Driver, F. and Maddrell, A. (1996) 'Geographical education and citizenship: introduction', *Journal of Historical Geography*, 22: 371–2.

Earle, F. (1994) *A Time to Travel? An Introduction to Britain's Newer Travellers*. Eyemouth: Enabler Publications.

Edensor, T. (2006) 'Performing rurality', in P. Cloke, M. Goodwin and B. Moody (eds) *Handbook of Rural Studies*. London: Sage, 484–95.

Edwards, B. (1998) 'Charting the discourse of community action: perspectives from practice in rural Wales', *Journal of Rural Studies*, 14: 63–77.

Edwards, B., Goodwin, M., Pemberton, S. and Woods, M. (2001) 'Partnerships, power, and scale in rural governance', *Environment and Planning C: Government and Policy*, 19: 289–310.

Ehrkamp, P. (2006) '"We Turks are no Germans": assimilation discourses and the dialectical construction of identities in Germany', *Environment and Planning A*, 38: 1673–92.

Ehrkamp, P. and Leitner, H. (2006) 'Rethinking immigration and citizenship: new spaces of migrant transnationalism and belonging', *Environment and Planning A*, 38: 1591–7.

Ehrkamp, P. and Nagel, C. (2012) 'Immigration, places of worship and the politics of citizenship in the US South' *Transactions of the Institute of British Geographers*, 37: 624–38.

Elden, S. (2010) 'Land, terrain, territory', *Progress in Human Geography*, 34: 799–817.

Ellis, G. (2004) 'Discourses of objection: towards an understanding of third-party rights in planning', *Environment and Planning A*, 36: 1549–70.

Elmhirst, E. (2011) 'Migrant pathways to resource access in Lampung's political forest: gender, citizenship and creative conjugality', *Geoforum*, 42: 173–83.

Epstein, K. and Iveson, K. (2009) 'Locking down the city (well, not quite): APEC 2007 and urban citizenship in Sydney', *Australian Geographer*, 40: 271–95.

Equal Opportunities Commission (2005) *Then and Now: Thirty Years of the Sex Discrimination Act*. Manchester: Equal Opportunities Commission.

Equality and Human Rights Commission (2010) *How Fair is Britain? The First Triennial Review. Executive Summary*. Manchester: Equality and Human Rights Commission.

Escobar, C. (2006) 'Migration and citizen rights: the Mexican case', *Citizenship Studies*, 10: 503–22.

European Union (2010) *Charter of Fundamental Rights of the European Union (2010/C 83/02)*. Brussels: European Union.

Evans, C. (1933) 'Geography and world citizenship' in F. Evans (ed.) *The Teaching of Geography in Relation to the World Community*. Cambridge: Cambridge University Press, 16–20.

Evans, D. (1993) *Sexual Citizenship: the Material Construction of Sexualities*. London: Routledge.

Evans, D. (2011) 'Consuming conventions: sustainable consumption, ecological citizenship and the worlds of worth', *Journal of Rural Studies*, 27: 109–15.

Evans, N. and Yarwood, R. (2000) 'The politicization of livestock: rare breeds and countryside conservation', *Sociologia Ruralis*, 40: 228–48.

Fairgrieve, J. and Young, E. (1927) *Human Geography: the World*. London: George Phillips and Son.

Fairtrade Foundation (2011) *What is Fairtrade?* Available online at http://www.fairtrade.org.uk/what_is_fairtrade/faqs.aspx (accessed 3 June 2012).

Fairtrade International (2012) *Annual Report 2011–2012*. Bonn: Fairtrade International.

Faulks, K. (2000) *Citizenship*. London: Routledge.

Favell, A. (2001) *Philosophies of Integration*. Basingstoke: Palgrave.

Favell, A. (2003) 'Games without frontiers? Questioning the transnational social power of migrants in Europe', *Archives Européennes de Sociologie*, 44: 397–427.

Favell, A. (2004) 'Europe without borders: remapping territory, citizenship, and identity in a transnational age', *Social Forces*, 83: 869–71.

Ferbrache, F. (2011) 'British immigrants in France: issues and debates in a broadening research field', *Geography Compass*, 5: 737–49.

Finlayson, G. (1994) *Citizen, State and Social Welfare in Britain, 1830–1990*. Oxford: Clarendon Press.

Fisher, D. (2012) 'Running amok or just sleeping rough? Long-grass camping and the politics of care in northern Australia', *American Ethnologist*, 39: 171–86.

Fletcher, S. and Potts, J. (2007) 'Ocean citizenship: an emergent geographical concept', *Coastal Management*, 35: 511–24.

Fleure, H. (1916) 'Geography and citizenship', lecture to National Union of Teachers, Caernarfonshire County Association, 24 June 1916. Aberystwyth: National Library of Wales.

Flowerdew, R. (ed.) (1982) *Institutions and Geographical Patterns*. London: Croom Helm.

Foucault, M. (1991) 'Governmentality', in G. Burchell, C. Gordon and P. Miller (eds) *The Foucault Effect: Studies in Governmentality*. Hemel Hempstead: Harvester Wheatsheaf, 87–104.

Fozdar, F. and Spittles, B. (2009) 'The Australian citizenship test: process and rhetoric', *Australian Journal of Politics and History*, 55: 496–512.

Fozdar, F. and Spittles, B. (2010) 'Patriotic vs. proceduralist citizenship: Australian representations', *Nations and Nationalism*, 16: 127–47.

Fuller, D. and Kitchin, R. (eds) (2004) *Radical Theory/Critical Praxis: Making a Difference Beyond the Academy?* Vernon and Victoria: Praxis E-Press.

Fyfe, N. (1995) 'Law and order policy and the spaces of citizenship in contemporary Britain', *Political Geography*, 14: 177–89.

Fyfe, N. and Milligan, C. (2003a) 'Out of the shadows: exploring contemporary geographies of voluntarism', *Progress in Human Geography*, 27: 397–413.

Fyfe, N. and Milligan, C. (2003b) 'Space, citizenship, and voluntarism: critical reflections on the voluntary welfare sector in Glasgow', *Environment and Planning A*, 35: 2069–86.

Gabrielson, T. and Parady, K. (2010) 'Corporeal citizenship: rethinking green citizenship through the body', *Environmental Politics*, 19: 374–91.

Gallagher, S. (2002) 'Towards a common European asylum system: fortress Europe redesigns the ramparts', *International Journal*, 57: 375–94.

Gallent, N. and Robinson, S. (2011) 'Local perspectives on rural housing affordability and implications for the localism agenda in England', *Journal of Rural Studies*, 27: 297–307.

Gallup (2013) *Home Internet Access Still Out of Reach for Many Worldwide*. Available online at http://www.gallup.com/poll/159815/home-internet-access-remains-reach-worldwide.aspx (accessed 22 April 2013).

Gardner, G. (2003) *Inventing Elliot*. London: Orion.

Garland, D. (1996) 'The limits of the sovereign state – strategies of crime control in contemporary society', *British Journal of Criminology*, 36: 445–71.

Genus, A. and Rogers-Hayden, T. (2005) 'Genetic engineering in Aotearoa, New Zealand: a case of opening up or closing down debate?', in M. Leach, I. Scoones and B. Wynne (eds) *Science and Citizens: Globalisation and the Challenge of Engagement*. London: Zed Books, 244–8.

Geographical Associations's Citizenship Working Group (2006) *What is Geography's Contribution to Making Citizens?* Available online at http://www.geography.org.uk/download/GA_AUCWGJan07ViewpointGuide.pdf (accessed 12th September 2013).

Germann Molz, J. (2005) 'Getting a "flexible eye": round-the-world travel and scales of cosmopolitan citizenship', *Citizenship Studies*, 9: 517–31.

Ghose, R. (2005) 'The complexities of citizen participation through collaborative governance', *Space and Polity*, 9: 61–75.

Gibbs, L. (2010) '"A beautiful soaking rain": environmental value and water beyond Eurocentrism', *Environment and Planning D: Society and Space*, 28: 363–78.

Gibson, C. (1998) '"We sing our home, we dance our land": indigenous self-determination and contemporary geopolitics in Australian popular music', *Environment and Planning D: Society and Space*, 16: 163–84.

Gibson, C. (1999) 'Cartographies of the colonial/capitalist state: a geopolitics of indigenous self-determination in Australia', *Antipode*, 31: 45–79.

Giddens, A. (1982) *Profiles and Critiques and Social Theory*. London: Macmillan.

Gilling, D. (2011) 'Governing crime in the UK: risk and representation', in R. Mawby and R. Yarwood (eds) *Rural Policing and Policing the Rural: a Constable Countryside?* Farnham: Ashgate, 69–80.

Gleeson, B. and Kearns, R. (2001) 'Remoralising landscapes of care', *Environment and Planning D: Society and Space*, 19: 61–80.

Goodman, M. (2010) 'The mirror of consumption: celebritization, developmental consumption and the shifting cultural politics of fair trade', *Geoforum*, 41: 104–16.

Goodman, M., Maye, D. and Holloway, L. (2010) 'Ethical foodscapes?: premises, promises, and possibilities', *Environment and Planning A*, 42: 1782–96.

Goodwin, M. (1998) 'The governance of rural areas: some emerging research issues and agendas', *Journal of Rural Studies*, 14: 5–12.

Goodwin, M. (2005) 'Citizenship and governance', in P. Cloke, P. Crang and M. Goodwin (eds) *Introducing Human Geographies*. Abingdon: Hodder Arnold, 365–77.

Goodwin, M. (2009) 'Governance', in R. Kitchin and N. Thrift (eds) *International Encyclopaedia of Human Geography*. London: Elsevier, 593–9.

Goodwin, M., Jones, M. and Jones, R. (2005) 'Devolution, constitutional change and economic development: explaining and understanding the new institutional geographies of the British state', *Regional Studies*, 39: 421–36.

Goodwin, M. and Painter, J. (1996) 'Local governance, the crises of Fordism and the changing geographies of regulation', *Transactions of the Institute of British Geographers*, 21: 635–48.

Gordon, S., Hallahan, K. and Henry, D. (2002) *Putting the Picture Together: Inquiry into Response by Government Agencies to Complaints of Family Violence and Child Abuse in Aboriginal Communities*. Perth: Department of Premium and Cabinet: Western Australia.

Gray, I. and Lawrence, G. (2001) *A Future for Regional Australia: Escaping Global Misfortune*. Cambridge: Cambridge University Press.

Green, J., Steinbach, R. and Datta, J. (2012) 'The travelling citizen: emergent discourses of moral mobility in a study of cycling in London', *Sociology: the Journal of the British Sociological Association*, 46: 272–89.

Griffiths, H. (2010) 'Identity, style and "youth" subculture: what does it mean to be British?', *Geography*, 95: 140–1.

Grimshaw, P. (1999) 'Colonising motherhood: evangelical social reformers and Koorie women in Victoria, Australia, 1880s to the early 1900s', *Women's History Review*, 8: 329–46.

Gruffudd, P. (1996) 'The countryside as educator: schools, rurality and citizenship in inter-war Wales', *Journal of Historical Geography*, 22: 412–23.

Gunther, C. (2012) 'France's repatriation of Roma: violation of fundamental freedoms?', *Cornell International Law Journal*, 45: 205–25.

Haarstad, H. and Fløysand, A. (2007) 'Globalization and the power of rescaled narratives: a case of opposition to mining in Tambogrande, Peru', *Political Geography*, 26: 289–308.

Hale, A. and Wills, J. (2007) 'Women Working Worldwide: transnational networks, corporate social responsibility and action research', *Global Networks*, 7: 453–76.

Halfacree, K. (1993) 'Locality and social representation – space, discourse and alternative definitions of the rural', *Journal of Rural Studies*, 9: 23–37.

Halfacree, K. (1996a) 'The distribution of gypsy caravans in England, 1979–94', *Geography*, 81: 37–46.

Halfacree, K. (1996b) 'Out of place in the country: travellers and the "rural idyll"', *Antipode*, 28: 42–72.

Halfacree, K. (1999) '"Anarchy doesn't work unless you think about it": intellectual interpretation and DIY culture', *Area*, 31: 209–20.

Halfacree, K. (2006) 'From dropping out to leading on? British counter-cultural back-to-the-land in a changing rurality', *Progress in Human Geography*, 30: 309–36.

Halfacree, K. (2007) 'Back-to-the-land in the twenty-first century: making connections with rurality', *Tijdschrift Voor Economische En Sociale Geografie*, 98: 3–8.
Halfacree, K. (2009) '"Glow worms show the path we have to tread": the counterurbanisation of Vashti Bunyan', *Social and Cultural Geography*, 10: 771–89.
Hall, J., Basarin, V. J. and Lockstone-Binney, L. (2010) 'An empirical analysis of attendance at a commemorative event: Anzac Day at Gallipoli', *International Journal of Hospitality Management*, 29: 245–53.
Hammer, T. (1990) *Democracy and the Nation State: Aliens, Denizens and Natural Resources*. Aldershot: Avebury.
Hammett, D. (2011) 'Resistance, power and geopolitics in Zimbabwe', *Area*, 43: 202–10.
Harper, S. (1989) 'The British rural community: an overview of perspectives', *Journal of Rural Studies*, 5: 161–84.
Harrington, J. (2012) 'Orientalism, political subjectivity and the birth of citizenship between 1780 and 1830', *Citizenship Studies*, 16: 573–86.
Harrington, J. A. (2005) 'Citizenship and the biopolitics of post-nationalist Ireland', *Journal of Law and Society*, 32: 424–49.
Harris, L. M. (2011) 'Neo(liberal) citizens of Europe: politics, scales, and visibilities of environmental citizenship in contemporary Turkey', *Citizenship Studies*, 15: 837–59.
Hartwick, E. (1998) 'Geographies of consumption: a commodity-chain approach', *Environment and Planning D: Society and Space*, 16: 423–37.
Hastings, J. and Thomas, H. (2005) 'Accessing the nation: disability, political inclusion and built form', *Urban Studies*, 42: 527–44.
Hawthorne, M. and Alabaster, T. (1999) 'Citizen 2000: development of a model of environmental citizenship', *Global Environmental Change: Human and Policy Dimensions*, 9: 25–43.
Hayward, F. (1935) 'Education for citizenship: instruction or inspiration?', *Times Educational Supplement*, 14 December: 438.
He, S. (2012) 'Two waves of gentrification and emerging rights issues in Guangzhou, China', *Environment and Planning A*, 44: 2817–33.
Heater, D. (2002) *World Citizenship: Cosmopolitan Thinking and its Opponents*. London: Continuum.
Heintzman, R. (1999) 'The effects of gobalisation on management practices: should the public sector operate on different parameters?', Paper presented at IPAC National Conference, 31 August 1999.
Hemming, P. (2011) 'Meaningful encounters? Religion and social cohesion in the English primary school', *Social and Cultural Geography*, 12: 63–81.
Hemming, P. (2012) 'Educating for religious citizenship: multiculturalism and national identity in an English multi-faith primary school', *Transactions of the Institute of British Geographers*, 36: 441–54.
Henry, M. (2011) 'Policing the producer: the bio-politics of farm production in New Zealand's productivist landscape', in R. Mawby and R. Yarwood (eds)

Rural Policing and Policing the Rural: a Constable Countryside? Farnham: Ashgate, 205–16.

Herbert, S. (2007) 'The "Battle of Seattle" revisited: or, seven views of a protest-zoning state', *Political Geography*, 26: 601–19.

Herbert, S. and Brown, E. (2006) 'Conceptions of space and crime in the punitive neoliberal city', *Antipode*, 38: 755–77.

Herbert-Cheshire, L. (2000) 'Contemporary strategies for rural community development in Australia: a governmentality perspective', *Journal of Rural Studies*, 16: 203–15.

Herbert-Cheshire, L. and Higgins, V. (2004) 'From risky to responsible: expert knowledge and the governing of community-led rural development', *Journal of Rural Studies*, 20: 289–302.

Herbertson, A. J. (1907) 'Geography', in J. Adamson (ed.) *The Practice of Instruction*. London: National Society's Depository, 191–248.

Herman, A. (2010) 'Connecting the complex lived worlds of fairtrade', *Journal of Environmental Policy and Planning*, 12: 405–22.

Herman, A. (2012) 'Tactical ethics: how the discourses of fairtrade and black economic empowerment change and interact in wine networks from South Africa to the UK', *Geoforum*, 43: 1121–30.

Hertz, N. (2001) *The Silent Takeover: Global Capitalism and the Death of Democracy*. London: William Heinemann.

Higgins, V. and Lockie, S. (2002) 'Re-discovering the social: neo-liberalism and hybrid practices of governing in rural natural resource management', *Journal of Rural Studies*, 18: 419–28.

Hill, D. (1994) *Citizens and Cities: Urban Policy in the 1990s*. Hemel Hempstead: Harvester Wheatsheaf.

Hill, R. (2011) 'Towards equity in indigenous co-management of protected areas: cultural planning by Miriuwung-Gajerrong people in the Kimberley, Western Australia', *Geographical Research*, 49: 72–85.

Ho, E. (2008) 'Citizenship, migration and transnationalism: a review and critical interventions', *Geography Compass*, 2: 1286–300.

Ho, E. (2009) 'Constituting citizenship through the emotions: Singaporean transmigrants in London', *Annals of the Association of American Geographers*, 99: 788–804.

Ho, E. (2011) '"Claiming" the diaspora: elite mobility, sending state strategies and the spatialities of citizenship', *Progress in Human Geography*, 35: 757–72.

Hobbes, Thomas (1651 [2008]) *Leviathan*. Oxford: Oxford World Classics.

Hofschrer, P. (1999) *1815: the Waterloo Campaign – the German Victory*. Barnsley: Greenhill Books.

Hogg, R. and Carrington, K. (1998) 'Crime, rurality and community', *Australian and New Zealand Journal of Criminology*, 31: 160–81.

Hoggart, K. (1988) 'Not a definition of rural', *Area*, 20: 35–40.

Hoggart, K. (1990) 'Let's do away with rural', *Journal of Rural Studies*, 6: 245–57.

Holloway, S. (2004) 'Rural roots, rural routes: discourses of rural self and travelling other in debates about the future of Appleby New Fair, 1945–1969', *Journal of Rural Studies*, 20: 143–56.

Holloway, S. (2005) 'Articulating otherness? White rural residents talk about gypsy-travellers', *Transactions of the Institute of British Geographers*, 30: 351–67.

Holloway, S., Hubbard, P., Jöns, H. and Pimlott-Wilson, H. (2010) 'Geographies of education and the significance of children, youth and families', *Progress in Human Geography* 34: 583–600.

Holloway, S. and Pimlott-Wilson, H. (2012) 'Neoliberalism, policy localisation and idealised subjects: a case study on educational restructuring in England', *Transactions of the Institute of British Geographers*, 37: 639–54.

Holsten, J. (1999) 'Spaces of insurgent citizenship', in J. Holsten (ed.) *Spaces of Insurgent Citizenship: Cities and Citizenship*. Durham, NC: Duke University Press.

Holsten, J. (2008) *Insurgent Citizenship: Disjunctions of Democracy and Modernity in Brazil*. Princetown, NJ: Princetown University Press.

Hopkins, P. (2010) 'The politics of identifying Muslim identities', *Geography*, 95: 137–9.

Hopkins, P., Baillie Smith, M., Laurie, N. and Olson, E. (2010) *Young Christians in Latin America: the Experiences of Young Christians who Participate in Faith-based International Volunteering Projects in Latin America*. Newcastle: Newcastle University.

Hopkins, R. (2008) *The Transition Handbook: From Oil Dependency to Local Resilience*. Dartington: Green Books.

Hörschelmann, K. (2008) 'Populating the landscapes of critical geopolitics – young people's responses to the war in Iraq (2003)', *Political Geography*, 27: 587–609.

Hörschelmann, K. and van Blerk, L. (2012) *Children, Youth and the City*. London: Routledge.

Hörschelmann, K. and Schäfer, N. (2007) '"Berlin is not a foreign country, stupid!": growing up "global" in eastern Germany', *Environment and Planning A*, 39: 1855–72.

Hourihan, K. (1987) 'Local community involvement and participation in neighborhood watch: a case-study in Cork, Ireland', *Urban Studies*, 24: 129–36.

Howitt, R., Havnen, O. and Veland, S. (2012) 'Natural and unnatural disasters: responding with respect for indigenous rights and knowledges', *Geographical Research*, 50: 47–59.

Hsu, Y. (2008) 'Acts of Chinese citizenship: the tank-man and democracy-to-come', in E. Isin and G. Nielson (eds) *Acts of Citizenship*. London: Zed Books, 247–65.

Hubbard, P. (1998) 'Community action and the displacement of street prostitution: evidence from British cities', *Geoforum*, 29: 269–86.

Hubbard, P. (2000) 'Desire/disgust: mapping the moral contours of heterosexuality', *Progress in Human Geography*, 24: 191–217.

Hubbard, P. (2001) 'Sex zones: intimacy, citizenship and public space', *Sexualities*, 4: 51–71.

Hubbard, P. (2005) 'Accommodating otherness: anti-asylum centre protest and the maintenance of white privilege', *Transactions of the Institute of British Geographers*, 30: 52–65.

Hubbard, P. (2006) 'NIMBY by another name? A reply to Wolsink', *Transactions of the Institute of British Geographers*, 31: 92–4.

Hubbard, P. (2012) 'Kissing is not a universal right: sexuality, law and the scales of citizenship', *Geoforum*, forthcoming. Earlyview details at: http://www.sciencedirect.com/science/article/pii/S0016718512001790 (last accessed 6 August 2013).

Hughes, A. (1997) 'Rurality and cultures of womanhood: domestic identities and moral order in rural life', in P. Cloke and J. Little (eds) *Contested Countryside Cultures: Others, Marginalisation and Rurality*. London: Routledge, 123–37.

Hughes, A., Wrigley, N. and Buttle, M. (2008) 'Global production networks, ethical campaigning, and the embeddedness of responsible governance', *Journal of Economic Geography*, 8: 345–67.

Huitema, D., Cornelisse, C. and Ottow, B. (2010) 'Is the jury still out? Toward greater insight in policy learning in participatory decision processes – the case of Dutch citizens' juries on water management in the Rhine Basin', *Ecology and Society*, 15: 16.

Human Rights and Equal Opportunities Commission (1997) *Bringing Them Home: Report of the National Inquiry into the Separation of Aboriginal and Torres Strait Islander Children from their Families*. Sydney: Human Rights and Equal Opportunity Commission.

Huq, S. (2005) 'Bodies as sites of struggle', in N. Kabeer (ed.) *Inclusive Citizenship*. London: Zed Books, 164–80.

Ikegame, A. (2012) 'Mathas, gurus and citizenship: the state and communities in colonial India', *Citizenship Studies*, 16: 689–703.

Imrie, R. and Edwards, C. (2007) 'The geographies of disability: reflections on the development of a sub-discipline', *Geography Compass*, 1: 623–40.

Imrie, R., Pinch, S. and Boyle, M. (1996) 'Identities, citizenship and power in the cities', *Urban Studies*, 33: 1255–61.

Isbister, W. (1883) *Fourth Standard Geographical Reader, The British Empire*. London: WM Imbister Ltd.

Isin, E. (2002) 'Citizenship after orientalism', in E. Isin and B. Turner (eds) *Handbook of Citizenship Studies*. London: Sage, 117–28.

Isin, E. (2005) 'Citizenship after orientalism: Ottoman citizenship', in F. Keyman and A. Icduygu (eds) *Challenges to Citizenship in a Globalising World: European Questions and Turkish Experiences*. London: Routledge, 32–51.

Isin, E. (2008) 'Theorising acts of citizenship', in E. Isin and G. Nielson (eds) *Acts of Citizenship*. London: Zed Books, 15–43.

Isin, E. (2009) 'Citizenship in flux: the figure of the activist citizen', *Subjectivity*, 29: 367–88.

Isin, E. (2012a) 'Citizens without frontiers: inaugural lecture'. Available online at http://www.oecumene.eu/files/oecumene/Engin percent20Isin percent20Inaugural percent207 percent20February percent202012.pdf (accessed 12 September 2012).

Isin, E. (2012b) 'Citizenship after orientalism: an unfinished project', *Citizenship Studies*, 16: 563–72.

Isin, E. and Nielson, G. (eds) (2008) *Acts of Citizenship*. London: Zed Books.

Isin, E. and Turner, B. (eds) (2002) *Handbook of Citizenship Studies*. London: Sage.

Isin, E. and Turner, B. (2007) 'Investigating citizenship: an agenda for citizenship studies', *Citizenship Studies*, 11: 5–17.

Isin, E. and Wood, P. (1999) *Citizenship and Identity*. London: Sage.

Jackson, P. (2010) 'Citizenship and the geographies of everyday life', *Geography*, 95: 139–40.

Jaffee, D. (2007) *Brewing Justice: Fair Trade Coffee, Sustainability and Survival*. San Francisco: University of California Press.

Jakimów, M. (2012) 'Chinese citizenship "after orientalism": academic narratives on internal migrants in China', *Citizenship Studies*, 16: 657–71.

Jakobsen, J. (2004) 'Embodied spaces: religion, sex and nationalism in public and in court: a response to Sallie A. Marston', *Political Geography*, 23: 17–25.

James, Z. (2011) 'Gypsies and travellers in the countryside: managing a risky population', in R. Mawby and R. Yarwood (eds) *Rural Policing and Policing the Rural: a Constable Countryside?* Farnham: Ashgate, 137–46.

Janoski, T. (1998) *Citizenship and Civil Society*. Cambridge: Cambridge University Press.

Janoski, T. and Gran, B. (2002) 'Political citizenship: foundations of rights', in E. Isin and B. Turner (eds) *Handbook of Citizenship Studies*. London: Sage, 13–52.

Jeffrey, C. (2013) 'Geographies of children and youth III: alchemists of the revolution?', *Progress in Human Geography* 37: 145–52.

Jessop, B. (1997) 'Capitalism and its future: remarks on regulation, government and governance', *Review of International Political Economy*, 4: 561–81.

Jessop, B. (2003) 'Governance and metagovernance: on reflexivity, requisite variety, and requisite irony', in *Governance as Social and Political Communication*. Manchester: Manchester University Press, 142–72.

Jeyasingham, D. (2010) 'Building heteronormativity: the social and material reconstruction of men's public toilets as spaces of heterosexuality', *Social and Cultural Geography*, 11: 307–25.

Johnsen, S., Cloke, P. and May, J. (2005) 'Transitory spaces of care: serving homeless people on the street', *Health and Place*, 11: 323–36.

Johnston, L. (2000a) *Policing Britain: Risk, Governance and Security*. Harlow: Longman.

Johnston, R. (2000b) 'Electoral geography', in D. Gregory, R. Johnston, G. Pratt, M. Watts and S. Whatmore (eds) *Dictionary of Human Geography*, fifth edition. Oxford: Blackwell, 187–8.

Johnston, R. and Pattie, C. (2006) *Putting Voters in their Place: Geography and Elections in Great Britain*. Oxford: Oxford University Press.

Jones, M., Jones, R. and Woods, M. (2004) *An Introduction to Political Geography*. London: Routledge.

Jones, R., Goodwin, M., Jones, M. and Pett, K. (2005) '"Filling in" the state: economic governance and the evolution of devolution in Wales', *Environment and Planning C: Government and Policy*, 23: 337–60.

Jones, R., Pykett, J. and Whitehead, M. (2011a) 'The geographies of soft paternalism in the UK: the rise of the avuncular state and changing behaviour after neoliberalism', *Geography Compass*, 5: 50–62.

Jones, R., Pykett, J. and Whitehead, M. (2011b) 'Governing temptation: changing behaviour in an age of libertarian paternalism', *Progress in Human Geography*, 35: 483–501.

Kabeer, N. (2005a) *Inclusive Citizenship: Meanings and Expressions*. London: Zed Books.

Kabeer, N. (2005b) 'Introduction', in N. Kabeer (ed.) *Inclusive Citizenship: Meanings and Expression*. London: Zed Books, 1–30.

Kearns, A. (1992) 'Active citizenship and urban governance', *Transactions of the Institute of British Geographers*, 17: 20–34.

Kearns, A. (1995) 'Active citizenship and local governance: political and geographical dimensions', *Political Geography*, 14: 155–75.

Kearns, R. and Joseph, A. (1997) 'Restructuring health and rural communities in New Zealand', *Progress in Human Geography*, 21: 18–32.

Khagram, S., Riker, J. and Sikkink, K. (2002) 'From Santiago to Seattle: transnational advocacy groups restructuring world politics', in S. Khagram, J. Riker and K. Sikkink (eds) *Restructuring World Politics: Transnational Social Movements, Networks and Norms*. Minneapolis: University of Minnesota Press, 3–23.

Kitchin, R. (1998) '"Out of place", "knowing one's place": space, power and the exclusion of disabled people', *Disability and Society*, 13: 343–56.

Kitchin, R. (2000) *Disability, Space and Society*. Sheffield: Geographical Association.

Klein, N. (2001) *No Logo: No Space, No Choice, No Jobs*. London: Flamingo.

Koenig-Archibugi, M. (2010) 'Accountability in transnational relations: how distinctive is it?', *West European Politics*, 33: 1142–64.

Koenig-Archibugi, M. (2011) 'Is global democracy possible?', *European Journal of International Relations*, 17: 519–42.

Koff, H. (2008) *Fortress Europe or a Europe of Fortresses? The Integration of Migrants in Western Europe*. Brussels: P.I.E. Peter Lang.

Kofman, E. (2002) 'Contemporary European migrations, civic stratification and citizenship', *Political Geography*, 21: 1035–54.

Kofman, E. (2005) 'Citizenship, migration and the reassertion of national identity', *Citizenship Studies*, 9: 453–67.

Kofman, E. and Sales, R. (1992) 'Towards fortress Europe?', *Women's Studies International Forum*, 15: 29–39.

Kurtz, H. and Hankins, K. (2005) 'Guest editorial: geographies of citizenship', *Space and Polity*, 9: 1–8.

Kyung-Sup, C. and Turner, B. (eds) (2012) *Contested Citizenship in East Asia: Development Politics, National Unity and Globalization*. Abingdon: Routledge.

Lambert, D. and Machon, P. (eds) (2001) *Citizenship through Secondary Geography*. London: Routledge.

Lambie-Mumford, H. and Jarvis, D. (2012) 'The role of faith-based organisations in the Big Society: opportunities and challenges', *Policy Studies*, 33: 249–62.

Lane, M. and Williams, L. (2009) 'The Natural Heritage Trust and indigenous lands: the trials and tribulations of "new technologies of governance"', *Australian Geographer*, 40: 85–107.

Latour, B. (2005) *Reassembling the Social: an Introduction to Actor-Network-Theory*. Oxford: Oxford University Press.

Lea, T. (2012) 'When looking for anarchy, look to the state: fantasies of regulation in forcing disorder within the Australian indigenous estate', *Critique of Anthropology*, 32: 109–24.

Leach, M., Scoones, I. and Wynne, B. (2005) 'Introduction: science, citizenship and globalisation', in M. Leach, I. Scoones and B. Wynne (eds) *Science and Citizens: Globalization and the Challenge of Engagement*. London: Zed Books, 3–14.

Lee, R. (2008) *Where Are We? Geography, Space and Political Relations. A Short Essay for the GA Citizenship Working Group*. Sheffield: Geographical Association.

Leitner, H. (1997) 'Reconfiguring the spatiality of power: the construction of a supranational migration framework for the European Union', *Political Geography*, 16: 123–43.

Leitner, H. and Ehrkamp, P. (2006) 'Transnationalism and migrants? Imaginings of citizenship', *Environment and Planning A*, 38: 1615–32.

Lepofsky, J. and Fraser, J. C. (2003) 'Building community citizens: claiming the right to place-making in the city', *Urban Studies*, 40: 127–42.

Lewis, G. (ed.) (2004a) *Citizenship: Personal Lives and Social Policy*. Milton Keynes: Open University.

Lewis, G. (2004b) '"Do not go gently . . . " Terrains of citizenship and landscape of the personal', in G. Lewis (ed.) *Citizenship: Personal Lives and Social Policy*. Milton Keynes: Open University, 1–38.

Liepins, R. (2000a) 'Exploring rurality through "community": discourses, practices and spaces shaping Australian and New Zealand rural "communities"', *Journal of Rural Studies*, 16: 325–41.

Liepins, R. (2000b) 'New energies for an old idea: reworking approaches to "community" in contemporary rural studies', *Journal of Rural Studies*, 16: 23–35.

Linklater, A. (2002) 'Cosmopolitan citizenship', in E. Isin and B. Turner (eds) *Handbook of Citizenship Studies*. London: Sage, 317–33.

List, C. and Koenig-Archibugi, M. (2010) 'Can there be a global demos? An agency-based approach', *Philosophy and Public Affairs*, 38: 76–110.

Lister, R. (2002) 'Sexual citizenship', in E. Isin and B. Turner (eds) *Handbook of Citizenship Studies*. London: Sage, 191–208.

Lister, R. (2003) *Citizenship: Feminist Perspectives*, second edition. Basingstoke: Palgrave.

Lister, R. (2007) 'Inclusive citizenship: realizing the potential', *Citizenship Studies*, 11: 49–61.

Lister, R., Smith, N., Middleton, S. and Cox, L. (2005) 'Young people talking about citizenship in Britain', in N. Kabeer (ed.) *Inclusive Citizenship*. London: Zed Books, 114–32.

Little, J. (2002) *Gender and Rural Geography: Identity, Sexuality and Power in the Countryside*. Harlow: Prentice Hall.

Loader, I. (2006) 'Fall of the "platonic guardians" – liberalism, criminology and political responses to crime in England and Wales', *British Journal of Criminology*, 46: 561–86.

Locke, J. (1690 [2008]) *Second Treatise on Government* Oxford: Oxford University Press.

Lockie, S. and Higgins, V. (2007) 'Roll-out neoliberalism and hybrid practices of regulation in Australian agri-environmental governance', *Journal of Rural Studies*, 23: 1–11.

Lockie, S., Lawrence, G. and Cheshire, L. (2006) 'Reconfiguring rural resource governance: the legacy of neo-liberalism in Australia', in P. Cloke, T. Marsden and P. Mooney (eds) *Handbook of Rural Studies*. London: Sage, 29–43.

London2012 (2012a) 'About the Torch Relay'. Available online at http://www.london2012.com/torch-relay/about/ (accessed 8 June 2012).

London2012 (2012b) 'Search begins for 8,000 inspirational people to carry the Olympic Flame'. Available online at http://www.london2012.com/news/articles/2011/05/search-begins-for-8-000-inspirational-people-to-carry-th.html (accessed 8 June 2012).

Lorimer, H. (1997) '"Happy hostelling in the Highlands": nationhood, citizenship and the inter-war youth movement', *Scottish Geographical Magazine*, 113: 42–50.

Lorimer, J. (2010) 'International conservation "volunteering" and the geographies of global environmental citizenship', *Political Geography*, 29: 311–22.

Lowe, B. and Ginsberg C. (2002) 'Animal rights as a post-citizenship movement', *Society and Animals*, 10: 203–15.

Lowe, R. and Shaw, W. (1993) *Travellers: Voices of the New Age Nomads*. New York: Fourth Estate.

Löwenheim, O. and Gazit, O. (2009) 'Power and examination: a critique of citizenship tests', *Security Dialogue*, 40: 145–67.

Maaka, R. and Fleras, A. (2005) *The Politics of Indigeneity: Challenging the State in Canada and Aotearoa, New Zealand*. Dunedin: University of Otago Press.

McCallum, D. (2011) 'Liberal forms of governing Australian indigenous peoples', *Journal of Law and Society*, 38: 604–30.

McDonald's Corporation (2004) *McDonald's Worldwide Corporate Responsibility Report*. Oak Brook, Illinois: McDonald's.

McEwan, C. (2005) 'New spaces of citizenship? Rethinking gendered participation and empowerment in South Africa', *Political Geography*, 24: 969–91.

McIlwaine, C. and Bermúdez, A. (2011) 'The gendering of political and civic participation among Colombian migrants in London', *Environment and Planning A*, 43: 1499–513.

MacKian, S. (1995) '"That great dust-heap called history": recovering the multiple spaces of citizenship', *Political Geography*, 14: 209–16.
MacKian, S. (1998) 'The citizen's new clothes: care in a Welsh community', *Critical Social Policy*, 18: 27–50.
MacKian, S. (2012) *Everyday Spirituality: Social and Spatial Worlds of Enchantment*. Basingstoke: Palgrave Macmillan.
Mackinder, H. (1906) *Our Own Islands: An Elementary Geography*. London: Phelps.
McKinley, E. and Fletcher, S. (2012) 'Improving marine environmental health through marine citizenship: a call for debate', *Marine Policy*, 36: 839–43.
McLaughlin, B. (1986) 'Rural policy in the 1980s – the renewal of the rural idyll', *Journal of Rural Studies*, 2: 81–90.
McLaughlin, B. (1987) 'Rural policy into the 1990s – self help or self deception?', *Journal of Rural Studies*, 3: 361–4.
MacLaughlin, J. (1998a) 'The political geography of anti-traveller racism in Ireland: the politics of exclusion and the geography of closure', *Political Geography*, 17: 417–35.
MacLaughlin, J. (1998b) 'Racism, ethnicity and multiculturalism in contemporary Europe: a review essay', *Political Geography*, 17: 1013–24.
MacLeod, G. (2002) 'From urban entrepreneurialism to a "revanchist city"? On the spatial injustices of Glasgow's renaissance', *Antipode*, 34: 602–24.
Macoun, A. (2011) 'Aboriginality and the Northern Territory Intervention', *Australian Journal of Political Science*, 46: 519–34.
Maddrell, A. (1996) 'Empire, emigration and school geography: changing discourses of imperial citizenship, 1880–1925', *Journal of Historical Geography*, 22: 373–87.
Makita, R. (2012) 'Fair trade and organic initiatives confronted with Bt cotton in Andhra Pradesh, India: a paradox', *Geoforum*, 43: 1232–41.
Malpass, A., Cloke, P., Barnett, C. and Clarke, N. (2007) 'Fairtrade urbanism? The politics of place beyond place in the Bristol fairtrade city campaign', *International Journal of Urban and Regional Research*, 31: 633–45.
Mann, M. (1996) 'Ruling class strategies and citizenship', in M. Bulmer and A. Rees (eds) *Citizenship Today: the Contemporary Relevance of T. H. Marshall*. London: UCL Press, 65–80.
Mansvelt, J. (1997) 'Working at leisure: critical geographies of ageing', *Area*, 29: 289–98.
Mansvelt, J. (2005) *Geographies of Consumption*. London: Routledge.
Mansvelt, J. (2008) 'Geographies of consumption: citizenship, space and practice', *Progress in Human Geography*, 32: 105–17.
Marino, A. (2012) '"The cost of dams": acts of writing as resistance in postcolonial India', *Citizenship Studies*, 16: 705–19.
Marsden, W. (2001a) 'Citizenship education: permeation or perversion', in D. Lambert and P. Machon (eds) *Citizenship through Secondary Education*. London: RoutledgeFalmer, 11–30.

Marsden, W. (2001b) "Book Review of Education for citizenship", *Geography*, 86: 270.

Marshall, T. (1950 [1992]) 'Citizenship and social class', in T. Marshall and T. Bottomore (eds) *Citizenship and Social Class*. London: Pluto, 3–54.

Marston, S. (2002) 'Making difference: conflict over Irish identity in the New York City St Patrick's Day parade', *Political Geography*, 21: 373–92.

Martin, D. (2004) 'Nonprofit foundations and grassroots organizing: reshaping urban governance', *Professional Geographer*, 56: 394–405.

Marx, K. (1990) *Capital: Critique of Political Economy*. London: Penguin.

Massey, D. (1991) 'A global sense of place?', *Marxism Today*, 24–9.

Matless, D. (1996) 'Visual culture and geographical citizenship: England in the 1940s', *Journal of Historical Geography*, 22: 424–39.

Matless, D. (1997) 'Moral geographies of English landscape', *Landscape Research*, 22: 141–55.

Matless, D. (2001) *Landscape and Englishness*. London: Reaktion Books.

Matthews, H. and Limb, M. (2003) 'Another white elephant? Youth councils as democratic structures', *Space and Polity*, 7: 173–92.

Matthews, M. and Vujakovic, P. (1995) 'Private worlds and public places: mapping the environmental values of wheelchair users', *Environment and Planning A*, 27: 1069–83.

Mawby, R. and Yarwood, R. (eds) (2010) *Rural Policing and Policing the Rural: a Constable Countryside?* Farnham: Ashgate.

Mayo, M. (2005) *Global Citizens: Social Movements and the Challenge of Globalisation*. London: Zed Books.

Mazzarino, J., Morigi, V., Kaufmann, C., Farias, A. and Fernandes, D. (2011) 'Daily practices, consumption and citizenship', *Anais da Academia Brasileira de Ciencias*, 83: 1481–91.

Melucci, A. (2008) 'A strange kind of newness: what's "new" in new social movements?', in V. Ruggiero and N. Montagna (eds) *Social Movements*. London: Routledge, 218–25.

Mercer, D. (1993) 'Terra nullius, aboriginal sovereignty and land rights in Australia: the debate continues', *Political Geography*, 12: 299–318.

Mercer, D. (1997) 'Aboriginal self-determination and indigenous land title in post-Mabo Australia', *Political Geography*, 16: 189–212.

Merriman, P. and Jones, R. (2009) '"Symbols of justice": the Welsh Language Society's campaign for bilingual road signs in Wales, 1967–1980', *Journal of Historical Geography*, 35: 350–75.

Micheletti, M. (2003) *Political Virtue and Shopping: Individuals, Consumerism and Collective Action*. London: Palgrave.

Miller, D. (2000) *Citizenship and National Identity*. Cambridge: Polity Press.

Miller, D. (2010) *The Idea of Global Citizenship*. Oxford: Nuffield College, Oxford University.

Miller, T. (2002) 'Cultural citizenship', in E. Isin and B. Turner (eds) *Handbook of Citizenship Studies*. London: Sage, 231–43.

Milligan, C. (2008) 'Geographies of voluntarism: mapping the terrain', *Geography Compass*, 1/2: 183–99.

Milligan, C. (2009) 'Voluntary sector', in R. Kitchin and N. Thrift (eds) *International Encyclopedia of Human Geography*. Oxford: Elsevier 165–70.

Milligan, C. and Fyfe, N. R. (2005) 'Preserving space for volunteers: exploring the links between voluntary welfare organisations, volunteering and citizenship', *Urban Studies*, 42: 417–33.

Milligan, C. and Wiles, J. (2010) 'Landscapes of care', *Progress in Human Geography*, 34: 736–54.

Mills, S. (2011a) 'Be prepared: communism and the politics of Scouting in 1950s Britain', *Contemporary British History*, 25: 429–50.

Mills, S. (2011b) 'Scouting for girls? Gender and the Scout movement in Britain', *Gender Place and Culture*, 18: 537–56.

Mills, S. (2013) '"An instruction in good citizenship": Scouting and the historical geographies of citizenship education', *Transactions of the Institute of British Geographers*, 38: 120–34.

Mingay, A. (1989) *The Unquiet Countryside*. London: Routledge.

Mitchell, D. (1995) 'The end of public space – people's park, definitions of the public and democracy', *Annals of the Association of American Geographers*, 85: 108–33.

Mitchell, D. (1997) 'The annihilation of space by law: the roots and implications of anti-homeless laws in the United States', *Antipode*, 29: 303–35.

Mitchell, D. (2005) 'The SUV model of citizenship: floating bubbles, buffer zones, and the rise of the "purely atomic" individual', *Political Geography*, 24: 77–100.

Mitchell, D. and Staeheli, L. A. (2005) 'Permitting protest: parsing the fine geography of dissent in America', *International Journal of Urban and Regional Research*, 29: 796–813.

Mitchell, K. (2009) 'Citizenship', in K. Gregory, R. Johnston, G. Pratt, M. Watts and S. Whatmore (eds) *The Dictionary of Human Geography*, fifth edition. Oxford: Wiley Blackwell, 84–5.

Mohan, G. (2007) 'Participatory development: from epistemological reversals to active citizenship', *Geography Compass*, 1: 779–96.

Mohan, G. and Mohan, J. (2002) 'Placing social capital', *Progress in Human Geography*, 26: 191–210.

Mohan, J. (1995) 'Thinking local – service-learning education for citizenship and geography', *Journal of Geography in Higher Education*, 19: 129–42.

Mohan, J. (2000) 'Geographies of welfare and social exclusion: dimensions, consequences and methods', *Progress in Human Geography*, 26: 65–75.

Mohan, J. (2002) *Planning, markets and hospitals*, London: Routledge.

Mohan, J. (2003a) 'Geography and social policy: spatial divisions of welfare', *Progress in Human Geography*, 27: 363–74.

Mohan, J. (2003b) 'Voluntarism, municipalism and welfare: the geography of hospital utilization in England in 1938', *Transactions of the Institute of British Geographers*, 28: 56–74.

Mohan, J., Twigg, L., Barnard, S. and Jones, K. (2005) 'Social capital, geography and health: a small-area analysis for England', *Social Science and Medicine*, 60: 1267–83.

Mohan, J., Twigg, L., Jones, K. and Barnard, S. (2006) 'Volunteering, geography and welfare: a multilevel investigation of geographical variations in voluntary action', in C. Milligan and D. Conradson (eds) *Landscapes of Voluntarism: New Spaces of Health, Welfare and Governance*. Bristol: Policy Press, 267–84.

Mohan, John (1995) *A National Health Service? The Restructuring of Health Care In Britain since 1979*. London: St Martin's Press.

Moley, S. and Budd, S. (2008) 'Neighbourhood Watch membership', in S. Nicholas, J. Flatley, J. Hoare, A. Patterson, C. Southcott, S. Moley and K. Jansson (eds) *Circumstances of Crime, Neighbourhood Watch Membership and Perceptions of Policing: Supplementary Vol.3 to Crime in England and Wales 2006/07 Findings from the 2006/07British Crime Survey*. London: HMSO, 55–67.

Moon, S. (2012) 'Local meanings and lived experiences of citizenship: voices from a women's organization in South Korea', *Citizenship Studies*, 16: 49–67.

Moore, R. (1991) 'Foreward', in T. Bottomore (ed.) *Citizenship and Social Class*. London: Pluto, vi.

Moran, D., Piacentini, L. and Pallot, J. (2012) 'Disciplined mobility and carceral geography: prisoner transport in Russia', *Transactions of the Institute of British Geographers*, 37: 446–60.

Mormont, M. (1983) 'The emergence of rural struggles and their ideological effects', *International Journal of Urban and Regional Research*, 7: 559–75.

Morris, W. (1946) *The Future Citizen and his Surroundings*. London: Batsford.

Morton, J. (2008) 'Poofters taking the piss out of Anzacs: the (un-)Australian wit of Sydney's gay and lesbian Mardi Gras', *Anthropological Forum*, 18: 219–34.

Mountz, A. (2004) 'Embodying the nation-state: Canada's response to human smuggling', *Political Geography*, 23: 323–45.

Mowl, G. and Fuller, D. (2001) 'Geographies of disability', in R. Pain, M. Barke, D. Fuller, J. Gough, R. MacFarlane and G. Mowl (eds) *Introducing Social Geographies*. London: Arnold.

Mullard, M. (2004) *The Politics of Globalisation and Polarisation*. Cheltenham: Edward Elgar.

Munday, M., Bristow, G. and Cowell, R. (2011) 'Wind farms in rural areas: how far do community benefits from wind farms represent a local economic development opportunity?', *Journal of Rural Studies*, 27: 1–12.

Munton, T. and and Zurawan, A. (2003) *Active Communities: Headline Findings from the 2003 Home Office Citizenship Survey*. London: Home Office.

Murdoch, J. and Marsden, T. (1994) *Reconstituting Rurality: Class, Community, and Power in the Development Process*. London: UCL Press.

Murphy, L. and Kearns, R. A. (1994) 'Housing New Zealand Ltd – privatisation by stealth', *Environment and Planning A*, 26: 623–37.

Mutua, M. (2002) *Human Rights: a Political and Cultural Critique*. Philadelphia: University of Pennsylvania.

Mycock, A. and Tonge, J. (2011) 'A big idea for the Big Society? The advent of National Citizen Service', *Political Quarterly*, 82: 56–66.

Nacu, A. (2012) 'From silent marginality to spotlight scapegoating? A brief case study of France's policy towards the Roma', *Journal of Ethnic and Migration Studies*, 38: 1323–8.

Nagel, C. and Staeheli, L. (2008) 'Integration and the negotiation of "here" and "there": the case of British Arab activists', *Social and Cultural Geography*, 9: 415–30.

Nahaboo, Z. (2012) 'Subverting orientalism: political subjectivity in Edmund Burke's India and liberal multiculturalism', *Citizenship Studies*, 16: 587–603.

Naidoo, K. (2000) 'The new civic globalism – NGOs should be made more effective in strengthening democracy', *Nation*, 270: 34–36.

Nash, C. (1996) 'Geo-centric education and anti-imperialism: theosophy, geography and citizenship in the writings of J. H. Cousins', *Journal of Historical Geography*, 22: 399–411.

National Health Service (2013) *About the NHS*. Available online at http://www.nhs.uk/NHSEngland/thenhs/about/Pages/nhscoreprinciples.aspx (accessed 27 March 2013).

Neilson, J. and Pritchard, B. (2010) 'Fairness and ethicality in their place: the regional dynamics of fair trade and ethical sourcing agendas in the plantation districts of South India', *Environment and Planning A*, 42: 1833–51.

Nelson, V. and Pound, B. (2009) *The Last Ten Years: a Comprehensive Review of the Literature on the Impact of Fairtrade*. London: Natural Resources Institute (NRI), University of Greenwich.

Newby, H. (1978) *Property, Paternalism and Power: Class and Control in Rural England*. London: Hutchinson.

Newby, H. (1986) 'Locality and rurality – the restructuring of rural social relations', *Regional Studies*, 20: 209–15.

Ní Laoire, C., Carpena-Mendez, F., Tyrrell, N. and White, A. (eds) (2011) *Childhood and Migration in Europe: Portraits of Mobility, Identity and Belonging in Contemporary Ireland*. Farnham: Ashgate.

North, P. (2011) 'Geographies and utopias of Cameron's Big Society', *Social and Cultural Geography*, 12: 817–27.

Nyamnjoh, F. (2007) 'From bounded to flexible citizenship: lessons from Africa', *Citizenship Studies*, 11: 73–82.

Nyers, P. (2007) 'Introduction: why citizenship studies', *Citizenship Studies*, 11: 1–4.

O'Dougherty, M. (2006) 'Public relations, private security: managing youth and race at the Mall of America', *Environment and Planning D: Society and Space*, 24: 131–54.

Oliphant, M. (1999) The Atlas of the Ancient World: Charting the Great Civilizations of the Past. New York: Thunder Bay.

Oliver, D. and Heater, D. (1994) *The Foundations of Citizenship*. Hemel Hempstead: Harvester Wheatsheaf.

O'Nions, H. (2011) 'Roma expulsions and discrimination: the elephant in Brussels', *European Journal of Migration and Law*, 13: 361–88.

Oommen, T. (1997) *Citizenship, Nationality and Ethnicity*. Cambridge: Polity Press.
Oswin, N. (2010) 'The modern model family at home in Singapore: a queer geography', *Transactions of the Institute of British Geographers*, 35: 256–68.
O'Toole, K. and Burdess, N. (2004) 'New community governance in small rural towns: the Australian experience', *Journal of Rural Studies*, 20: 433–43.
Owen, S. and Kearns, R. (2008) 'Competition, adaption and resistance: (re)forming health organisation in New Zealand's third sector', in C. Milligan and D. Conradson (eds) *Landscapes of Voluntarism: New Spaces of Health, Welfare and Governance*. Bristol: Policy Press, 115–34.
Paasche, T. (2011) 'The governance of security in neoliberal Cape Town', Unpublished PhD Thesis, Plymouth University.
Paasche, T. (2012) 'Creating parallel public spaces through private governments: a South African case study', *South African Geographical Journal*, 94: 46–59.
Paasche, T. and Sidaway, J. (2010) 'Transecting security and space in Maputo', *Environment and Planning A*, 42: 1555–76.
Pain, R. (1997a) '"Old age" and ageism in urban research: the case of fear of crime', *International Journal of Urban and Regional Research*, 21: 117–28.
Pain, R. (1997b) 'Social geographies of women's fear of crime', *Transactions of the Institute of British Geographers*, 22: 231–44.
Pain, R. (2000) 'Place, social relations and the fear of crime: a review', *Progress in Human Geography*, 24: 365–87.
Pain, R. (2001) 'Gender, race, age and fear in the city', *Urban Studies*, 38: 899–913.
Pain, R. (2009) 'Globalized fear? Towards an emotional geopolitics', *Progress in Human Geography*, 33: 466–86.
Pain, R., Mowl, G. and Talbot, C. (2000) 'Difference and the negotiation of "old age"', *Environment and Planning D: Society and Space*, 18: 377–93.
Painter, J. (2002) 'Multilevel citizenship, identity and regions in contemporary Europe', in J. Anderson (ed.) *Transnational Democracy: Political Spaces and Border Crossings*. London: Routledge, 93–110.
Painter, J. (2007) 'What kind of citizenship for what kind of community?', *Political Geography*, 26: 221–4.
Painter, J. (2012) 'The politics of the neighbour', *Environment and Planning D: Society and Space*, 30: 515–33.
Painter, J. and Jeffrey, A. (2009) *Political Geography*. London: Sage.
Painter, J. and Philo, C. (1995) 'Spaces of citizenship: an introduction', *Political Geography*, 14: 107–20.
Pakulski, J. (1997) 'Cultural citizenship', *Citizenship Studies*, 1: 73–86.
Panelli, R. and Welch, R. (2005) 'Why community? Reading difference and singularity with community', *Environment and Planning A*, 37: 1589–611.
Pant, M. (2005) 'The quest for inclusion: nomadic communities and citizenship quests in Rajasthan', in N. Kabeer (ed.) *Inclusive Citizenship: Meanings and Expressions*. London: Zed Books, 85–98.
Parker, G. (1996) 'ELMs disease: stewardship, corporatism and citizenship in the English countryside', *Journal of Rural Studies*, 12: 399–411.

Parker, G. (1999a) 'Rights, symbolic violence, and the micropolitics of the rural: the case of the Parish Paths Partnership scheme', *Environment and Planning A*, 31: 1207–22.

Parker, G. (1999b) 'The role of the consumer-citizen in environmental protest in the 1990s', *Space and Polity*, 3: 67–83.

Parker, G. (2001) *Citizenships, Contingency and the Countryside: Rights, Culture, Land and the Environment*. London: Routledge.

Parker, G. (2006) 'The Country Code and the ordering of countryside citizenship', *Journal of Rural Studies*, 22: 1–16.

Parker, G. and Ravenscroft, N. (2001) 'Land, rights and the gift: the Countryside and Rights of Way Act 2000 and the negotiation of citizenship', *Sociologia Ruralis*, 41: 381–98.

Parr, H. and Butler, H. (eds) (1999) *Mind and Body Spaces: Geographies of Illness, Impairment and Disability*. London: Routledge.

Parr, H., Philo, C. and Burns, N. (2004) 'Social geographies of rural mental health: experiencing inclusions and exclusions', *Transactions of the Institute of British Geographers*, 29: 401–19.

Parsons, L. (2006) 'The voluntary spaces of charity shops: workplaces or domestic spaces?', in D. Conradson and C. Milligan (eds) *Landscapes of Voluntarism: New Spaces of Health, Welfare and Governance*. Bristol: Policy Press, 231–46.

Pattie, C. and Johnston, R. (2011) 'How big is the Big Society?' *Parliamentary Affairs*, 64: 403–24.

Pearson, C. (2012) 'Researching militarized landscapes: a literature review on war and the militarization of the environment', *Landscape Research*, 37: 115–33.

Peck, J. (2004) 'Geography and public policy: constructions of neoliberalism', *Progress in Human Geography*, 28: 392–405.

Peck, J. and Tickell, A. (2002) 'Neoliberalizing space', *Antipode*, 34: 380–404.

Peers, S. (1998) 'Building fortress Europe: the development of EU migration law', *Common Market Law Review*, 35: 1235–72.

Perreault, T. (2003) 'Changing places: transnational networks, ethnic politics, and community development in the Ecuadorian Amazon', *Political Geography*, 22: 61–88.

Petersen, M. and Warburton, J. (2012) 'Residential complexes in Queensland, Australia: a space of segregation and ageism?', *Ageing and Society*, 32: 60–84.

Phillips, A. and Ganesh, G. (2007) *Young People and British Identity*. London: Ipsos MORI.

Philo, C. (1992) 'Neglected rural geographies: a review', *Journal of Rural Studies*, 8: 193–207.

Philo, C. (1997) 'Of other rurals', in P. Cloke and J. Little (eds) *Contested Countryside Cultures: Otherness, Marginalisation and Rurality*. London: Routledge, 19–50.

Philo, C. (2012) 'Security of geography/geography of security', *Transactions of the Institute of British Geographers*, 37: 1–7.

Philo, C. and Parr, H. (2000) 'Institutional geographies: introductory remarks', *Geoforum*, 31: 513–21.

Philo, C. and Wilbert, C. (eds) (2000) *Animal Spaces, Beastly Places: New Geographies of Human–Animal Relations*. London: Routledge.

Pickerill, J. and Krinsky, J. (2012) 'Why does Occupy matter?', *Social Movement Studies*, 11: 279–87.

Pile, S. (1995) '"What we are asking for is decent human life": SPLASH, neighbourhood demands and citizenship in London's docklands', *Political Geography*, 14: 199–208.

Pilger, J. (2002) *The New Rulers of the World*. London: Verso.

Pilgram, L. (2012) 'British-Muslim family law and citizenship', *Citizenship Studies*, 16: 769–82.

Pine, A. (2010) 'The performativity of urban citizenship', *Environment and Planning A*, 42: 1103–20.

Pine, A. (2011) 'The temporary permanence of Dominican Bodegueros in Philadelphia: neighbourhood development in an era of transnational mobility', *Urban Studies*, 48: 641–60.

Pow, C. (2011) 'Living it up: super-rich enclave and transnational elite urbanism in Singapore', *Geoforum*, 42: 382–93.

Pratt, G (2005) 'Abandoned women and spaces of the exception', *Antipode*, 37, 1052–73.

Prince, R. (2010) 'National citizenship service for 16-year-olds launched today', *The Daily Telegraph*, 22 July.

Puddington, A. (2012) *Freedom in the World 2012: The Arab Uprisings and their Global Repercussions*. Available online at http://www.freedomhouse.org/sites/default/files/Full percent20Report percent20Essay percent20-percent20PDF percent20Version.pdf (last accessed 9 July 2012).

Putnam, R. (2001) *Bowling Alone: The Collapse and Revival of American Community*. New York: Simon and Schuster.

Pykett, J. (2007) 'Making citizens governable? The Crick Report as governmental technology', *Journal of Education Policy*, 22: 301–19.

Pykett, J. (2009a) 'From the nanny state to the avuncular state?' In R. Jones, M. Whitehead and J. Pykett, *Soft Paternalism Blog*. Available at http://governingtemptation.wordpress.com/2009/06/02/hello-world/. 2 June 2009 (accessed 4 August 2012).

Pykett, J. (2009b) 'Making citizens in the classroom: an urban geography of citizenship education?', *Urban Studies*, 46: 803–23.

Pykett, J (2010) 'Designing identity: exploring citizenship through geographies of identity', *Geography*, 95: 132–4.

Pykett, J. (2011) 'Citizenship education and narratives of pedagogy', *Citizenship Studies*, 14: 621–35.

Pykett, J. (2012) 'The new maternal state: the gendered politics of governing through behaviour change', *Antipode*, 44: 217–38.

Pykett, J., Cloke, P., Barnett, C., Clarke, N. and Malpass, A. (2010) 'Learning to be global citizens: the rationalities of fair-trade education', *Environment and Planning D: Society and Space*, 28: 487–508.

Pykett, J., Jones, R., Whitehead, M., Huxley, M., Strauss, K., Gill, N., McGeevor, K., Thompson, L. and Newman, J. (2011) 'Interventions in the political geography of "libertarian paternalism"', *Political Geography*, 30: 301–10.

Ransome, A. (1934) *Coot Club*. London: Jonathan Cape.

Rasmussen, C. and Brown, M. (2002) 'Radical democratic citizenship: amidst political theory and geography', in E. Isin and B. Turner (eds) *Handbook of Citizenship Studies*. London: Sage, 175–88.

Rasmussen, C. and Brown, M. (2005) 'The body politic as spatial metaphor', *Citizenship Studies*, 9: 469–84.

Reed, L. (1999) '"Part of our own story": representations of indigenous Australians and Papua New Guineans within Australia Remembers 1945–1995 – the continuing desire for a homogeneous national identity', *Oceania*, 69: 157–70.

Reid, L., Hunter, C. and Sutton, P. (2011) 'Rising to the challenge of environmental behaviour change: developing a reflexive diary approach', *Geoforum*, 42: 720–30.

Rhodes, R. (1996) 'The new governance: governing without government', *Political Studies*, 44: 652–67.

Rhodes, R. (2007) 'Understanding governance: ten years on', *Organization Studies*, 28: 1243–64.

Ribchester, C. and Edwards, B. (1999) 'The centre and the local: policy and practice in rural education provision', *Journal of Rural Studies*, 15: 49–63.

Richardson, D. (2005) 'Desiring sameness? The rise of a neoliberal politics of normalisation', *Antipode*, 37: 515–35.

Richmond, A. (1999) 'Citizens, denizens and exiles', *Citizenship Studies*, 3: 151–5.

Robins, S. (2005) 'AIDS, science and citizenship after apartheid', in M. Leach, I. Scoones and B. Wynne (eds) *Science and Citizens: Globalisation and the Challenge of Engagement*. London: Zed Books, 113–29.

Robinson, J and Mills, S (2012) 'Being observant and observed: embodied citizenship training in the Home Guard and the Boy Scout Movement, 1907–1945', *Journal of Historical Geography*, 38: 412–23.

Robinson, V. (1996) 'Population migration in the European Union', in P. Rees, J. Stillwell, A. Convey and M. Kupiszewski (eds) *Population Migration in the European Union*. Wiley: New York.

Rose, N. (1996) 'The death of the social? Re-figuring the territory of government', *Economy and Society*, 25: 327–56.

Rose, N. (2007) *The Politics of Life Itself: Biomedicine, Power, and Subjectivity in the Twenty-first Century*. Oxford: Princeton University Press.

Routledge, P. (1997) 'The imagineering of resistance: Pollok Free State and the practice of postmodern politics', *Transactions of the Institute of British Geographers*, 22: 359–76.

Routledge, P. (2000) 'Geopoetics of resistance: India's Baliapal movement', *Alternatives: Social Transformation and Humane Governance*, 25: 375–89.

Routledge, P. (2003) 'Convergence space: process geographies of grassroots globalization networks', *Transactions of the Institute of British Geographers*, 28: 333–49.

Routledge, P. (2005) 'Survival and resistance', in P. Cloke, P. Crang and M. Goodwin (eds) *Introducing Human Geography*. London: Hodder Arnold, 211–24.

Routledge, P. (2008) 'Acting in the network: ANT and the politics of generating associations', *Environment and Planning D: Society and Space*, 26: 199–217.

Routledge, P., Cumbers, A. and Nativel, C. (2007) 'Grassrooting network imaginaries: relationality, power, and mutual solidarity in global justice networks', *Environment and Planning A*, 39: 2575–92.

Routledge, P., Nativel, C. and Cumbers, A. (2006) 'Entangled logics and grassroots imaginaries of global justice networks', *Environmental Politics*, 15: 839–59.

Routledge, P. and Simons, J. (1995) 'Embodying spirits of resistance', *Environment and Planning D: Society and Space*, 13: 471–98.

Rowley, G. and Haynes, M. (1990) 'Neighbourhood conflict, neighbourhood activism and the case of the Fenton Holyman', *Area*, 22: 37–45.

Rubenstein, K. (2003) 'Review essay: the centrality of migration to citizenship', *Citizenship Studies*, 7: 255–65.

Ruggiero, V. and Montagna, N. (eds) (2008) *Social Movements*. London: Routledge.

Ruiz, C. (2005) 'Rights and citizenship of indigenous women in Chiapas: a history of struggles, fears and hopes', in N. Kabeer (ed.) *Inclusive Citizenship: Meanings and Exclusions*. London: Zed Books, 132–48.

Rutt, L. (2011) 'New ways of doing charity: governmentality and emerging subjectivities in spaces and places of 'ethical giving'', Unpublished PhD Thesis, University of Exeter.

Sadler, D. (2004) 'Anti-corporate campaigning and corporate "social" responsibility: towards alternative spaces of citizenship?', *Antipode*, 36: 851–70.

Sadler, D. and Lloyd, S. (2009) 'Neo-liberalising corporate social responsibility: a political economy of corporate citizenship', *Geoforum*, 40: 613–22.

Said, E. (1978) *Orientalism*. New York: Pantheon Books.

Samers, M. (2010) *Migration*. London: Routledge.

Sandell, J. (2010) 'Transnational ways of seeing: sexual and national belonging in Hedwig and the Angry Inch', *Gender Place and Culture*, 17: 231–47.

Sanders, M., O'Brien, M., Tennant, M., Sokolowski, S. and Salmon, L. (2008) *The New Zealand Non-Profit Sector in Comparative Perspective*. Wellington: Office for the Community and Voluntary Sector.

Sassen, S. (2002) 'Towards post-national and denationalized citizenship', in E. Isin and B. Turner (eds) *Handbook of Citizenship Studies*. London: Sage, 277–93.

Sassen, S. (2009) 'Incompleteness and the possibility of making: towards denationalized citizenship', *Political Power and Social Theory*, 20: 229–58.

Satsangi, M., Gallent, N. and Bevan, M. (2010) *The rural housing question: communities and planning in Britain's countrysides*. Bristol: Policy Press.
Saunders, M. (2008) 'Flash mobs', in E. Isin and G. Nielson (eds) *Acts of Citizenship*. London: Zed Books, 295–96.
Saunders, P. (1979) *Urban Politics: a Sociological Interpretation*. Hutchinson: London.
Schelly, D. and Stretesky, P. B. (2009) 'An analysis of the path of least resistance argument in three environmental justice success cases', *Society and Natural Resources*, 22: 369–80.
Scott, M., Redmond, D. and Russell, P. (2012) 'Active citizenship and local representational politics in twenty-first century Ireland: the role of residents groups within Dublin's planning arena', *European Planning Studies*, 20: 147–70.
Scout Association (2011) *Making Our Mark: the Scout Association's Annual Report and Accounts 2010/2011*. London: Scout Association.
Seal, G. (2011) '". . . and in the morning . . .": adapting and adopting the dawn service', *Journal of Australian Studies*, 35: 49–63.
Secor, A. (2004) '"There is an Istanbul that belongs to me": citizenship, space, and identity in the city', *Annals of the Association of American Geographers*, 94: 352–68.
Sekunda, N., Northwood, S. and Simkins, M. (2000) *Caesar's Legions: the Roman Soldier 753 BC to 117 AD*. Oxford: Osprey.
Sellick, J. and Yarwood, R. (2013) 'Placing livestock in landscape studies: pastures new or out to graze?', *Landscape Research*, 38, 404–20.
Shaw, J. and MacKinnon, D. (2011) 'Moving on with "filling in"? Some thoughts on state restructuring after devolution', *Area*, 43: 23–30.
Shaw, J. and Štiks, I. (2012) 'Citizenship in the new states of south eastern Europe', *Citizenship Studies*, 16: 309–21.
Shearing, C. and Wood, J. (2003) 'Nodal governance, democracy, and the new "denizens"', *Journal of Law and Society*, 30: 400–19.
Sheller, M. and Urry, J. (2006) 'The new mobilities paradigm', *Environment and Planning A*, 38: 207–26.
Short, J. (1989) 'Yuppies, Yuffies and the new urban order', *Transactions of the Institute of British Geographers*, 14: 173–88.
Short, J. (1991) *Imagined Country: Society, Culture and Environment*. London: Routledge.
Short, J. (1993) *Introduction to Political Geography*. London: Routledge.
Short, J. (1996) 'Idyllic ruralities', in P. Cloke, M. Goodwin and P. Mooney (eds) *Handbook of Rural Studies*. London: Sage, 133–48.
Shove, E. and Walker, G. (2007) 'CAUTION! Transitions ahead: politics, practice, and sustainable transition management', *Environment and Planning A*, 39: 763–70.
Shuck, P. (2002) 'Liberal citizenship', in E. Isin and B. Turner (eds) *Handbook of Citizenship Studies*. London: Sage, 131–44.
Sibley, D. (1981) *Outsiders in Urban Societies*. Oxford: Blackwell.
Sibley, D. (1994) 'The sin of transgression', *Area*, 26: 300–3.

Sibley, D. (1995) *Geographies of Exclusion: Society and Difference in the West.* London: Routledge.
Sibley, D. (2003) 'Psychogeographies of rural space and practices of exclusion', in P. Cloke (ed.) *Country Visions.* Harlow: Pearson, 218–30.
Sidaway, J. (2007) 'Enclave space: a new metageography of development?', *Area*, 39: 331–9.
Sidaway, J. (2009) 'Shadows on the path: negotiating geopolitics on an urban section of Britain's South West Coast Path', *Environment and Planning D: Society and Space*, 27: 1091–116.
Simmons, T. (2008) 'Sexuality and immigration: UK family reunion policy and the regulation of sexual citizens in the European Union', *Political Geography*, 27: 213–30.
Skelton, T. (2006) *What is Geography's Contribution to Making Citizens?* Available online at http://www.geography.org.uk/download/ga_aucwgviewpoints-jan07.pdf (accessed 12 August 2012).
Skelton, T. (2007) 'Children, young people, UNICEF and participation', *Children's Geographies*, 5: 165–81.
Skinner, M. and Fleuret, S. (2011) 'Health geography's voluntary turn: a view from western France', *Health and Place*, 17: 33–41.
Skinner, M. and Power, A. (2011) 'Voluntarism, health and place: bringing an emerging field into focus', *Health and Place*, 17: 1–6.
Smiley, S. (2010) 'Expatriate everyday life in Dar es Salaam, Tanzania: colonial origins and contemporary legacies', *Social and Cultural Geography*, 11: 327–42.
Smith, D. (2008) 'The politics of studentification and "(un) balanced" urban populations: lessons for gentrification and sustainable communities?', *Urban Studies*, 45: 2541–64.
Smith, J. (2008) 'Globalising resistance: the battle for Seattle and the future of social movements', in V. Ruggiero and N. Montagna (eds) *Social Movements.* London: Routledge, 316–26.
Smith, N. (2006) 'The endgame of globalization', *Political Geography*, 25: 1–14.
Smith, N. (2010) 'Ten years after', *Geographical Journal*, 177: 203–7.
Smith, R. (2002) 'Modern citizenship', in E. Isin and B. Turner (eds) *Handbook of Citizenship Studies.* London: Sage, 105–16.
Smith, R. and van der Anker, C. (eds) (2005) *The Essentials of Human Rights.* London: Hodder Arnold.
Smith, S. (1989) 'Space, society and citizenship: a human geography for the new times?', *Transactions of the Institute of British Geographers*, 14: 144–57.
Smith, S. (1995) 'Citizenship: all or nothing?', *Political Geography*, 14: 190–3.
Smith, S. (2000) 'Citizenship', in R. Johnston, K. Gregory, G. Pratt and M. Watts (eds) *The Dictionary of Human Geography*, fourth edition. Oxford: Blackwell, 83–4.
Snowdon, C. (2012) *Sock Puppets: How the Government Lobbies itself and Why.* London: Institute of Economic Affairs.
Soysal, N. (1994) *Limits of Citizenship: Migrants and Postnational Membership in Europe.* Chicago: University of Chicago Press.

Sparke, M. (2006) 'A neoliberal nexus: economy, security and the biopolitics of citizenship on the border', *Political Geography*, 25: 151–80.
Staeheli, L. (1994) 'Restructuring citizenship in Pueblo, Colorado', *Environment and Planning A*, 26: 849–71.
Staeheli, L. (2003a) 'Cities and citizenship', *Urban Geography*, 24: 97–102.
Staeheli, L. (2003b) 'The new politics of citizenship: structuring participation by household, work, and identity', *Urban Geography*, 24: 103–26.
Staeheli, L. (2005) 'Editorial: can American cities be sites of citizenship? What can we do about it?', *Urban Geography*, 26: 197–9.
Staeheli, L. (2008a) 'Citizenship and the problem of community', *Political Geography*, 27: 5–21.
Staeheli, L. (2008b) 'More on the "problems" of community', *Political Geography*, 27: 35–9.
Staeheli, L. (2010) 'Political geography: democracy and the disorderly public', *Progress in Human Geography*, 34: 67–78.
Staeheli, L. (2011) 'Political geography: where's citizenship?', *Progress in Human Geography*, 35: 393–400.
Staeheli, L. (2013) 'The 2011 Antipode AAG lecture "Whose responsibility is it? Obligation, citizenship and social welfare"', *Antipode*, 45: 521–40.
Staeheli, L. and Mitchell, D. (2007) *The People's Property: Power, Politics and the Public*. London: Routledge.
Staeheli, L. and Nagel, C. (2006) 'Topographies of home and citizenship: Arab-American activists in the United States', *Environment and Planning A*, 38: 1599–614.
Stamper, A. (2004) *Becoming Active Citizens: Social Action of the Women's Institutes in England and Wales, 1915–1925*. London: Women's Institute.
Stephens, J. (2007) 'Memory, commemoration and the meaning of a suburban war memorial', *Journal of Material Culture*, 12: 241–61.
Stevenson, N. (ed) (2001) *Culture and Citizenship*. London: Sage.
Storey, D. (2001) *Territory: the Claiming of Space*. Harlow: Prentice Hall.
Storey, D. (2009) 'Political geography', in R. Kitchin and N. Thrift (eds) *International Encyclopedia of Human Geography*. London: Elsevier 243–53.
Storey, D. (2011) *Territories: the Claiming of Space*, second edition. London: Routledge.
Stychin, C. (2006) '"Las Vegas is not where we are": queer readings of the Civil Partnership Act', *Political Geography*, 25: 899–920.
Tennant, M., O'Brien, M. and Sanders, J. (2008) *The History of the Non-profit Sector in New Zealand*. Wellington: Office for the Community and Voluntary Sector.
Tesfahuney, M. (1998) 'Mobility, racism and geopolitics', *Political Geography*, 17: 499–515.
Tewdwr-Jones, M. (1998) 'Rural government and community participation: the planning role of community councils', *Journal of Rural Studies*, 14: 51–62.
Thaler, R. and Sunstein, C. (2009) *Nudge: Improving Decisions about Health, Wealth and Happiness*. London: Penguin.

Thrift, N. (1994) 'Inhuman geographies – landscapes of speed, light and power', in P. Cloke, M. Doel, D. Matless, N. Thrift and M. Phillips (eds) *Writing the Rural: Five Cultural Geographies*. London: Paul Chapman Publishing, 191–248.

Tonts, M. (2001) 'The exclusive brethren and an Australian rural community', *Journal of Rural Studies*, 17: 309–22.

Tonts, M. and Greive, S. (2002) 'Commodification and creative destruction in the Australian rural landscape: the case of Bridgetown, Western Australia', *Australian Geographical Studies*, 40: 58–70.

Tonts, M. and Larsen, A. (2002) 'Rural disadvantage in Australia: a human rights perspective', *Geography*, 87: 132–41.

Tormey, A. (2007) '"Everyone with eyes can see the problem": moral citizens and the space of Irish nationhood', *International Migration*, 45: 69–100.

Transition Network (2012) *About Transition Network*. Available online at http://www.transitionnetwork.org/about (accessed 1 September 2012).

Troy, P. (2000) 'Suburbs of acquiescence, suburbs of protest', *Housing Studies*, 15: 717–38.

Trudeau, D. (2008a) 'Junior partner or empowered community? The role of non-profit social service providers amidst state restructuring in the US', *Urban Studies*, 45: 2805–27.

Trudeau, D. (2008b) 'Towards a relational view of the shadow state', *Political Geography*, 27: 669–90.

Turner, B. (1974) *Weber and Islam: a Critical Study*. London: Routledge and Kegan Paul.

Turner, B. (1986) *Citizenship and Capitalism: a Debate over Reformism*. London: Allen and Unwin.

Turner, B. (1990) 'Outline of a theory of citizenship', *Sociology*, 24: 189–217.

Turner, B. (1997) 'Citizenship studies: a general theory', *Citizenship Studies*, 1: 5–18.

Turner, B. (2001) 'Outline of a general theory of cultural citizenship', in N. Stevenson (ed.) *Culture and Citizenship*. London: Sage, 11–32.

Turner, B. (2002) 'Religion and politics: the elementary forms of citizenship', in E. Isin and B. Turner (eds) *Handbook of Citizenship Studies*. London: Sage, 259–76.

Turner, B. (2007) 'The enclave society: towards a sociology of immobility', *European Journal of Social Theory*, 10: 287–304.

Turner, B. (2009) 'T. H. Marshall, social rights and English national identity', *Citizenship Studies*, 13: 65–73.

Turner, B. (2012) 'National and social citizenship: some structural and cultural problems with modern citizenship', in C. Kyung-Sup and B. Turner (eds) *Contested Citizenship in East Asia: Development Politics, National Unity and Globalization*. Abingdon: Routledge, 15–42.

Tyrrell, N., White, A., Ní Laoire, C. and Carpena-Mendez, F. (eds) (2012) *Transnational Migration and Childhood*. London: Routledge.

Unstead, J. (1931) 'The primary geography schoolteacher: what should he know and be', *Geography*, 14: 315–22.

USAonWatch (2009) *About USAonWatch: Welcome to USAonWatch.org.* Available online at http://www.usaonwatch.org/ (accessed 9 October 2009).

Valdivia, G. (2008) 'Governing relations between people and things: citizenship, territory, and the political economy of petroleum in Ecuador', *Political Geography*, 27: 456–77.

Valentine, G. (1989) 'The geographies of women's fear', *Area*, 21: 385–90.

Valentine, G. (1993) '(Hetero)sexing space: lesbian perceptions and experiences of everyday spaces', *Environment and Planning D: Society and Space*, 11: 395–413.

Valentine, G. (2001) *Social Geographies: Space and Society*. Harlow: Prentice Hall.

Valentine, G. and Skelton, T. (2007) 'The right to be heard: citizenship and language', *Political Geography*, 26: 121–40.

Valentine, G. and Waite, L. (2012) 'Negotiating difference through everyday encounters: the case of sexual orientation and religion and belief', *Antipode*, 44: 474–92.

Vanderbeck, R., Andersson, J., Valentine, G., Sadgrove, J. and Ward, K. (2011) 'Sexuality, activism, and witness in the Anglican Communion: the 2008 Lambeth Conference of Anglican Bishops', *Annals of the Association of American Geographers*, 101: 670–89.

van Dijk, T. and van der Wulp, N. (2010) 'Not in my open space: anatomy of neighbourhood activism in defence of land use conversion', *Landscape and Urban Planning*, 96: 19–28.

van Krieken, R. (1999) 'The barbarism of civilization: cultural genocide and the "stolen generations"', *British Journal of Sociology*, 50: 297–315.

Verdonk, V. (2012) 'The animal is dead, long live the animals: the animal rights debate from the 1970s onwards', *Tijdschrift voor Geschiedenis*, 125: 552–66.

Veronis, L. (2006) 'The Canadian Hispanic Day Parade, or how Latin American immigrants practise (sub)urban citizenship in Toronto', *Environment and Planning A*, 38: 1653–71.

Vujakovic, P. and Matthews, M. (1994) 'Contorted, folded, torn – environmental values, cartographic representation and the politics of disability', *Disability and Society*, 9: 359–74.

Waitt, G. (2005) 'Sexual citizenship in Latvia: geographies of the Latvian closet', *Social and Cultural Geography*, 6: 161–81.

Waitt, G., Markwell, K. and Gorman-Murray, A. (2008) 'Challenging heteronormativity in tourism studies: locating progress', *Progress in Human Geography*, 32: 781–800.

Walford, R. (1996) 'Geographical education and citizenship: afterword', *Journal of Historical Geography*, 22: 440–2.

Walker, G., Hunter, S., Devine-Wright, P., Evans, B. and Fay, H. (2007) 'Harnessing community energies: explaining and evaluating community-based localism in renewable energy policy in the UK', *Global Environmental Politics*, 7: 64–82.

Walker, R. and Barcham, M. (2010) 'Indigenous-inclusive citizenship: the city and social housing in Canada, New Zealand, and Australia', *Environment and Planning A*, 42: 314–31.

Walsh, K. (2006) '"Dad says I'm tied to a shooting star"! Grounding (research on) British expatriate belonging', *Area*, 38: 268–78.

Walsh, K. (2012) 'Emotion and migration: British transnationals in Dubai', *Environment and Planning D: Society and Space*, 30: 43–59.

Walzer, M. (1994) 'Spheres of affection', *Boston Review*, 19: 29.

Weber, C. (2012) 'Design, translation, citizenship: reflections on the virtual (de) territorialization of the USA–Mexico border', *Environment and Planning D: Society and Space*, 30: 482–96.

Weeks, J. (1998) 'The sexual citizen', *Theory, Culture, Society*, 15: 35–52.

Wells, J. T. and Christie, M. F. (2000) 'Albert Namatjira and the burden of citizenship', *Australian Historical Studies*, 31: 110–30.

Whatmore, S. (2005) 'Hybrid geographies: author's responses and reflections', *Antipode*, 37: 842–5.

Whatmore, S. and Thorne, L. (1997) 'Nourishing networks: alternative geographies of food', in D. Goodman and M. Watts (eds) *Globalising Food: Agrarian Questions and Global Restructuring*. London: Routledge, 287–304.

Whelan, A., Wrigley, N., Warm, D. and Cannings, E. (2002) 'Life in a "food desert"', *Urban Studies*, 39: 2083–100.

White, J. (1997) 'Power/knowledge and public space: policing the "Aboriginal Towns"', *Australian and New Zealand Journal of Criminology*, 30: 275–91.

Widdicombe, D. (1986) *The Conduct of Local Authority Business: Report Cmnd 9797*. London: HMSO.

Williams, A., Cloke, P. and Thomas, S. (2012) 'Co-constituting neoliberalism: faith-based organisations, co-option, and resistance in the UK', *Environment and Planning A*, 44: 1479–501.

Wills, J. (2005) 'Globalization and protest', in P. Cloke, P. Crang and M. Goodwin (eds) *Introducing Human Geography*. London: Hodder Arnold, 573–87.

Wise, M. (2006) 'Defending national linguistic territories in the European Single Market: towards more transnational geolinguistic analysis', *Area*, 38: 204–12.

Wolch, J. (1989) 'The shadow state: transformations in the voluntary sector', in J. Wolch and M. Dear (eds) *The Power of Geography: How Territory Shapes*. Boston: Unwin Hyman, 197–221.

Wolch, J. (1990) *The shadow state: Government and Voluntary Sector in Transition*. New York: The Foundation Centre.

Wolch, J. (2006) 'Beyond the shadow state?', in C. Milligan and D. Conradson (eds) *Landscapes of Voluntarism: New Spaces of Health, Welfare and Governance*. Bristol: Policy Press, xii–xv.

Wolch, J. and Emel, J. (1998) *Animal Geographies: Place, Politics, and Identity in the Nature–Culture Borderlands*. New York: Verso.

Wolsink, M. (2006) 'Invalid theory impedes our understanding: a critique on the persistence of the language of NIMBY', *Transactions of the Institute of British Geographers*, 31: 85–91.

Wood, P. (2006) 'The "sarcee war": fragmented citizenship and the city', *Space and Polity*, 10: 229–42.
Woods, M. (1997) 'Discourses of power and rurality: local politics in Somerset in the 20th century', *Political Geography*, 16: 453–78.
Woods, M. (1998) 'Mad cows and hounded deer: political representations of animals in the British countryside', *Environment and Planning A*, 30: 1219–34.
Woods, M. (2003) 'Deconstructing rural protest: the emergence of a new social movement', *Journal of Rural Studies*, 19: 309–25.
Woods, M. (2005) *Rural Geography: Processes, Responses, and Experiences in Rural Restructuring*. London: Sage.
Woods, M. (2006a) 'Political articulation: the modalities of new critical politics of rural citizenship', in P. Cloke, M. Goodwin and E. Mooney (eds) *Handbook of Rural Studies*. London: Sage, 457–72.
Woods, M. (2006b) 'Redefining the "rural question": the new "politics of the rural" and social policy', *Social Policy and Administration*, 40: 579–95.
Woods, M. (2007) 'Engaging the global countryside: globalization, hybridity and the reconstitution of rural place', *Progress in Human Geography*, 31: 485–507.
Woods, M. (2008) 'Social movements and rural politics', *Journal of Rural Studies*, 24: 129–37.
Woods, M. (2010) 'Performing rurality and practising rural geography', *Progress in Human Geography*, 34: 835–46.
Woods, M. (2011a) 'Policing rural protest', in R. Mawby and R. Yarwood (eds) *Rural Policing and Policing the Rural: a Constable Countryside?* Farnham: Ashgate, 109–22.
Woods, M. (2011b) *Rural*. London: Routledge.
Woods, M. and Goodwin, M. (2003) 'Applying the rural: governance and policy in rural areas', in P. Cloke (ed.) *Country Visions*. Harlow: Pearson, 245–62.
Woods, M., Anderson, J., Guilbert, S. and Watkin, S. (2013) 'Rhizomic radicalism and arborescent advocacy: a Deleuzo-Guattarian reading of rural protest', *Environment and Planning D: Society and Space*, 31: 434–50.
Woodward, R. (2004) *Military Geographies*. London: Royal Geographical Society with Institute of British Geographers.
Woodward, R. (2005) 'From military geography to militarism's geographies: disciplinary engagements with the geographies of militarism and military activities', *Progress in Human Geography*, 29: 718–40.
World Food Programme (2010) *Fighting Hunger Worldwide*. Rome: World Food Programme.
Wrigley, N., Warm, D. and Margetts, B. (2003) 'Deprivation, diet, and food-retail access: findings from the Leeds "food deserts" study', *Environment and Planning A*, 35: 151–88.
Yarwood, R. (2002) 'Parish councils, partnership and governance: the development of "exceptions" housing in the Malvern Hills District, England', *Journal of Rural Studies*, 18: 275–91.

Yarwood, R. (2005) 'Geography, citizenship and volunteering: some uses of the higher education active community fund in geography', *Journal of Geography in Higher Education*, 29: 355–68.

Yarwood, R. (2007a) 'The geographies of policing', *Progress in Human Geography*, 31: 447–65.

Yarwood, R. (2007b) 'Getting just deserts? Policing, governance and rurality in Western Australia', *Geoforum*, 38: 339–52.

Yarwood, R. (2010a) 'An exclusive countryside? Crime concern, social exclusion and community policing in two English villages', *Policing and Society*, 20: 61–78.

Yarwood, R. (2010b) 'Risk, rescue and emergency services: the changing spatialities of mountain rescue teams in England and Wales', *Geoforum*, 41: 257–70.

Yarwood, R. (2011a) 'Voluntary sector geographies, intraorganisational difference, and the professionalisation of volunteering: a study of land search and rescue organisations in New Zealand', *Environment and Planning C: Government and Policy*, 29: 457–72.

Yarwood, R. (2011b) 'Whose blue line is it anyway? Community policing and partnership working in rural areas', in R. Mawby and R. Yarwood (eds) *Rural Policing and Policing the Rural: a Constable Countryside?* Farnham: Ashgate, 93–108.

Yarwood, R. (2012a) 'Neighbourhood Watch', in S. Smith, M. Elsinga, L. O'Mahony, O. Eng, S. Wachter and M. Pareja Eastaway (eds) *International Encyclopedia of Housing and Home, Vol 5*. Oxford: Elsevier, 90–5.

Yarwood, R. (2012b) 'One moor night: emergencies, training and rural space', *Area* 44: 22–8.

Yarwood, R. and Edwards, B. (1995) 'Voluntary action in rural areas: the case of Neighbourhood Watch', *Journal of Rural Studies*, 11: 447–59.

Yarwood, R. and Gardner, G. (2000) 'Fear of crime, cultural threat and the countryside', *Area*, 32: 403–11.

Yarwood, R. and Tyrell, N. (2012) 'Why children's geographies?', *Geography*, 97: 124–8.

Young, J. (1999) *The Exclusive Society*. London: Sage.

Yuval-Davis, N. (1997) 'Women, citizenship and difference', *Feminist Review*, 57: 4–27.

Zedner, L. (2009) *Security*. London: Routledge.

Index